CARNEGIE LEARNING
LONG + LIVE + MATH

High School Math Solution
Integrated Math I

Student Edition
Volume 1

Sandy Bartle Finocchi and Amy Jones Lewis

with Josh Fisher, Janet Sinopoli, and Victoria Fisher

501 Grant St., Suite 1075
Pittsburgh, PA 15219
Phone 888.851.7094
Customer Service Phone 412.690.2444
Fax 412.690.2444

www.carnegielearning.com

Cover Design by Anne Milliron

ISBN: 978-1-68459-282-1
Student Edition, Volume 1

Printed in the United States of America
3 4 5 6 7 8 9 BB 21 20 21

LONG + LIVE + MATH

ACKNOWLEDGMENTS

High School Math Solution Authors
- Sandy Bartle Finocchi, Senior Academic Officer
- Amy Jones Lewis, Director of Instructional Design
- Josh Fisher, Instructional Designer
- Victoria Fisher, Instructional Designer
- Janet Sinopoli, Instructional Designer

Foundational Authors
- William S. Hadley, Co-Founder
- David Dengler
- Mary Lou Metz

Vendors
- Lumina Datamatics, Ltd.
- Mathematical Expressions, LLC

Images
www.pixabay.com

Special Thanks

- Alison Huettner for project management and editorial review.
- Jacyln Snyder for her contributions to the Teacher's Implementation Guide facilitation notes.
- Harry Lynch for his contributions and review of the Statistics and Probability strand.
- The members of Carnegie Learning Cognitive Scientist Team—Brendon Towle, John Connelly, Bob Hausmann, Chas Murray, and Martina Pavelko—for their insight in learning science and collaboration on MATHia® Software.
- John Jorgenson, Chief Marketing Officer, for all his insight and messaging.
- Carnegie Learning Education Services Team for content review and providing customer feedback.
- The entire Carnegie Learning staff for their hard work and dedication to transforming math education.
- The families of the authoring team for their continued support.

"Mathematics is so much more than memorizing rules. It is learning to reason, to make connections, and to make sense of the world. We believe in Learning by Doing(TM)—you need to actively engage with the content if you are to benefi t from it. The lessons were designed to take you from your intuitive understanding of the world and build on your prior experiences to then learn new concepts. My hope is that these instructional materials help you build a deep understanding of math."

Sandy Bartle Finocchi, Senior Academic Officer

"You have been learning math for a very long time—both in school and in your interactions in the world. You know a lot of math! In this course, there's nothing brand new. It all builds on what you already know. So, as you approach each activity, use all of your knowledge to solve problems, to ask questions, to fix mistakes, and to think creatively."

Amy Jones Lewis, Director of Instructional Design

"At Carnegie Learning we have created an organization whose mission and culture is defined by your success. Our passion is creating products that make sense of the world of mathematics and ignite a passion in you. Our hope is that you will enjoy our resources as much as we enjoyed creating them."

Barry Malkin, CEO, Carnegie Learning

Module 1: Searching for Patterns

Topic 1: Quantities and Relationships

Topic 2: Sequences

Topic 3: Linear Regressions

© Carnegie Learning, Inc.

Module 2: Exploring Constant Change

Topic 1: Linear Functions

Topic 2: Solving Linear Equations and Inequalities

Topic 3: Systems of Equations and Inequalities

© Carnegie Learning, Inc.

Module 3: Investigating Growth and Decay

Module 4: Describing Distributions

Topic 1: One-Variable Statistics

Topic 2: Two-Variable Categorical Data

Module 5: Analyzing Geometric Functions

Topic 1: Constructions

Each lesson has the same structure. Key features are noted.

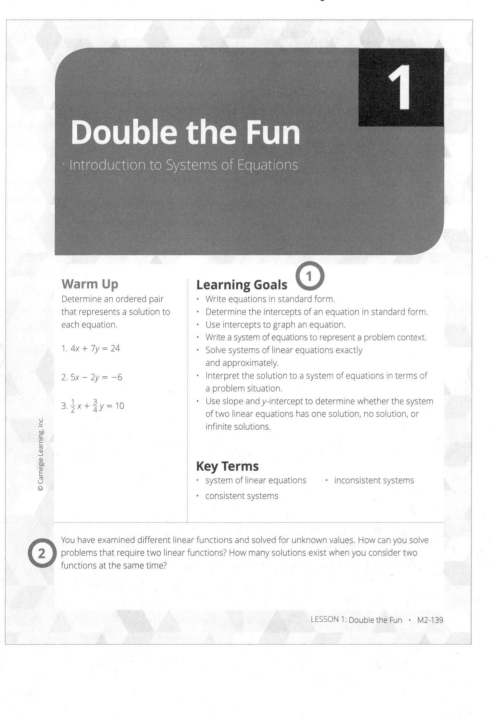

Double the Fun

Introduction to Systems of Equations

1

Warm Up

Determine an ordered pair that represents a solution to each equation.

1. $4x + 7y = 24$

2. $5x - 2y = -6$

3. $\frac{1}{2}x + \frac{3}{4}y = 10$

Learning Goals ①

- Write equations in standard form.
- Determine the intercepts of an equation in standard form.
- Use intercepts to graph an equation.
- Write a system of equations to represent a problem context.
- Solve systems of linear equations exactly and approximately.
- Interpret the solution to a system of equations in terms of a problem situation.
- Use slope and y-intercept to determine whether the system of two linear equations has one solution, no solution, or infinite solutions.

Key Terms

- system of linear equations
- inconsistent systems
- consistent systems

② You have examined different linear functions and solved for unknown values. How can you solve problems that require two linear functions? How many solutions exist when you consider two functions at the same time?

LESSON 1: Double the Fun • M2-139

© Carnegie Learning, Inc.

1. Learning Goals
Learning goals are stated for each lesson to help you take ownership of the learning objectives.

2. Connection
Each lesson begins with a statement connecting what you have learned with a question to ponder.

Return to this question at the end of this lesson to gauge your understanding.

3. Getting Started

Each lesson begins with a Getting Started. When working on the Getting Started, use what you know about the world, what you have learned previously, or your intuition. The goal is just to get you thinking and ready for what's to come.

---

③ GETTING STARTED

Ticket Tabulation

The Marshall High School Athletic Association sells tickets for the weekly football games. Students pay $5 and adults pay $10 for a ticket. The athletic association needs to raise $3000 selling tickets to send the team to an out-of-town tournament.

1. Write an equation to represent this situation.

2. What combination of student and adult ticket sales would achieve the athletic association's goal?

3. Compare your combination of ticket sales with your classmates'. Did you all get the same answer? Explain why or why not.

4. Activities

You are going to build a deep understanding of mathematics through a variety of activities in an environment where collaboration and conversations are important and expected.

You will learn how to solve new problems, but you will also learn why those strategies work and how they are connected to other strategies you already know.

Remember:

- It's not just about answer-getting. The process is important.

- Making mistakes are a critical part of learning, so take risks.

- There is often more than one way to solve a problem.

Activities may include real-world problems, sorting activities, worked examples, or analyzing sample student work.

Be prepared to share your solutions and methods with your classmates.

---

④

ACTIVITY 1.1 Analyzing the Graph of an Equation in Standard Form

ACTIVITY 1.2 Determining the Solution to a System of Linear Equations

ACTIVITY 1.3 Systems with No Solution, One Solution, or an Infinite Number of Solutions

Marcus and Phillip are in the Robotics Club. They are both saving money to buy materials to build a new robot.

Marcus opens a new bank account. He deposits $25 that he won at a robotics competition. He also plans on depositing $10 a week that he earns from tutoring. Phillip decides he wants to save money as well. He already has $40 saved from mowing lawns over the summer. He plans to also save $10 a week from his allowance.

1. **Write equations to represent the amount of money Marcus saves and the amount of money Phillip saves.**

2. **Use your equations to predict when Marcus and Phillip will have the same amount of money saved.**

You can prove your prediction by solving and graphing a system of linear equations.

3. **Analyze the equations in your system.**

   a. **How do the slopes compare? Describe what this means in terms of this problem situation.**

   b. **How do the y-intercepts compare? Describe what this means in terms of this problem situation.**

Adult Tickets Sold

M2-1

5. Talk the Talk

Talk the Talk gives you an opportunity to reflect on the main ideas of the lesson.

- Be honest with yourself.

- Ask questions to clarify anything you don't understand.

- Show what you know!

Don't forget to revisit the question posed on the lesson opening page to gauge your understanding.

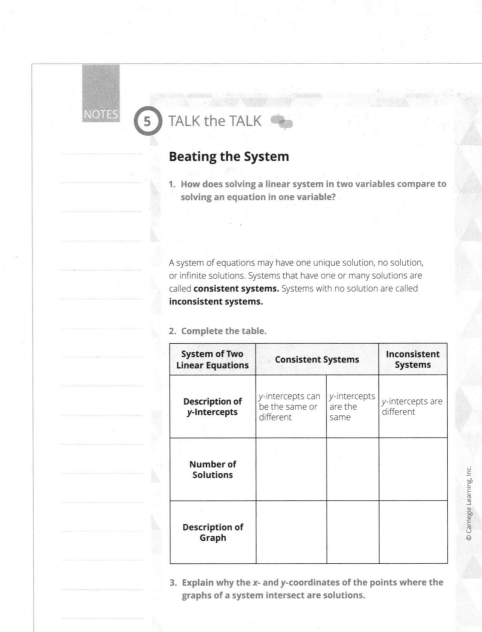

NOTES

5 TALK the TALK

Beating the System

1. How does solving a linear system in two variables compare to solving an equation in one variable?

A system of equations may have one unique solution, no solution, or infinite solutions. Systems that have one or many solutions are called **consistent systems.** Systems with no solution are called **inconsistent systems.**

2. Complete the table.

System of Two Linear Equations	Consistent Systems		Inconsistent Systems
Description of *y*-Intercepts	*y*-intercepts can be the same or different	*y*-intercepts are the same	*y*-intercepts are different
Number of Solutions			
Description of Graph			

3. Explain why the *x*- and *y*-coordinates of the points where the graphs of a system intersect are solutions.

© Carnegie Learning, Inc.

ASSIGNMENT

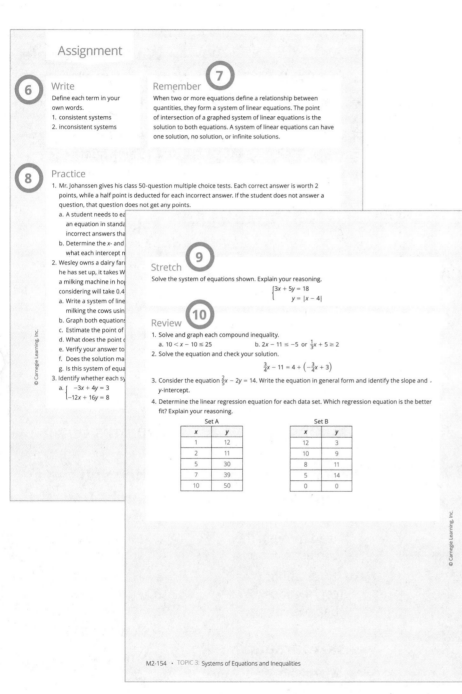

Assignment

6 Write
Define each term in your own words.
1. consistent systems
2. inconsistent systems

7 Remember
When two or more equations define a relationship between quantities, they form a system of linear equations. The point of intersection of a graphed system of linear equations is the solution to both equations. A system of linear equations can have one solution, no solution, or infinite solutions.

8 Practice
1. Mr. Johanssen gives his class 50-question multiple choice tests. Each correct answer is worth 2 points, while a half point is deducted for each incorrect answer. If the student does not answer a question, that question does not get any points.
   a. A student needs to ea... an equation in standa... incorrect answers tha...
   b. Determine the x- and ... what each intercept m...
2. Wesley owns a dairy far... he has set up, it takes W... a milking machine in ho... considering will take 0.4...
   a. Write a system of line... milking the cows usin...
   b. Graph both equations...
   c. Estimate the point of ...
   d. What does the point o...
   e. Verify your answer to ...
   f. Does the solution ma...
   g. Is this system of equa...
3. Identify whether each sy...
   a. $\begin{cases} -3x + 4y = 3 \\ -12x + 16y = 8 \end{cases}$

9 Stretch
Solve the system of equations shown. Explain your reasoning.
$$\begin{cases} 3x + 5y = 18 \\ y = |x - 4| \end{cases}$$

10 Review
1. Solve and graph each compound inequality.
   a. $10 < x - 10 \le 25$ b. $2x - 11 \le -5$ or $\frac{1}{3}x + 5 \ge 2$
2. Solve the equation and check your solution.
$$\frac{3}{4}x - 11 = 4 + \left(-\frac{3}{4}x + 3\right)$$
3. Consider the equation $\frac{2}{5}x - 2y = 14$. Write the equation in general form and identify the slope and y-intercept.
4. Determine the linear regression equation for each data set. Which regression equation is the better fit? Explain your reasoning.

Set A

x	y
1	12
2	11
5	30
7	39
10	50

Set B

x	y
12	3
10	9
8	11
5	14
0	0

6. Write
Reflect on your work and clarify your thinking.

7. Remember
Take note of the key concepts from the lesson.

8. Practice
Use the concepts learned in the lesson to solve problems.

9. Stretch
Ready for a challenge?

10. Review
Remember what you've learned by practicing concepts form previous lessons and topics.

Worked Example

You can represent a_n using function notation.

$$a_n = 2 + 4(n - 1)$$
$$f(n) = 2 + 4(n - 1)$$

Next, rewrite the expression $2 + 4(n - 1)$.

$f(n) = 2 + 4n - 4$	Distributive Property
$= 4n + 2 - 4$	Commutative Property
$= 4n - 2$	Combine Like Terms

So, $a_n = 2 + 4(n - 1)$ written in function notation is $f(n) = 4n - 2$.

Worked Example

When you see a Worked Example:
- Take your time to read through it.
- Question your own understanding.
- Think about the connections between steps.

Ask Yourself:
- What is the main idea?
- How would this work if I changed the numbers?
- Have I used these strategies before?

Maya and Sherry each convert the given formula to degrees Fahrenheit.

Maya 👍

$$C = \frac{5}{9}(F - 32)$$
$$C = \frac{5}{9}F - \frac{160}{9}$$
$$9(C) = 9\left(\frac{5}{9}F - \frac{160}{9}\right)$$
$$9C = 5F - 160$$
$$9C + 160 = 5F$$
$$\frac{9C}{5} + \frac{160}{5} = \frac{5F}{5}$$
$$\frac{9}{5}C + 32 = F$$

Sherry 👎

$$C = \frac{5}{9}(F - 32)$$
$$C = \frac{5}{9}F - 32$$
$$9(C) = 9\left(\frac{5}{9}F - 32\right)$$
$$9C = 5F - 288$$
$$9C + 288 = 5F$$
$$\frac{9C}{5} + \frac{288}{5} = \frac{5F}{5}$$
$$\frac{9}{5}C + 57.6 = F$$

Thumbs Up

When you see a Thumbs Up icon:
- Take your time to read through the correct solution.
- Think about the connections between steps.

Ask Yourself:
- Why is this method correct?
- Have I used this method before?

Thumbs Down

When you see a Thumbs Down icon:
- Take your time to read through the incorrect solution.
- Think about what error was made.

Ask Yourself:
- Where is the error?
- Why is it an error?
- How can I correct it?

4. Carlos and Mikala do not like working with fractions. Each rewrites the equation so that it does not have fractions. Their work is shown.

Carlos
$$F = \frac{9}{5}C + 32$$
$$(5)F = 5\left(\frac{9}{5}C + 32\right)$$
$$5F = 9C + 160$$
$$5F - 9C = 160$$

Mikala
$$C = \frac{5}{9}(F - 32)$$
$$(9)C = (9)\left(\frac{5}{9}(F - 32)\right)$$
$$9C = 5(F - 32)$$
$$9C = 5F - 160$$
$$9C - 5F = -160$$

Carlos and Mikala got two different equations. Who is correct? Explain your reasoning.

Who's Correct

When you see a Who's Correct icon:
- Take your time to read through the situation.
- Question the strategy or reason given.
- Determine correct or not correct.

Ask Yourself:
- Does the reasoning make sense?
- If the reasoning makes sense, what is the justification?
- If the reasoning does not make sense, what error was made?

HABITS OF MIND

The types of activities within this book require you to make sense of mathematics and to demonstrate your reasoning through problem solving, writing, discussing, and presenting. Effective communication and collaboration are essential skills of a successful learner.

Each activity is denoted with an icon that represents a practice or pair of practices intentionally being developed. To help develop these habits of mind ask yourself the types of questions listed as you work.

With practice, you can develop the habits of mind of a productive mathematical thinker.

▶ Make sense of problems and perservere in solving them.

This practice is evident every day in every lesson. No icon used.

Questions to ask:
- What is this problem asking and what is my plan for answering it?
- What tools do I need to solve this problem?
- Does my answer make sense?

▶ Reason abstractly and quantitatively.
▶ Construct viable arguments and critique the reasoning of others.

Questions to ask:
- What representation can I use to solve this problem?
- How can this problem be represented with symbols and numbers?
- How can I explain my thinking?
- How does my strategy compare to my partner's?

" In this class, you won't experiment with beakers full of unearthly liquids, but you'll still be thinking and working like a scientist. So, you will notice patterns, predict how they will behave, test out the predictions, and then unscramble the results. Patterns are everywhere throughout this book, so be **constantly** on the lookout—ready to spot them. There may even be a pleasing pattern buried somewhere in this quotation. "

Josh Fisher, Instructional Designer

► **Model with mathematics.**
► **Use appropriate tools strategically.**

Questions to ask:

- What expression or equation could represent this situation?
- What tools would help me solve this problem?
- What representations best show my thinking?
- How does this answer make sense in the context of the original problem?

► **Attend to precision.**

Questions to ask:

- Is my answer accurate?
- Did I use the correct units or labels?
- Is there a more efficient way to solve this problem?
- Is there more sophisticated vocabulary that I could use in my explanation?

► **Look for and make use of structure.**
► **Look for and express regularity in repeated reasoning.**

Questions to ask:

- What characteristics of this expression or equation are made clear through this representation?
- How can I use what I know to explain why this works?
- Can I develop a more efficient method?
- How could this problem help me to solve another problem?

"It's okay to make mistakes. There is great value in taking risks, making mistakes, and communicating about your mathematical thinking. Only when you reveal your misconceptions, can they be addressed and clarified. You will be amazed at the power you have when you can reason to make sense of the math!

Janet Sinopoli, Instructional Designer

There are important terms you will encounter throughout this book. It is important that you have an understanding of these words as you get started on your journey through the mathematical concepts. Knowing what is meant by these terms and using these terms will help you think, reason, and communicate your ideas.

Related Phrases

- Examine
- Evaluate
- Determine
- Observe
- Consider
- Investigate
- What do you notice?
- What do you think?
- Sort and match

ANALYZE

Definition

To study or look closely for patterns. Analyzing can involve examining or breaking a concept down into smaller parts to gain a better understanding of it.

Ask Yourself

- Do I see any patterns?
- Have I seen something like this before?
- What happens if the shape, representation, or numbers change?

Related Phrases

- Show your work
- Explain your calculation
- Justify
- Why or why not?

EXPLAIN YOUR REASONING

Definition

To give details or describe how to determine an answer or solution. Explaining your reasoning helps justify conclusions.

Ask Yourself

- How should I organize my thoughts?
- Is my explanation logical?
- Does my reasoning make sense?
- How can I justify my answer to others?

REPRESENT

Related Phrases

Definition

To display information in various ways. Representing mathematics can be done using words, tables, graphs, or symbols.

- Show
- Sketch
- Draw
- Create
- Plot
- Graph
- Write an equation
- Complete the table

Ask Yourself

- How should I organize my thoughts?
- How do I use this model to show a concept or idea?
- What does this representation tell me?
- Is my representation accurate?

ESTIMATE

Related Phrases

Definition

To make an educated guess based on the analysis of given data. Estimating first helps inform reasoning.

- Predict
- Approximate
- Expect
- About how much?

Ask Yourself

- Does my reasoning make sense?
- Is my solution close to my estimation?

DESCRIBE

Related Phrases

Definition

To represent or give an account of in words. Describing communicates mathematical ideas to others.

- Demonstrate
- Label
- Display
- Compare
- Determine
- Define
- What are the advantages?
- What are the disadvantages?
- What is similar?
- What is different?

Ask Yourself

- How should I organize my thoughts?
- Is my explanation logical?
- Did I consider the context of the situation?
- Does my reasoning make sense?

> " Imagine a room full of art tools. You and your peers must each use the tools to represent a frog. Some may choose to paint the frog. Others may sculpt or write a poem about it. As a mathematician, you are an artist representing your world with your choice of tools–numbers, equations, graphs, tables, or even words. We can express ourselves in different ways even if we are representing the same idea. "

Victoria Fisher, Instructional Designer

Thought Bubbles

Look for these icons as you journey through the textbook. Sometimes they will remind you about things you already learned. Sometimes they will ask you questions to help you think about different strategies. Sometimes they will share fun facts. They are here to help and guide your learning.

Side notes are included to provide helpful insights as you work.

Remember:

Think about:

Ask yourself:

MODULE 1

53ARCH1NG
FOR PATT3RN5

The lessons in this module build on your experiences searching for patterns in the real-world, in numbers, in geometric figures, and in data. In this module, you will consider different scenarios, graphs, and equations and sort them according to key characteristics and define five function families. You will explore numeric sequences and consider how to classify them based on similarities. You will analyze patterns in data and formalize your understanding of lines of best fit.

Quantities and Relationships

The amount of sand in the lower bulb of an hourglass is directly proportional to the time since the glass was turned over.

Module 1: Searching for Patterns

TOPIC 1: QUANTITIES AND RELATIONSHIPS

In this topic, students explore a variety of different functions. The intent is merely to introduce these new functions, providing an overview but not a deep understanding at this point. The topic is designed to help students recognize that different function families have different key characteristics. In later study in this course, they will formalize their understanding of the defining characteristics of each type of function.

Where have we been?

In previous grades, students defined a function and used linear functions to model the relationship between two quantities. They have written linear functions in slope-intercept form and should be able to identify the slope and *y*-intercept in the equation. Students have also characterized graphs as functions using the terms *increasing, decreasing, constant, discrete, continuous, linear,* and *nonlinear.*

Where are we going?

The study of functions is a main focus of high school mathematics. This topic builds the foundation for future, more in-depth study by familiarizing students with the concept of a function. Students will continue to use formal function notation throughout this course and in higher-level math courses.

Function Notation

The linear equation $y = 8x + 15$ can be written to represent a relationship between the variables x and y. You can write this linear equation as a function with the name f to represent it as a mathematical object that has a specific set of inputs (the domain of the function) and a specific set of outputs (the range of the function).

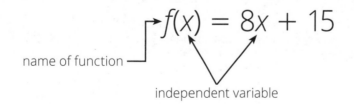

name of function

$$f(x) = 8x + 15$$

independent variable

The input of the function, x, is represented by a single variable, but this variable often represents a whole collection of values.

Functions Are Everywhere. Google It.

Every time you open a web page, you are calling hundreds, if not thousands, of functions. At the time of this writing, there were 88 functions mentioned in the background on the homepage of a popular search engine, which contains just a name and a search box.

Functions that programmers write are very similar to the functions students study in mathematics. They take inputs and produce outputs. And they are often written in the same way too—with a function name and an input variable in parentheses, like $f(x)$. Search functions take in search terms as inputs and output hundreds of thousands or millions of results. Mathematical functions can only output one result for each input.

Talking Points

Functions is an important topic to know about for college admissions tests.
Here is a sample question:

For the function $f(x) = 2x^2 - 3x$, what is the value of $f(-5)$?

To solve this, students need to know that the input -5 is substituted for x in the equation:

$$f(-5) = 2(-5)^2 - 3(-5)$$
$$= 2(25) + 15$$
$$= 50 + 15$$
$$= 65$$

The point $(-5, 65)$ is on the graph of the function.

Key Terms

increasing function
If a function increases across the entire domain, then the function is called an increasing function.

decreasing function
If a function decreases across the entire domain, then the function is called a decreasing function.

function family
A function family is a group of functions that all share some characteristics.

x-intercept
The x-intercept is the point where a graph crosses the x-axis.

y-intercept
The y-intercept is the point where a graph crosses the y-axis.

A Picture Is Worth a Thousand Words

Understanding Quantities and Their Relationships

Warm Up

Emma bought a new video game. The graph shown describes the number of hours Emma spent playing the game over a period of 7 days.

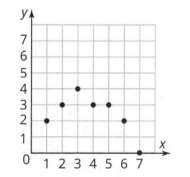

1. Label the axes.

2. What does the highest point on the graph represent with respect to the scenario? The lowest point?

Learning Goals

- Understand quantities and their relationships with each other.
- Identify the independent and dependent quantities for a scenario.
- Match a graph with an appropriate scenario.
- Use a reasonable scale for a graph modeling a scenario.
- Identify key characteristics of graphs.
- Describe similarities and differences between pairs of graphs and scenarios.

Key Terms

- dependent quantity
- independent quantity

You have analyzed graphs of relationships and identified important features such as intercepts and slopes. How can the key characteristics of a graph tell a story?

What Comes First?

Have you ever planned a party? You may have purchased ice, gone grocery shopping, selected music, made food, or even cleaned in preparation. Many times, these tasks depend on another task being done first. For instance, you wouldn't make food before grocery shopping, now would you?

Consider the two quantities that are changing in each relationship.

> When one quantity depends on another in a problem situation, it is said to be the **dependent quantity**. The quantity it depends upon is called the **independent quantity**.

- the number of movie tickets purchased and the total cost

- the number of eggs used and the number of cakes baked

- the number of students in attendance at school and the number of lunches served

- the number of hours driven and the number of miles to a vacation destination

- the number of minutes a swimming pool is filled with water and the number of gallons of water in the swimming pool

1. **Circle the independent quantity and underline the dependent quantity in each relationship.**

2. **Describe how you can determine which quantity is independent and which quantity is dependent in any problem situation.**

© Carnegie Learning, Inc.

Connecting Scenarios and Their Graphs

While a person can describe the monthly cost to operate a business, or talk about a marathon pace a runner ran to break a world record, graphs on a coordinate plane enable people to see the data. Graphs relay information about data in a visual way.

You can use lines or smooth curves to represent relationships between points on a graph. In some problem situations, all the points on the line will make sense. In other problem situations, not all the points will make sense. So, when you model a relationship with a line or a curve, it is up to you to consider the situation and interpret the meaning of the data values shown.

This activity includes eight scenarios and eight graphs that are located at the end of the lesson.

1. **Read each scenario. Determine the independent and dependent quantities. Then match each scenario to its corresponding graph. Glue the graph next to the scenario. For each graph, label the *x*- and *y*-axis with the appropriate quantity and a reasonable scale, and then interpret the meaning of the origin.**

Think about:

Be sure to include the appropriate units of measure for each quantity.

Daredevil
Greyson completes a dive from a cliff 75-feet above a river. It takes him only 1.5 seconds to hit the water and then another 0.5 second to descend 10 feet into the river.

- **independent quantity:**

- **dependent quantity:**

Ask yourself:

What strategies will you use to match each graph with one of the eight scenarios?

Something's Fishy

Candice is a building manager for the Crowley Enterprise office building. One of her responsibilities is cleaning the office building's 200-gallon aquarium. For cleaning, she must remove the fish from the aquarium and drain the water. The water drains at a constant rate of 10 gallons per minute.

- **independent quantity:**

- **dependent quantity:**

Smart Phone, but Is It a Smart Deal?

You have your eye on an upgraded smart phone. However, you currently do not have the money to purchase it. Your cousin will provide the funding, as long as you pay him back with interest. He tells you that you only need to pay $1 in interest initially, and then the interest will double each week after that. You consider his offer and wonder if this *really* is a good deal.

- **independent quantity:**

- **dependent quantity:**

Can't Wait to Hit the Slopes!

Andrew loves skiing—he just hates the ski lift. To make matters worse, the ski lift has been acting up today. Andrew is using the GPS on his phone to track the ski lift's progress as it travels up the mountain. It moves at a steady rate of 400 feet per minute until it stops suddenly. Andrew calls his friends to tell them that he is stuck. They talk on the phone for 10 minutes until finally the ski lift begins moving again.

- **independent quantity:**

- **dependent quantity:**

It's Magic

The Amazing Aloysius is practicing one of his tricks. As part of this trick, he cuts a rope into many pieces and then magically puts the pieces of rope back together. He begins the trick with a 20-foot rope and then cuts it in half. He then takes one of the halves and cuts that piece in half. He repeats this process until he is left with a piece so small he can no longer cut it.

- **independent quantity:**

- **dependent quantity:**

Baton Twirling

Jill is a drum major for the Altadena High School marching band. For the finale of the halftime performance, Jill tosses her baton in the air so that it reaches a maximum height of 22 feet. This gives her 2 seconds to twirl around twice and catch the baton when it comes back down.

- **independent quantity:**

- **dependent quantity:**

Cold Weather

The number of guests at a ski resort on any given day is related to the day's high temperature. If the high temperature is −20°F or below, no one comes to the resort. As the temperature increases, so does the number of guests. Once the temperature reaches 0°F and increases through the single digits, the number of guests soars. If the temperature is 10°F or higher, the ski resort is at full capacity with 400 guests.

- **independent quantity:**

- **dependent quantity:**

Jelly Bean Challenge

Mr. Wright judges the annual Jelly Bean Challenge at the summer fair. Every year, he encourages the citizens in his town to guess the number of jelly beans in a jar. He records all the possible guesses and the number of jelly beans that each guess was off by.

- **independent quantity:**

- **dependent quantity:**

© Carnegie Learning, Inc.

Now that you have matched a graph with the appropriate problem situation, let's go back and examine all the graphs.

1. **What similarities do you notice in the graphs?**

Think

about:

Look closely when analyzing the graphs. What do you see?

2. **What differences do you notice in the graphs?**

3. **How did you label the independent and dependent quantities in each graph?**

4. **Analyze each graph from left to right. Describe any graphical characteristics you notice.**

5. Compare the graphs for each pair of scenarios given and describe any similarities and differences you notice.

Think about:

What do the points on each graph represent?

a. *Smart Phone, but Is It a Smart Deal?* and *Cold Weather*

b. *Something's Fishy* and *It's Magic*

c. *Baton Twirling* and *Jelly Bean Challenge*

TALK the TALK

A Writer and a Mathematician

1. Write a scenario and sketch a graph to describe a possible trip to school.

Scenario   **Graph**

_____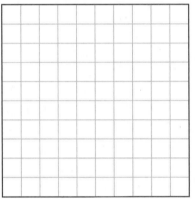

_____

_____

_____

_____

_____

_____

_____

2. Describe the meaning of the points, or smooth curve, represented by your graph.

3. Compare your scenario and sketch with your classmates' scenarios and sketches. What similarities do you notice? What differences do you notice?

Graph Cutouts

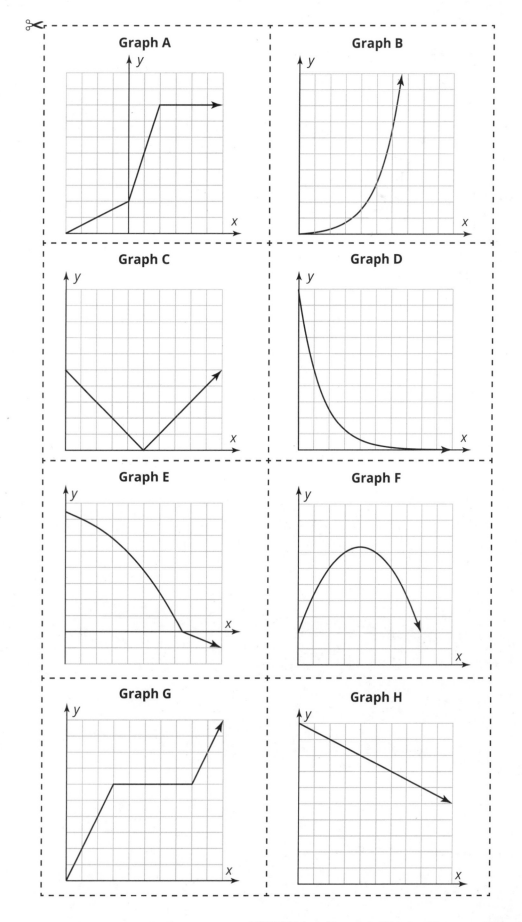

384-772
862-425

Assignment

Write

Describe how you can distinguish between an independent quantity and a dependent quantity. Use an example in your description.

Remember

When one quantity depends on another in a problem situation, it is said to be the dependent quantity. The quantity it depends upon is called the independent quantity. The independent quantity is represented on the *x*-axis and the dependent quantity is represented on the *y*-axis.

Practice

1. Read each scenario and identify the independent and dependent quantities. Be sure to include the appropriate units of measure. Then analyze each graph and determine which of the provided scenarios it models. For each graph, label the *x*- and *y*-axis with the appropriate quantity and unit of measure.

a. Endangered Species
   The Elkwood Aquatic Society is working with various reptile species to increase their populations. The initial population of 450 endangered turtles tripled each year for the past five years.

c. Sales Commission
   Julian works as a salesman. He receives a monthly salary of $3000 as well as a 10% commission on the amount of sales.

e. Commuter Flight
   A commuter flight between two cities in Oregon takes about 40 minutes. The plane increases its altitude for the first half of the flight until it gets to 18,000 feet, and then it descends for the second half of the flight. The plane ascends and descends at a constant rate of 900 feet per minute.

b. Video Games
   Gillian is playing video games at an arcade. Gillian starts with $40 and is playing games that cost 50 cents per game.

d. Cooling Tea
   A freshly made cup of tea is served at a temperature of about 180°F. The tea cools rapidly at first, and then slows down gradually as it approaches room temperature.

f. Cross Country
   Brady runs for his high school cross country team. His strategy for each 5-kilometer race is always to begin by increasing his speed so that by the time he reaches the first kilometer, he is running at a speed of 0.3 km/min. He maintains that speed for the next 2 km. He then gradually speeds up for the remaining 2 km so that when he crosses the finish line, he is running at a speed of 0.5 km/min.

A.
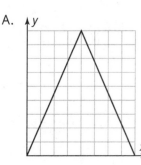

B.
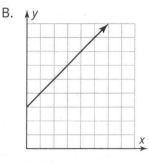

C.
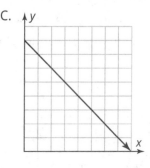

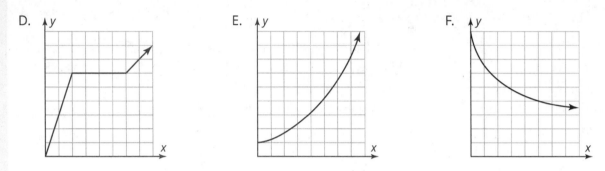

D.   E.   F.

2. Compare each pair of graphs and describe any similarities and differences you notice.

a.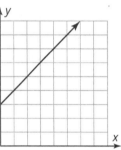

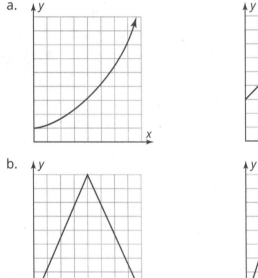

b.

Stretch

Read the scenario and identify the independent and dependent quantities. Be sure to include the appropriate units of measure.

1. A student performs several experiments in which he swings a pendulum for a 20-second duration. He uses a string that is 27 cm long, and he tests pendulum masses of different sizes, varying from 2 to 12 grams. He records the number of swings each pendulum makes in 20 seconds.

2. The student then decides to make a second graph showing the string length (in cm) as the independent quantity. What changes must the student make to his experiment?

Review

1. Solve the equation $-2x + 8 = -3x + 14$.
2. Evaluate the expression $x^2 - 3y + 12$ for $x = -2$ and $y = 5$.

A Sort of Sorts

Analyzing and Sorting Graphs

2

Warm Up

Write the coordinates of each point and name the quadrant or axis where the point is located.

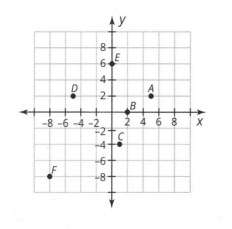

Learning Goals

- Review and analyze graphs and graphical behavior.
- Determine similarities and differences among various graphs.
- Sort graphs and give reasons for the similarities and differences between the groups of graphs.

You have used graphs to analyze the relationship between independent and dependent quantities. Do the graphs of certain types of relationships share any characteristics?

Let's Sort Some Graphs

Mathematics is the science of patterns and relationships. Looking for patterns and sorting patterns into different groups based on similarities and differences can provide valuable insights. In this lesson, you will analyze many different graphs and sort them into various groups.

1. **Cut out the 19 graphs at the end of the lesson. Then analyze and sort the graphs into at least 2 different groups. You may group the graphs in any way you feel is appropriate.**

    Record the following information for each of your groups.
    *   **Name each group of graphs.**
    *   **List the letters of the graphs in each group.**
    *   **Provide a rationale for why you created each group.**

Keep your graphs, you will need them in the next lesson.

© Carnegie Learning, Inc.

In this activity, consider the different ways the graphs are grouped.

1. **Matthew grouped these graphs together. Why do you think Matthew put these graphs in the same group?**

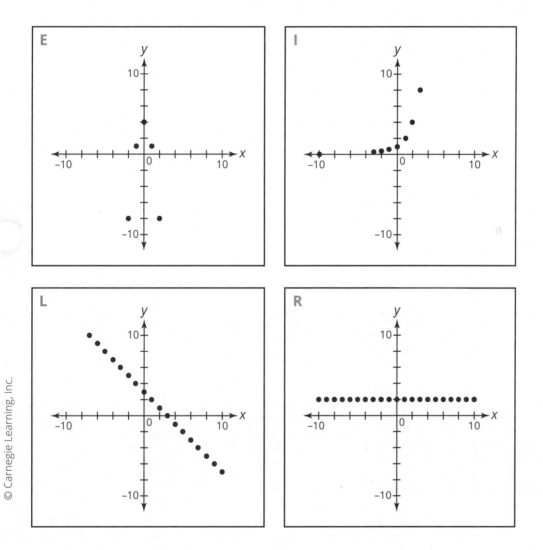

2. Consider Ashley's correct grouping.

Ashley

I grouped these graphs together because they all have a vertical axis of symmetry. If I draw a vertical line through the middle of the graph, the image is the same on both sides.

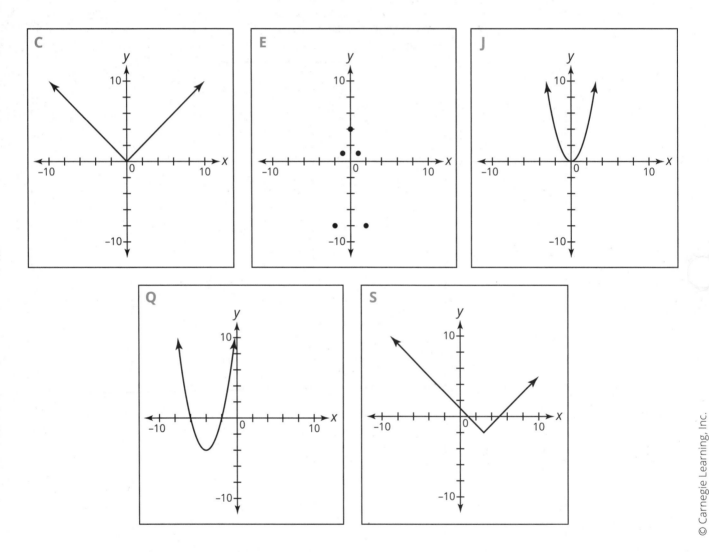

a. Show why Ashley's reasoning is correct.

b. If possible, identify other graphs that have a vertical axis of symmetry.

3. Consider Duane's incorrect grouping.

Duane
I grouped these graphs together because each graph goes through only two quadrants.

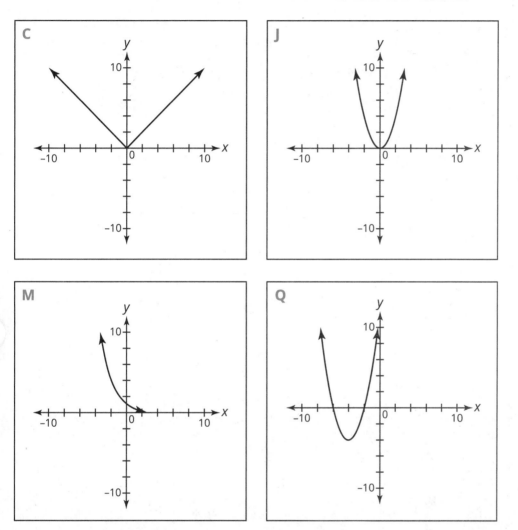

a. Explain why Duane's reasoning is not correct.

b. If possible, identify other graphs that go through only two quadrants.

4. Judy grouped these graphs together, but did not provide any rationale.

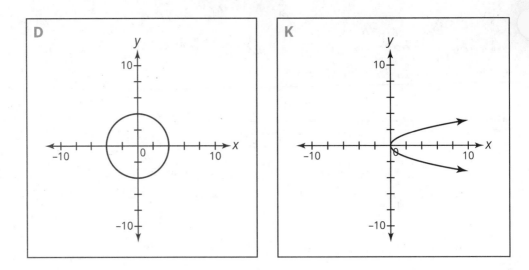

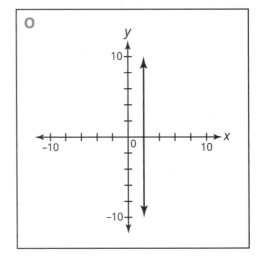

a. What do you notice about the graphs?

b. What rationale could Judy have provided?

TALK the TALK

Compare and Contrast

1. Compare your groups with your classmates' groups. Create a list of the different graphical behaviors you noticed.

Ask yourself:

Are any of the graphical behaviors shared among your groups? Or, are they unique to each group?

Graph Cards

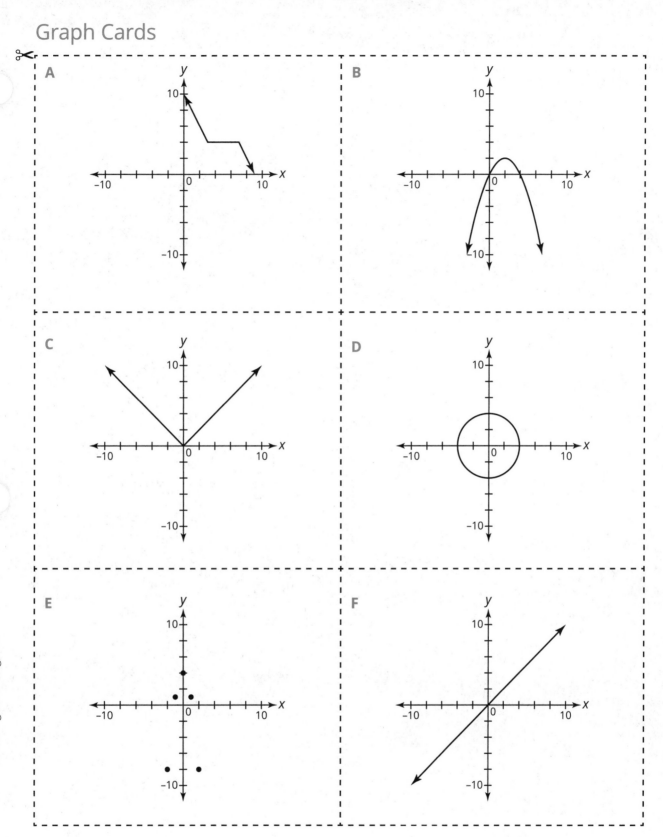

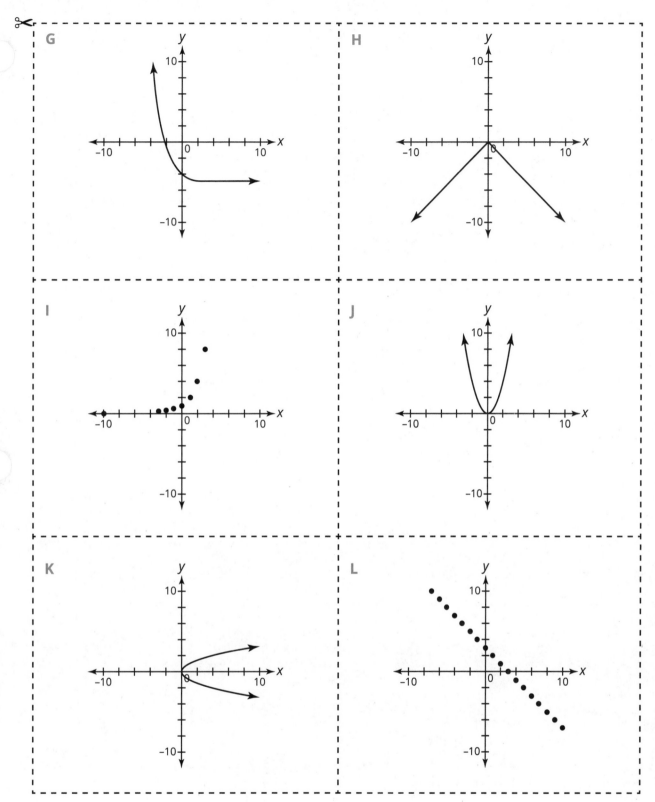

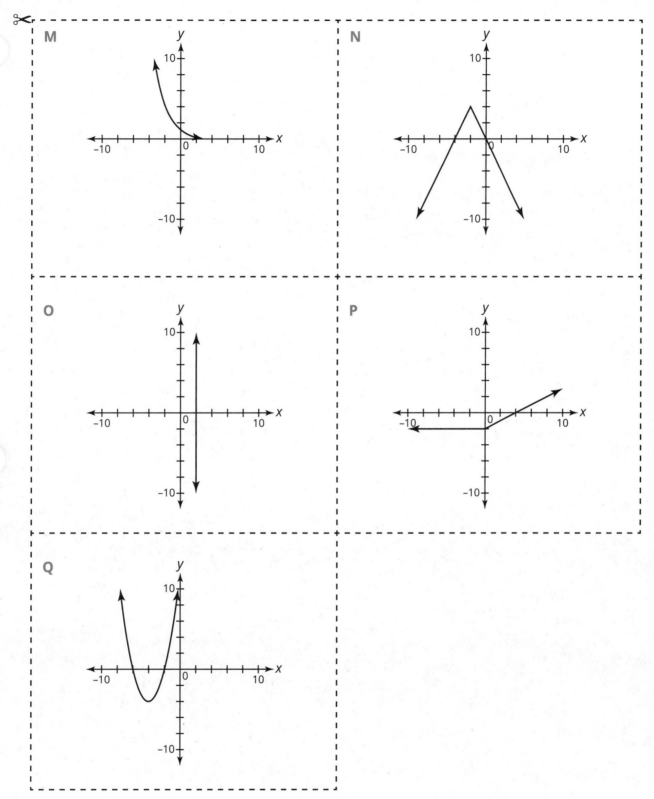

M

N

O

P

Q

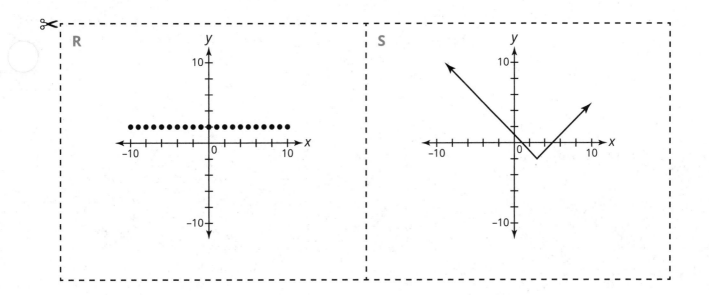

R

S

Write

Describe the importance of graphical representations.

Remember

Graphs of relationships between quantities have characteristics that can give you important information about the relationship. For example, a graph can be increasing, decreasing, neither increasing nor decreasing, or both increasing and decreasing. A graph can have straight lines or smooth curves, a maximum or minimum, or no maximum or minimum, and so on.

Practice

1. Record the letter of each graph with the given characteristic.
   a. has a vertical axis of symmetry
   b. has a horizontal axis of symmetry
   c. passes through exactly 1 quadrant
   d. passes through all 4 quadrants

A.
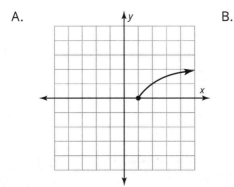

B.
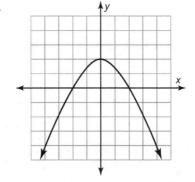

C.
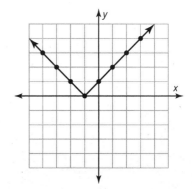

D.
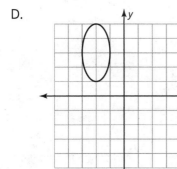

E.
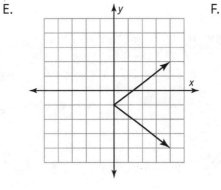

F.
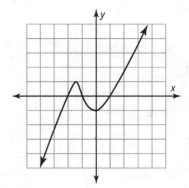

Stretch

Describe characteristics of each graph, including whether or not it has a vertical or horizontal axis of symmetry and the number of quadrants it passes through.

1. diagonal line through the origin that increases from left to right
2. diagonal line through the origin that decreases from left to right
3. diagonal line that does not pass through the origin
4. horizontal line below the origin
5. vertical line to the right of the origin

Review

1. Read each scenario and identify the independent and dependent quantities. Be sure to include the appropriate units of measure. Then determine which graph models the scenario.

   a. Henry is cooking a turkey for his family. His recipe says to cook the turkey for 15 minutes per pound.

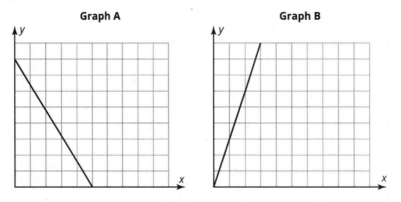

   Graph A   **Graph B**

   b. When Jane exercises on an elliptical machine, her initial heart rate is 90 beats per minute. She warms up at this rate for 5 minutes. Over the next 5 minutes, she gradually increases to 150 beats per minute. She maintains that rate for 15 minutes before gradually decreasing back to her original heart rate at the end of her 30-minute workout.

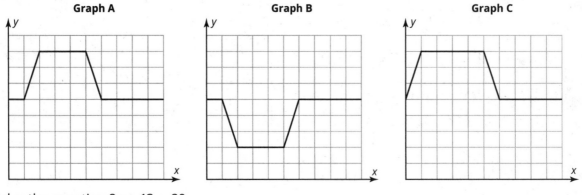

   Graph A   **Graph B**   **Graph C**

2. Solve the equation $8y + 13 = 29$.

3. Evaluate the expression $6z + 5(-2z - 7)$ for $z = -1$.

G of X

Recognizing Functions and Function Families

Warm Up

Identify the domain and range of the relation described by each set of ordered pairs. Write an equation using the variables x and y that could map the domain to the range.

1. $\{(-3, -6), (-2, -4), (-1, -2), (0, 0), (1, 2)\}$

2. $\{(-3, 9), (-2, 4), (-1, 1), (0, 0), (1, 1), (2, 4)\}$

3. $\{(-3, 3), (-2, 2), (-1, 1), (0, 0), (1, -1), (2, -2)\}$

Learning Goals

- Define a function as a relation that assigns each element of the domain to exactly one element of the range.
- Write equations using function notation.
- Recognize multiple representations of functions.
- Determine and recognize characteristics of functions.
- Determine and recognize characteristics of function families.

Key Terms

- relation
- domain
- range
- function
- function notation
- Vertical Line Test
- discrete graph
- continuous graph
- increasing function
- decreasing function
- constant function
- function family
- linear functions
- exponential functions
- absolute minimum
- absolute maximum
- quadratic functions
- linear absolute value functions
- linear piecewise functions
- x-intercept
- y-intercept

You have sorted graphs by their graphical behaviors. How can you describe the common characteristics of the graphs of the functions?

Odd One Out

1. **Which of the graphs shown does not belong with the others? Explain your reasoning.**

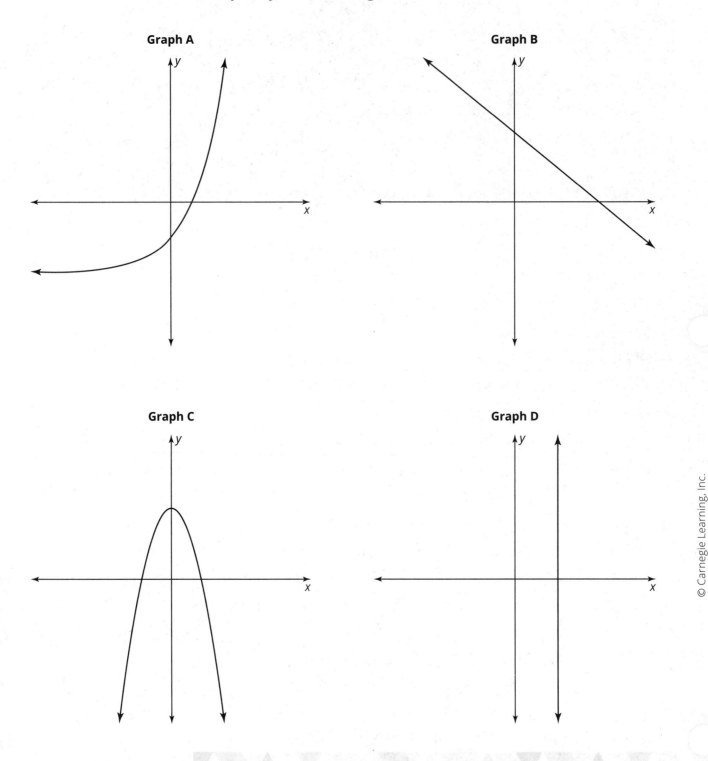

Graph A

Graph B

Graph C

Graph D

A relation can be represented in the following ways.

> A **relation** is the mapping between a set of input values called the **domain** and a set of output values called the **range**.

Ordered Pairs
{(−2, 2), (0, 2), (3, −4), (3, 5)}

Equation
$y = \frac{2}{3}x - 1$

Verbal
The relation between students in your school and each student's birthday.

Mapping

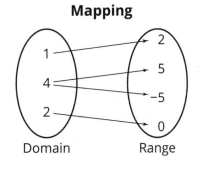

Domain   Range

Graph

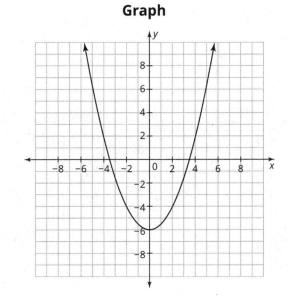

Table

Domain	Range
−1	1
2	0
5	−5
6	−5
7	−8

A **function** is a relation that assigns to each element of the domain exactly one element of the range. Functions can be represented in a number of ways.

1. **Analyze the relation represented as a table. Is the relation a function? Explain your reasoning.**

2. **Analyze the relation represented as a mapping. Is the relation a function? Explain your reasoning.**

3. **Analyze the relation represented verbally. Is the relation a function? Explain your reasoning.**

You can write an equation representing a function using *function notation.* Let's look at the relationship between an equation and function notation.

Consider this scenario. U.S. Shirts charges $8 per shirt plus a one-time charge of $15 to set up a T-shirt design.

The equation $y = 8x + 15$ can be written to model this situation. The independent variable x represents the number of shirts ordered, and the dependent variable y represents the total cost of the order, in dollars.

This is a function because for each number of shirts ordered (independent value) there is exactly one total cost (dependent value) associated with it. Because this relationship is a function, you can write $y = 8x + 15$ in function notation.

$$f(x) = 8x + 15$$

name of function

independent variable

The cost, defined by f, is a function of x, defined as the number of shirts ordered.

You can write a function in a number of different ways. You could write the T-shirt cost function as $C(s) = 8s + 15$, where the cost, defined as C, is a function of s, the number of shirts ordered.

4. **Consider the U.S. Shirts function, $C(s) = 8s + 15$. What expression in the function equation represents:**

   a. **the domain of the function?**

   b. **the range of the function?**

5. **Describe the possible domain and range for this situation.**

© Carnegie Learning, Inc.

The **Vertical Line Test** is a visual method used to determine whether a relation represented as a graph is a function. To apply the Vertical Line Test, consider all of the vertical lines that could be drawn on the graph of a relation. If any of the vertical lines intersect the graph of the relation at more than one point, then the relation is not a function.

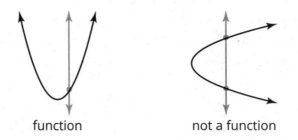

function   not a function

The Vertical Line Test applies for both *discrete* and *continuous graphs*.

A **discrete graph** is a graph of isolated points. A **continuous graph** is a graph of points that are connected by a line or smooth curve on the graph. Continuous graphs have no breaks.

6. **How can you determine if a relation represented as ordered pairs is a function? Explain your reasoning.**

7. **How can you determine if a relation represented as an equation is a function? Explain your reasoning.**

8. **Determine which relations represent functions. If the relation is not a function, state why not.**

a. $y = 3^x$

b. For every house, there is one and only one street address.

c.

Domain	Range
−1	4
0	0
3	−2
0	4

d.

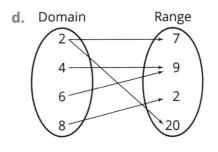

e. {(−7, 5), (−5, 5), (2, −2), (3, 5)}

f.

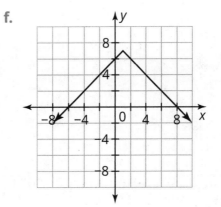

9. **Analyze the three graphs Judy grouped together in the previous lesson, graphs D, K, and O. Are the graphs she grouped functions? Explain your conclusion.**

10. **Use the Vertical Line Test to sort the graphs in the previous lesson into two groups: functions and non-functions. Record your results by writing the letter of each graph in the appropriate column in the table shown.**

Functions	Non-Functions

Domain and Range of a Function

You have identified the domain and range of a function given its equation.

1. **Explain how you can identify the domain and range of a function given:**

   a. a verbal statement.   **b. a graph.**

Worked Example

There are different ways to write the domain and range of a function given its graph.

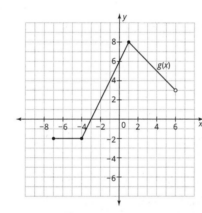   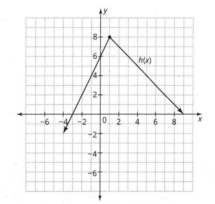

	Domain		Range	
	g(x)	**h(x)**	**g(x)**	**h(x)**
In Words	The domain is all real numbers greater than or equal to −7 and less than 6.	The domain is the set of all real numbers.	The range is all real numbers greater than or equal to -2 and less than or equal to 8	The range is all real numbers less than or equal to 8.
Using Notation	$-7 \le x < 6$	$-\infty < x < \infty$	$-2 \le y \le 8$	$y \le 8$

---

2. **Consider the Graph Cards from the previous activity that include continuous functions. Label each of these cards with the appropriate domain and range.**

Gather all of the graphs that you identified as functions.

A function is described as increasing when the value of the dependent variable increases as the value of the independent variable increases. If a function increases across the entire domain, then the function is called an **increasing function**.

A function is described as decreasing when the value of the dependent variable decreases as the value of the independent variable increases. If a function decreases across the entire domain, then the function is called a **decreasing function**.

If the value of the dependent variable of a function remains constant over the entire domain, then the function is called a **constant function**.

> When determining whether a graph is increasing or decreasing, read the graph from left to right.

1. **Analyze each graph from left to right. Sort all the graphs into one of the four groups listed.**

   • **increasing function**

   • **decreasing function**

   • **constant function**

   • **a combination of increasing, decreasing, and constant**

   Record the function letter in the appropriate column of the table shown.

Increasing Function	Decreasing Function	Constant Function	Combination of Increasing, Decreasing, and Constant Functions

2. Each function shown represents one of the graphs in the increasing function, decreasing function, or constant function categories. Use graphing technology to determine the shape of its graph. Then match the function to its corresponding graph by writing the function directly on the graph that it represents.

- $f(x) = x$

- $f(x) = \left(\frac{1}{2}\right)^x$

- $f(x) = \left(\frac{1}{2}\right)^x - 5$

- $f(x) = 2$, where x is an integer

- $f(x) = 2^x$, where x is an integer

- $f(x) = -x + 3$, where x is an integer

Think about:

Be sure to correctly interpret the domain of each function. Also, remember to use parentheses when entering fractions into your calculator.

3. Consider the six graphs and functions that are increasing functions, decreasing functions, or constant functions.

a. Sort the graphs into two groups based on the equations representing the functions and record the function letter in the table.

Group 1	Group 2

b. What is the same about all the functions in each group?

You have just sorted the graphs into their own *function families*. A **function family** is a group of functions that share certain characteristics.

The family of **linear functions** includes functions of the form $f(x) = ax + b$, where a and b are real numbers.

The family of **exponential functions** includes functions of the form $f(x) = a \cdot b^x + c$, where a, b, and c are real numbers, and b is greater than 0 but not equal to 1.

4. **Go back to your table in Question 3 and identify which group represents linear and constant functions and which group represents exponential functions.**

5. **If $f(x) = ax + b$ represents a linear function, describe the a and b values that produce a constant function.**

Place these two groups of graphs off to the side. You will need them again.

Quadratic and Absolute Value Functions

A function has an **absolute minimum** if there is a point on the graph of the function that has a *y*-coordinate that is less than the *y*-coordinate of every other point on the graph. A function has an **absolute maximum** if there is a point on the graph of the function that has a *y*-coordinate that is greater than the *y*-coordinate of every other point on the graph.

1. **Sort the graphs from the combination of increasing, decreasing, and constant category in the previous activity into one of the three groups listed.**

   • **those that have an absolute minimum value**

   • **those that have an absolute maximum value**

   • **those that have no absolute minimum or maximum value**

   Then record the function letter in the appropriate column of the table shown.

Absolute Minimum	Absolute Maximum	No Absolute Minimum or Absolute Maximum

2. **Each function shown represents one of the graphs with an absolute maximum or an absolute minimum value. Use graphing technology to determine the shape of its graph. Then match the function to its corresponding graph by writing the function directly on the graph that it represents.**

- $f(x) = x^2 + 8x + 12$
- $f(x) = -|x|$

- $f(x) = |x - 3| - 2$
- $f(x) = -3x^2 + 4$, where x is integer

- $f(x) = x^2$
- $f(x) = -\frac{1}{2}x^2 + 2x$

- $f(x) = |x|$
- $f(x) = -2|x + 2| + 4$

3. **Consider the graphs of functions that have an absolute minimum or an absolute maximum.**

a. **Sort the graphs into two groups based on the equations representing the functions and record the function letter in the table.**

Group 1	Group 2

b. **What is the same about all the functions in each group?**

You have just sorted functions into two more function families.

The family of **quadratic functions** includes functions of the form $f(x) = ax^2 + bx + c$, where a, b, and c are real numbers, and a is not equal to 0.

The family of **linear absolute value functions** includes functions of the form $f(x) = a|x + b| + c$, where a, b, and c are real numbers, and a is not equal to 0.

4. **Go back to your table in Question 3 and identify which group represents quadratic functions and which group represents linear absolute value functions.**

ACTIVITY 3.5

Linear Piecewise Functions

Analyze each of the functions shown. These functions represent the last two graphs of functions from the no absolute minimum and no absolute maximum category.

$$f(x) = \begin{cases} -2, & x < 0 \\ \frac{1}{2}x - 2, & x \geq 0 \end{cases} \qquad f(x) = \begin{cases} -2x + 10, & x < 3 \\ 4, & 3 \leq x < 7 \\ -2x + 18, & x \geq 7 \end{cases}$$

1. **Use graphing technology to determine the shapes of their graphs. Then match each function to its corresponding graph by writing the function directly on the graph that it represents.**

You have just sorted the remaining functions into one more function family. The family of **linear piecewise functions** includes functions that have equation changes for different parts, or pieces, of the domain.

You have now sorted each of the graphs and equations representing functions into one of five function families: linear, exponential, quadratic, linear absolute value, and linear piecewise. Let's now focus on linear and exponential functions, which are the functions that you will explore in-depth in this course.

1. **Glue your sorted graphs and functions to the appropriate function family graphic organizer located at the end of the lesson. Write a description of the graphical behavior for each function family.**

Hang on to your graphic organizers. They will be a great resource moving forward!

Don't worry—you don't need to know everything there is to know about these function families right now. As you progress through this course, you will learn more about linear and exponential function families.

TALK the TALK

Interception!

Recall that the **x-intercept** is the point where a graph crosses the x-axis. The **y-intercept** is the point where a graph crosses the y-axis.

1. **The graphs shown represent relations with just the x- and y-intercepts plotted. If possible, draw a function that has the given intercepts. If it is not possible, explain why not.**

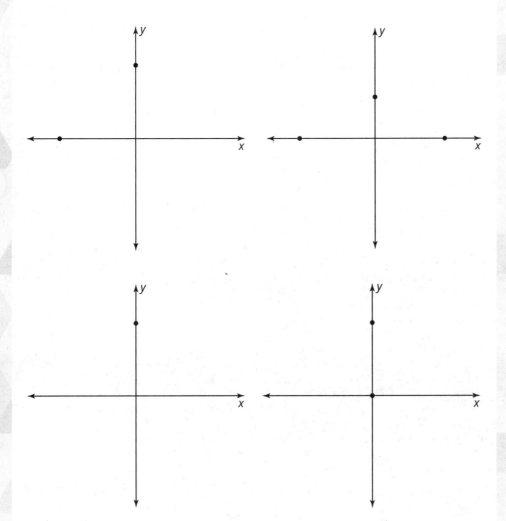

The family of **linear functions** includes functions of the form $f(x) = ax + b$, where a and b are real numbers.

Graphs

Linear
Functions

Graphical Behaviors

Increasing/Decreasing/Constant:

Domain and Range:

Maximum/Minimum:

Curve/Line:

The family of **exponential functions** includes functions of the form $f(x) = a \cdot b^x + c$, where a, b, and c are real numbers, and b is greater than 0 but not equal to 1.

Graphs

Exponential
Functions

Increasing/Decreasing/Constant:

Domain and Range:

Maximum/Minimum:

Curve/Line:

Graphical Behaviors

Assignment

Write

function notation   increasing function   constant function

absolute maximum   decreasing function   absolute minimum

Choose the term that best completes each statement.

1. _____ is a way to represent equations algebraically that makes it more efficient to recognize the independent and dependent variables.

2. When both the independent and dependent variables of a function increase across the entire domain, the function is called a(n) _____.

3. A function has a(n) _____ if there is a point on its graph that has a y-coordinate that is greater than the y-coordinates of every other point on the graph.

4. When the dependent variable of a function decreases as the independent variable increases across the entire domain, the function is called a(n) _____.

5. If the dependent variable of a function does not change or remains constant over the entire domain, then the function is called a(n) _____.

6. A function has a(n) _____ if there is a point on its graph that has a y-coordinate that is less than the y-coordinate of every other point on the graph.

Remember

A function is a relation that assigns to each element of the domain exactly one element of the range. The different function families include linear functions, exponential functions, quadratic functions, linear absolute value functions, and linear piecewise functions.

Practice

For each scenario, use graphing technology to determine the shape of its graph. Then identify the function family, whether it is increasing, decreasing, or a combination of both, has an absolute maximum or absolute minimum, and whether it is a smooth curve or straight line.

1. A fitness company is selling DVDs for one of its new cardio routines. Each DVD will sell for $15. Due to fixed and variable costs, the profit that the company will see after selling x DVDs can be represented by the function $P(x) = 11.5x - 0.1x^2 - 150$.

2. The PARK SAFE commuter lot charges different rates depending on the number of hours a car is parked during the 5-day work week. The lot charges $3 per hour for the first day, $2 per hour for the next 2 days, and will charge $1 per hour if the car is parked more than 3 days in the lot. The fees after x hours can be represented by the function shown.

$$f(x) = \begin{cases} 3x, & 0 \le x \le 24 \\ 72 + 2(x - 24), & 24 < x \le 72 \\ x + 168 & 72 < x \le 120 \end{cases}$$

3. Shari is going to put $500 into an account with The People's Bank. The bank is offering a 3% interest rate compounded annually. The amount of money that Shari will have after x years can be represented by the function $A(x) = 500(1.03)^x$.

4. The Ace Calendar Company is going to buy a new 3D printer for $20,000. In order to plan for the future, the owners are interested in the salvage value of the printer each year. The salvage value after x years can be represented by the function $S(x) = 20,000 - 2000x$.

5. An underwater camera has been placed in the center of the 25-meter pool at the Grandtown Aquatic Center to take pictures of swimmers during a swim meet. The camera will go off at different times depending on the distance of the swimmer to the camera. If the swimmer is moving at a constant rate of 1.28 meters per second, then the distance the swimmer is from the camera after x seconds can be represented by the function $d(x) = 1.28|x - 9.77|$.

Stretch

Graph both functions on the same screen using graphing technology. Use reasoning to classify the second function as a new family. Then describe the similarities and differences between the shapes of the graphs in terms of intervals of increase and decrease, maximums or minimums, and whether they are curves or lines.

$$h(x) = x^2 + 9x + 14 \qquad\qquad p(x) = |x^2 + 9x| + 14$$

Review

1. Identify the axis of symmetry each graph has, if any, and identify the number of quadrants it passes through.

a.

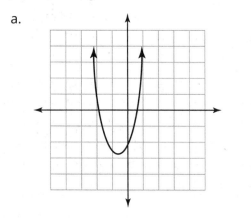

b.

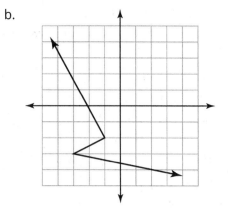

2. Solve the equation $2(9n - 6) + 52 = 2(7n + 8)$.

3. Evaluate the expression $\dfrac{3x^2 - 8(y + 2)}{2y}$ for $x = 8$ and $y = -2$.

Function Families for 800, Alex

Recognizing Functions by Characteristics

4

Warm Up

1. Sketch a graph and write an equation for each function.

   a. decreasing linear function

   b. increasing exponential function

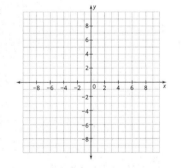

Learning Goals

- Recognize similar characteristics among function families.
- Recognize different characteristics among function families.
- Determine function types given certain characteristics.

You have identified key characteristics of graphs. How can the key characteristics help you sketch the graph of a function?

Name That Function!

You have sorted graphs according to their function family. Now, consider which function families have the given characteristics.

Function Families

linear

exponential

quadratic

linear absolute value

linear piecewise

1. **Which function families can be described by the characteristic provided? Choose from the given list.**

   a. **The graph is a smooth curve.**

   b. **The graph is made up of one or more straight lines.**

   c. **The graph increases or decreases over the entire domain.**

   d. **The graph has an absolute maximum or minimum.**

2. **One or more characteristics have been added to the graphical description of each function. Name the possible function families.**

   a. **The graph has an absolute minimum or absolute maximum and is a smooth curve.**

   b. **The graph either increases or decreases over the entire domain and is a straight line.**

   c. **The graph is a smooth curve, and either increases or decreases over the entire domain.**

   d. **The graph has either an absolute minimum or an absolute maximum, has symmetry, and is made up of 2 straight lines.**

Each function family has certain graphical behaviors, with some behaviors common among different function families. Notice, the more specific characteristics that are given, the more specifically you can name that function!

ACTIVITY 4.1

Categorizing Scenarios into Their Function Families

You have been introduced to several function families: linear, exponential, quadratic, linear absolute value, and linear piecewise. Let's revisit the first lesson: *A Picture Is Worth a Thousand Words*. Each of the scenarios in that lesson represents one of these function families.

1. **Describe how each scenario represents a function.**

2. **Complete the table on the following pages to describe each scenario.**

   a. **Identify the appropriate function family under the scenario name.**

   b. **Based on the context, identify the domain.**

   c. **Describe the graphical behavior as increasing, decreasing, constant, or a combination.**

© Carnegie Learning, Inc.

Scenario	Domain of the Real-World Situation	Graph of the Mathematical Model	Graphical Behavior
Daredevil		**Graph E** 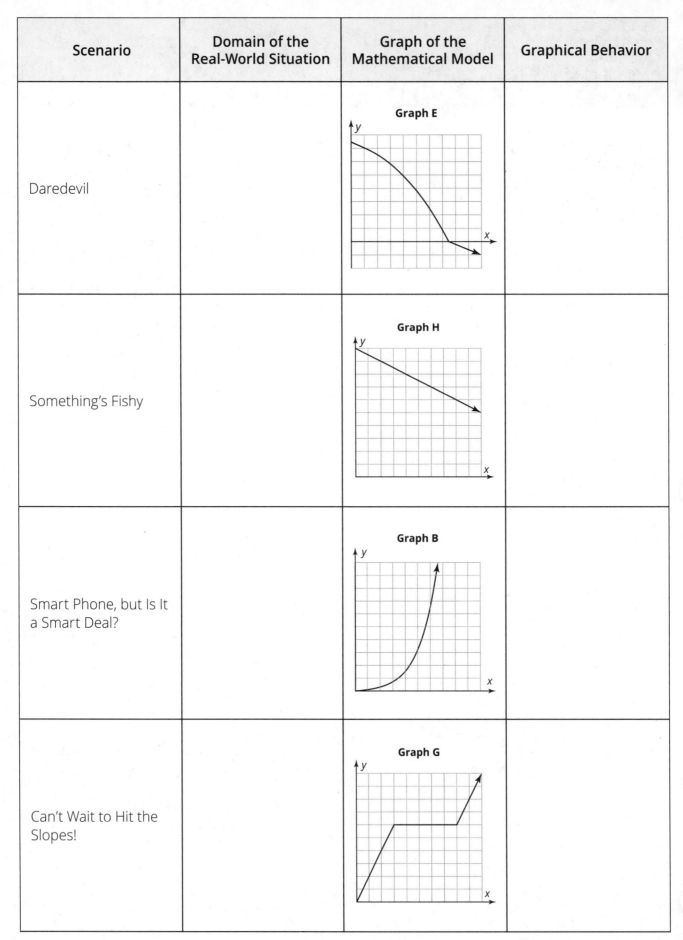	
Something's Fishy		**Graph H**	
Smart Phone, but Is It a Smart Deal?		**Graph B**	
Can't Wait to Hit the Slopes!		**Graph G**	

Scenario	Domain of the Real-World Situation	Graph of the Mathematical Model	Graphical Behavior
It's Magic		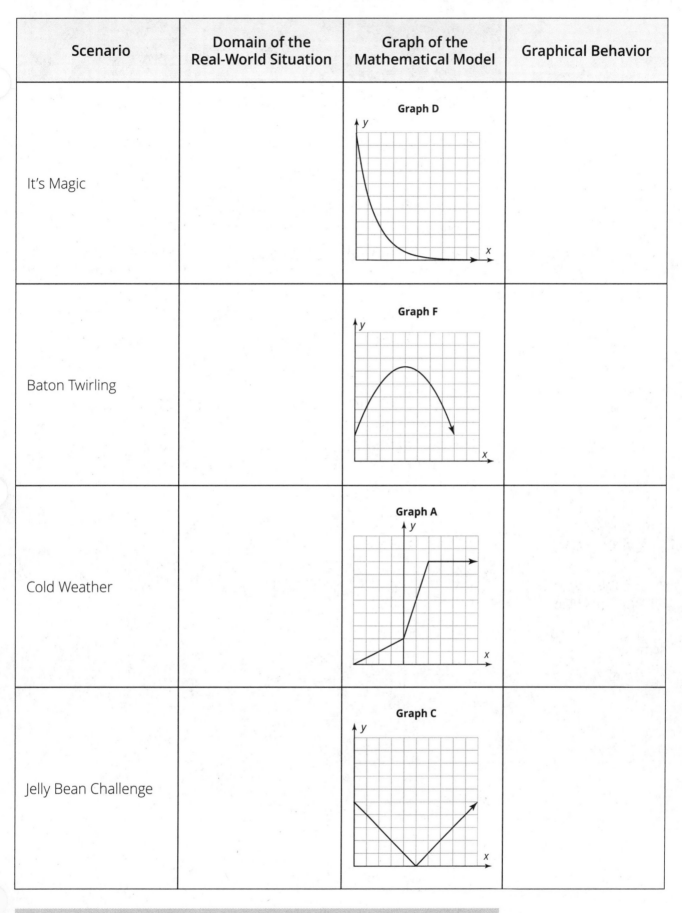**Graph D**	
Baton Twirling		**Graph F**	
Cold Weather		**Graph A**	
Jelly Bean Challenge		**Graph C**	

Building Graphs from Characteristics

In this activity, you will write equations and sketch a graph based on given characteristics.

1. **Use the given characteristics to create an equation and sketch a graph. Use the equations given in the box as a guide. When creating your equation, use a, b, and c values that are any real numbers between −3 and 3. Do not use any functions that were used previously in this topic.**

| **Linear Function** |
| $f(x) = ax + b$ |
| **Exponential Function** |
| $f(x) = a \cdot b^x + c$ |

   a. **Create an equation and sketch a graph that is:**
      • **a function,**
      • **exponential,**
      • **continuous, and**
      • **decreasing.**

   Equation: _____

Think about:

Don't forget about the function family graphic organizers you created if you need some help.

b. Create an equation and sketch a graph that is:
- **linear,**
- **discrete,**
- **increasing, and**
- **a function.**

Ask yourself:

Is the domain the same or different for each function?

Equation: _____

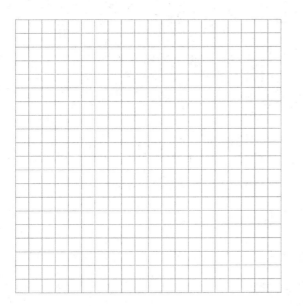

c. Create an equation and sketch a graph that is:
- **not a function,**
- **continuous, and**
- **a straight line**

Equation: _____

© Carnegie Learning, Inc.

2. **Create your own function. Describe certain characteristics of the function and see if your partner can sketch it. Then sketch your partner's function based on characteristics provided.**

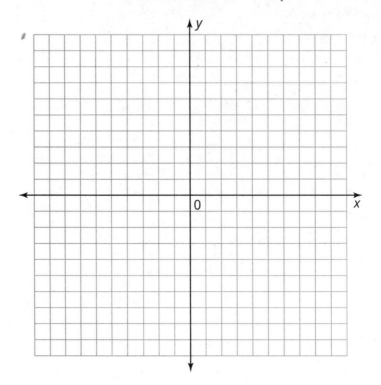

TALK the TALK

Trying to Be Unique

Throughout this lesson, you used characteristics to describe graphs.

1. **Write a list of four characteristics to describe a graph.**

   * _____

   _____

   * _____

   _____

   * _____

   _____

   * _____

   _____

2. **Sketch two possible graphs based on your characteristics.**

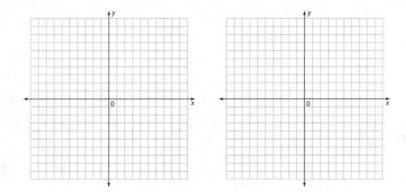

3. **How could you modify your list of characteristics to describe a unique graph?**

© Carnegie Learning, Inc.

NOTES

Assignment

Write

Identify the characteristics of the linear function family.

Remember

Function families have key characteristics that are common among all functions in the family. Knowing these key characteristics is useful when sketching a graph of the function.

Practice

For each scenario and its graph, identify the appropriate function family. Then, based on the problem situation, identify whether the data values represented in the graph are discrete or continuous. Finally, identify the graphical behavior of the function that models the scenario based on the characteristics of its function family.

1. Greg is training for a mountain bike race. He leaves his car at the beginning of a trail and proceeds to bike 8 miles away and then comes back the same way to his car. If he bikes at a constant rate, the function graphed models the distance he is away from his car after x minutes.

2. A local television company determines that the revenue it gets from running ads doubles each year. The function graphed models the revenue from advertising after x years.

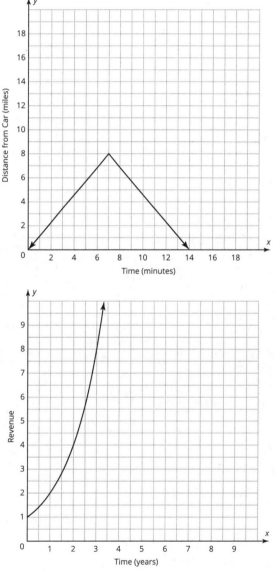

3. The Redwood Heights Women's Club is hosting a summer nighttime party in the park. They are handing out glow sticks to all the children who attend. They start with 200 glow sticks and each child receives 3 glow sticks. The function graphed models the number of glow sticks they have left after x children have entered.

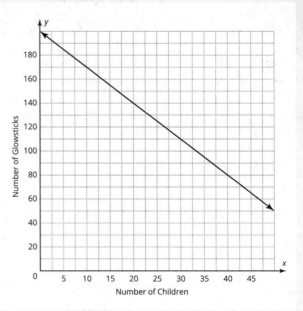

Stretch

Write an equation and sketch a graph that has a minimum in Quadrant IV, is continuous, and is a linear absolute value function.

Review

1. Determine whether each graph represents an increasing function, a decreasing function, a constant function, or a combination of increasing and decreasing functions.

a.

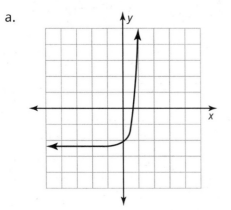

b.

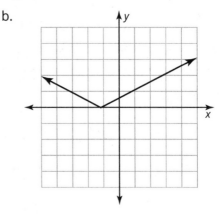

2. Solve each equation.

a. $-6 + 4x = 22$

b. $68 = -7 - 15b$

3. Evaluate each expression.

a. $x^2 + 5x - 19$ for $x = -4$

b. $(3 + y)^2 + 4y$ for $y = -5$

Quantities and Relationships Summary

KEY TERMS

- dependent quantity
- independent quantity
- relation
- domain
- range
- function
- function notation
- Vertical Line Test

- discrete graph
- continuous graph
- increasing function
- decreasing function
- constant function
- function family
- linear functions
- exponential functions

- absolute maximum
- absolute minimum
- quadratic functions
- linear absolute value functions
- linear piecewise functions
- *x*-intercept
- *y*-intercept

LESSON 1

A Picture Is Worth a Thousand Words

Many problem situations include two quantities that change. When one quantity depends on another, it is said to be the **dependent quantity**. The quantity that the dependent quantity depends upon is called the **independent quantity**.

Graphs relay information about data in a visual way. Connecting points on a coordinate plane with a line or smooth curve is a way to model or represent relationships. The independent quantity is graphed on the horizontal, or *x*-axis, while the dependent quantity is graphed on the vertical, or *y*-axis. Graphs can be straight lines or curves, and can increase or decrease from left to right.

For example, consider the graph which models the situation where Pedro is hiking in a canyon. At the start of his hike, he was at 3500 feet. During the first 20 minutes of the hike, he descended 500 feet at a constant rate. Then he rested for half an hour before continuing the hike at the same rate.

Time is the independent quantity and elevation is the dependent quantity.

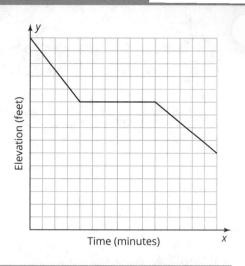

Looking for patterns can help when sorting and comparing graphs. Some graphs show vertical symmetry (if a vertical line were drawn through the middle of the graph the image is the same on both sides). Other possible patterns to look for include: only goes through two quadrants, always increasing from left to right, always decreasing from left to right, straight lines, smooth curves, the graph goes through the origin, the graph forms a U shape, the graph forms a V shape.

For example, Graph A has vertical symmetry. Graph B is a smooth curve that increases from left to right.

Graph A

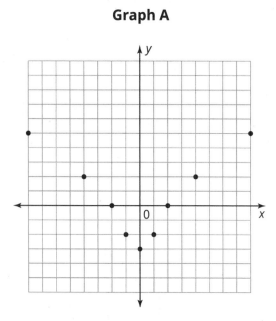

Graph B

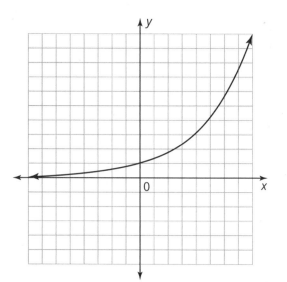

A **relation** is the mapping between a set of input values called the **domain** and a set of output values called the **range**.

A **function** is a relation between a given set of elements, such that for each element in the domain there exists exactly one element in the range. If each value in the domain has one and only one range value, then the relation is a function. If any value in the domain has more than one range value, then the relation is not a function.

The value −2 in the domain has more than one range value. The mapping does not represent a function.

Each element in the domain has exactly one element in the range. The table represents a function.

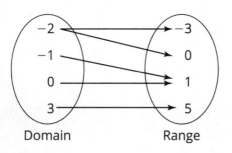

Domain   Range

Domain	Range
2	1
6	3
10	5
14	7

Functions can be represented in a number of ways. An equation representing a function can be written using **function notation**. Function notation is a way of representing functions algebraically. This form allows you to more efficiently identify the independent and dependent quantities. The function $f(x)$ is read as "f of x" and indicates that x is the independent variable.

For example, consider the situation in which U.S. Shirts charges $8 per shirt plus a one-time charge of $15 to set up a T-shirt design. The equation that models the situation, $y = 8x + 15$, where x represents the number of shirts ordered and y represents the total cost of the order, can be written in function notation as $f(x) = 8x + 15$. The cost, defined by f, is a function of x, defined as the number of shirts ordered.

The **Vertical Line Test** is a visual method used to determine whether a relation represented as a graph is a function. To apply the Vertical Line Test, consider all of the vertical lines that could be drawn on the graph of a relation. If any of the vertical lines intersect the graph of the relation at more than one point, then the relation is not a function. The Vertical Line Test applies to both discrete and continuous graphs. A **discrete graph** is a graph of isolated points. A **continuous graph** is a graph of points that are connected by a line or smooth curve with no breaks in the graph.

A line drawn vertically through the graph touches more than one point. The graph does not represent a function.

A line drawn vertically through the graph only touches one point. The graph represents a function.

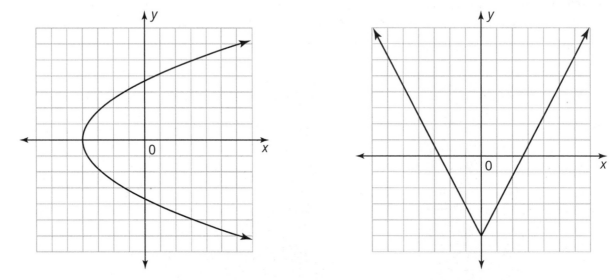

A function is described as increasing when both the independent and dependent variables are increasing. If a function increases across the entire domain, then the function is called an **increasing function**. A function is described as decreasing when the dependent variable decreases as the independent variable increases. If a function decreases across the entire domain, then the function is called a **decreasing function**. If the dependent variable of a function does not change or remains constant over the entire domain, then the function is called a **constant function**.

A **function family** is a group of functions that share certain characteristics.

The family of **linear functions** includes functions of the form $f(x) = ax + b$, where a and b are real numbers.

The family of **exponential functions** includes functions of the form $f(x) = a \cdot b^x + c$, where a, b, and c are real numbers, and b is greater than 0, but not equal to 1.

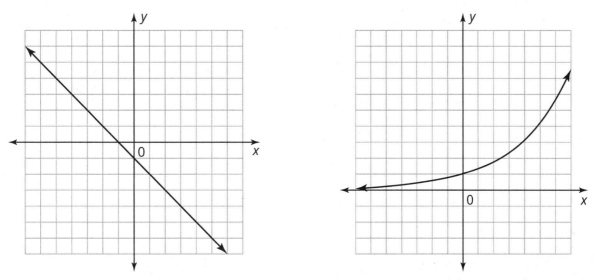

Quadratic and linear absolute value functions have an absolute maximum or an absolute minimum. An **absolute maximum** is a point on the graph of the function that has a y-coordinate that is greater than the y-coordinate of every other point on the graph. An **absolute minimum** is a point on the graph of the function that has a y-coordinate that is less than the y-coordinate of every other point on the graph.

The family of **quadratic functions** includes functions of the form $f(x) = ax^2 + bx + c$, where a, b, and c are real numbers, and a is not equal to 0.

The family of **linear absolute value functions** includes functions of the form $f(x) = a|x + b| + c$, where a, b, and c are real numbers, and a is not equal to 0.

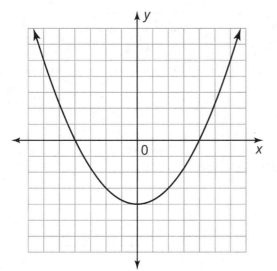

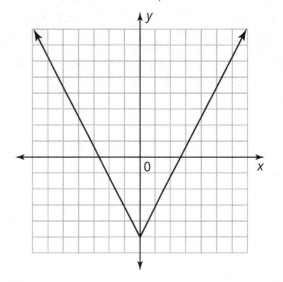

The family of **linear piecewise functions** includes functions that have an equation that changes for different parts, or pieces, of the domain.

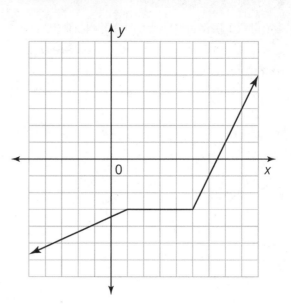

Function Families for 800, Alex

Function families have key characteristics that are common among all functions in the family. Knowing these key characteristics is useful when sketching a graph of the function.

For example, to sketch a graph of a continuous exponential function that increases, the graph should be a smooth curve that increases from left to right.

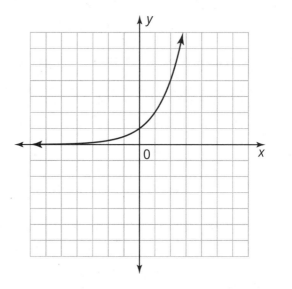

Sequences

Everyday sequences might include sizes or ages. What other sequences have you noticed today?

Module 1: Searching for Patterns

TOPIC 2: SEQUENCES

In this topic, students explore sequences represented as lists of numbers, in tables of values, by equations, and as graphs on the coordinate plane. Students move from an intuitive understanding of patterns to a more formal approach of representing sequences as functions. In the final lesson of the topic, students are introduced to the modeling process. Defined in four steps—Notice and Wonder, Organize and Mathematize, Test and Interpret, and Predict and Analyze—the modeling process gives students a structure for approaching real-world mathematical problems.

Where have we been?

Students have been analyzing and extending numeric patterns since elementary school. They have discovered and explained features of patterns. They have formed ordered pairs with terms of two sequences and compared the terms. In middle school, students have connected term numbers and term values as the inputs and outputs of a function.

Where are we going?

As students deepen their understanding of functions throughout this course and beyond, recognizing that all sequences are functions is an important building block. A rich understanding of arithmetic sequences is the foundation for linear functions. As students gain experience with more complex functions, the modeling process will help them approach and solve problems they encounter in the real world.

Formulas for Sequences

A formula can be written to determine any number in an arithmetic or geometric sequence. You just need to know the first number in the sequence, the position of the number in the sequence, and the common difference or common ratio.

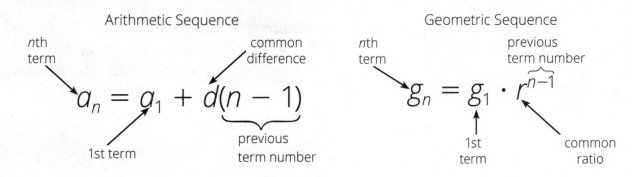

Arithmetic Sequence

nth term — $a_n = g_1 + d(n - 1)$ — common difference — 1st term — previous term number

Geometric Sequence

nth term — $g_n = g_1 \cdot r^{n-1}$ — previous term number — 1st term — common ratio

Given the arithmetic sequence 2, 5, 8, 11, 14 . . . , the 10th number is $2 + 3(10 - 1)$, or 29.

Given the geometric sequence 2, 6, 18, 54, 162 . . . , the 10th number is $2 \cdot 3^{10-1}$, or 39,366.

The Dress, with Sequence

Not too long ago, a picture of a dress caused a lot of controversy on the internet. Was it white and gold or blue and black? (Spoiler: It was actually blue and black.) As a result of all the attention, the company that made the dress saw sales go up nearly 350%.

Public demand for products usually changes much more slowly than this. But still, companies have to be ready to deliver. So production managers use sequences to determine how much of their product to have available to meet the demand.

These sequences never match the perfect mathematical sequences you see in math class, but companies analyze the mathematical sequences to model the actual demand for products and make predictions and estimates for their inventory.

Talking Points

Sequences is an important topic to know about for college admissions tests.

Here is a sample question:

What is the second term in this geometric sequence?

$$\frac{1}{3}, \underline{\hspace{2cm}}, \frac{1}{48}, \frac{1}{192}, \cdots$$

To solve this, students need to know that each term in a geometric sequence is calculated by using the same multiplier, or constant ratio. The multiplier can be determined by dividing a term by the term before it.

In this case, $192 \div 48 = 4$. Therefore, $\frac{1}{192} \div \frac{1}{48} = \frac{1}{4}$. This means the multiplier is $\frac{1}{4}$. The second term can be calculated by multiplying the first term by $\frac{1}{4}$. Because $\frac{1}{3} \times \frac{1}{4} = \frac{1}{12}$, the second term is $\frac{1}{12}$.

Key Terms

sequence
A sequence is a pattern involving an ordered arrangement of numbers, geometric figures, letters, or other objects.

arithmetic sequence
An arithmetic sequence is a sequence of numbers in which the difference between any two consecutive terms is a constant.

geometric sequence
A geometric sequence is a sequence of numbers in which you multiply each term by a constant to determine the next term.

mathematical modeling
Mathematical modeling is explaining patterns in the real world based on mathematical ideas.

Is There a Pattern Here?

Recognizing Patterns and Sequences

1

Warm Up

Write the next three terms in each pattern and explain how you generated each term.

1. J, F, M, A, M, J, J, A, S, . . .

2. S, M, T, W, . . .

3. 5, 10, 15, 20, . . .

4. 100, 81, 64, 49, . . .

Learning Goals

- Recognize and describe patterns.
- Represent patterns as sequences.
- Predict the next term in a sequence.
- Represent a sequence as a table of values.

Key Terms

- sequence
- term of a sequence
- infinite sequence
- finite sequence

Since early elementary school, you have been recognizing and writing patterns involving shapes, colors, letters, and numbers. How are patterns related to sequences and how can sequences be represented using a table of values?

A Pyramid of Patterns

Pascal's Triangle is a famous pattern named after the French mathematician and philosopher Blaise Pascal. A portion of the pattern is shown.

1. **List at least 3 patterns that you notice.**

2. **Describe the pattern for the number of terms in each row.**

3. **Describe the pattern within each row.**

4. **Describe the pattern that results from determining the sum of each row.**

5. **Determine the next two rows in Pascal's Triangle. Explain your reasoning.**

ACTIVITY 1.1

Patterns to Sequences to Tables

A **sequence** is a pattern involving an ordered arrangement of numbers, geometric figures, letters, or other objects. A **term of a sequence** is an individual number, figure, or letter in the sequence.

Ten examples of sequences are given in this activity. For each sequence, describe the pattern, draw or describe the next terms, and represent each sequence numerically.

1. **Positive Thinking**

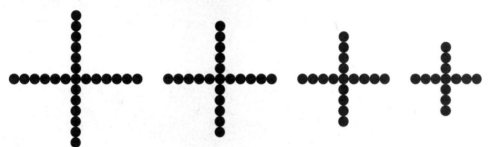

a. **Analyze the number of dots. Describe the pattern.**

b. **Draw the next three figures of the pattern.**

c. **Represent the number of dots in each of the seven figures as a numeric sequence.**

d. **Represent the number of dots in each of the first seven figures as a function using a table of values.**

Term Number	1	2	3	4	5	6	7
Term Value							

> All numeric sequences can be represented as functions. The independent variable is the term number beginning with 1, and the dependent variable is the term of the sequence.

2. Family Tree

Jessica is investigating her family tree by researching each generation, or set, of parents. She learns all she can about the first four generations, which include her two parents, her grandparents, her great-grandparents, and her great-great-grandparents.

Term Number	Term Value

a. **Think about the number of parents. Describe the pattern.**

b. **Determine the number of parents in the fifth and sixth generations.**

c. **Represent the number of parents in each of the 6 generations as a numeric sequence. Then represent the sequence using a table of values.**

3. A Collection of Squares

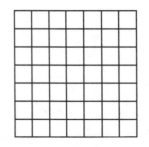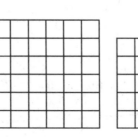

Term Number	Term Value

a. **Analyze the number of small squares in each figure. Describe the pattern.**

b. **Draw the next three figures of the pattern.**

c. **Represent the number of small squares in each of the first seven figures as a numeric sequence. Then represent the sequence using a table of values.**

4. **Al's Omelets**

   Al's House of Eggs N'at makes omelets. Al begins each day with 150 eggs to make his famous *Bestern Western Omelets*. After making 1 omelet, he has 144 eggs left. After making 2 omelets, he has 138 eggs left. After making 3 omelets, he has 132 eggs left.

   a. **Think about the number of eggs Al has left after making each omelet. Describe the pattern.**

   b. **Determine the number of eggs left after Al makes the next two omelets.**

   c. **Represent the number of eggs left after Al makes each of the first 5 omelets as a numeric sequence. Then represent the sequence using a table of values.**

Term Number	Term Value

5. **Donna's Daisies**

   Donna is decorating the top border of her bedroom walls with a daisy pattern. She is applying decals with each column having a specific number of daisies.

   a. **Think about the number of daisies in each column. Describe the pattern.**

   b. **Determine the number of daisies in each of the next two columns.**

   c. **Represent the number of daisies in each of the first 8 columns as a numeric sequence. Then represent the sequence using a table of values.**

Term Number	Term Value

6. Troop of Triangles

a. **Analyze the number of dark triangles. Describe the pattern.**

Term Number	Term Value

b. **Draw the next two figures of the pattern.**

c. **Represent the number of dark triangles in each of the first 6 figures as a numeric sequence. Then represent the sequence using a table of values.**

7. Gamer Guru

Mica is trying to beat his high score on his favorite video game. He unlocks some special mini-games where he earns points for each one he completes. Before he begins playing the mini-games, Mica has 500 points. After completing 1 mini-game he has a total of 550 points, after completing 2 mini-games he has 600 points, and after completing 3 mini-games he has 650 points.

a. **Think about the total number of points Mica gains from mini-games. Describe the pattern.**

b. **Determine Mica's total points after he plays the next two mini-games.**

c. **Represent Mica's total points after completing each of the first 5 mini-games as a numeric sequence. Be sure to include the number of points he started with. Then represent the sequence using a table of values.**

Term Number	Term Value

8. **Polygon Party**

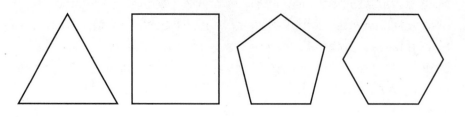

a. Analyze the number of sides in each polygon. Describe the pattern.

Term Number	Term Value

b. Draw the next two figures of the pattern.

c. Represent the number of sides of each of the first 6 polygons as a numeric sequence. Then represent the sequence using a table of values.

9. **Pizza Contest**

   Jacob is participating in a pizza-making contest. Each contestant has to bake the largest and most delicious pizza they can. Jacob's pizza has a 6-foot diameter! After the contest, he plans to cut the pizza so that he can pass the slices out to share. He begins with 1 whole pizza. Then, he cuts it in half. After that, he cuts each of those slices in half. Then he cuts each of those slices in half, and so on.

   a. **Think about the size of each slice in relation to the whole pizza. Describe the pattern.**

   b. **Determine the size of each slice compared to the whole pizza after the next two cuts.**

   c. **Represent the size of each slice compared to the whole pizza after each of the first 5 cuts as a numeric sequence. Include the whole pizza before any cuts. Then represent the sequence using a table of values.**

Term Number	Term Value

10. **Coin Collecting**

Miranda's uncle collects rare coins. He recently purchased a rare coin for $5. He claims that the value of the coin will triple each year. So even though the coin is currently worth $5, next year it will be worth $15. In 2 years it will be worth $45, and in 3 years it will be worth $135.

a. Think about how the value of the coin changes each year. Describe the pattern.

Term Number	Term Value

b. Determine the value of the coin after 4 years and after 5 years.

c. Represent the value of the coin after each of the first 5 years as a numeric sequence. Include the current value. Then represent the sequence using a table of values.

There are many different patterns that can generate a sequence of numbers. For example, you may have noticed that some of the sequences in the previous activity were generated by performing the same operation using a constant number. In other sequences, you may have noticed a different pattern.

The next term in a sequence is calculated by determining the pattern of the sequence, and then using that pattern on the last known term of the sequence.

1. **For each sequence in the previous activity, write the numeric sequence, record whether the sequence increases or decreases, and describe the sequence by stating the first term and the operation(s) used to create the sequence. The first one has been completed for you.**

Problem Name	Numeric Sequence	Increases or Decreases	Sequence Description
Positive Thinking	25, 21, 17, 13, 9, 5, 1	Decreases	Begin at 25. Subtract 4 from each term.
Family Tree			
A Collection of Squares			
Al's Omelets			
Donna's Daisies			
Troop of Triangles			
Gamer Guru			
Polygon Party			
Pizza Contest			
Coin Collecting			

2. Which sequences are similar? Explain your reasoning.

3. What do all sequences have in common?

4. Consider a sequence in which the first term is 64 and each term after that is calculated by dividing the previous term by 4. Margaret says that this sequence ends at 1 because there are no whole numbers that come after 1. Jasmine disagrees and says that the sequence continues beyond 1. Who is correct? If Margaret is correct, explain why. If Jasmine is correct, predict the next two terms of the sequence.

5. What is the domain of a sequence? What is the range?

© Carnegie Learning, Inc.

If a sequence continues on forever, it is called an **infinite sequence**. If a sequence terminates, it is called a **finite sequence**.

For example, consider an auditorium where the seats are arranged according to a specific pattern. There are 22 seats in the first row, 26 seats in the second row, 30 seats in the third row, and so on. Numerically, the sequence is 22, 26, 30, . . . , which continues infinitely. However, in the context of the problem, it does not make sense for the number of seats in each row to increase infinitely. Eventually, the auditorium would run out of space! Suppose that this auditorium can hold a total of 10 rows of seats. The correct sequence for this problem situation is:

An ellipsis is three periods, which means "and so on." An infinite sequence can be represented using an ellipsis.

22, 26, 30, 34, 38, 42, 46, 50, 54, 58.

Therefore, because of the problem situation, the sequence is a finite sequence.

6. **Does the pattern shown represent an infinite or finite sequence? Explain your reasoning.**

TALK the TALK

Searching for a Sequence

In this lesson you have seen that many different patterns can generate a sequence of numbers.

1. **Explain why the definition of a function applies to all sequences.**

2. **Create a sequence to fit the given criteria. Describe your sequence using figures, words, or numbers. Provide the first four terms of the sequence. Explain how you know that it is a sequence.**

   a. **Create a sequence that begins with a positive integer, is decreasing by multiplication, and is finite.**

   b. **Create a sequence that begins with a negative rational number, is increasing by addition, and is infinite.**

Assignment

Write

Explain why all sequences can be described as functions.

Remember

A sequence is a pattern involving an ordered arrangement of numbers, geometric figures, letters, or other objects. All numeric sequences can be represented as functions.

Practice

Consider the three sequences given. For each sequence, describe the pattern. Then, represent the sequence as a numeric sequence and as a table of values, including the first 6 terms.

1. Matchstick Mayhem

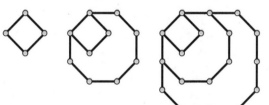

2. Hancox Homes

Hancox Homes is a popular construction company that builds affordable housing. When the company first started, they sold 1 home the first month, 3 homes the second month, 9 homes the third month, and 27 homes the fourth month.

3. Violet's Videos

Violet is a yoga instructor who regularly posts new exercise videos on a website for her clients. One week after launching the website, she had posted a total of 6 videos. At the end of week 2, she had a total of 10 videos. At the end of week 3, she had a total of 14 videos. At the end of week 4, she had a total of 18 videos.

Stretch

Robin's Restaurant

Robin is opening a restaurant and tells her staff they have to go above and beyond to please their customers, especially on opening day. She reasons that if one customer is pleased with the restaurant, that person is likely to tell 4 people about it. Then each of those people is likely to tell 4 people about it, and so on.

- Describe the pattern for the number of customers Robin's Restaurant will reach with each telling.
- Determine how many customers are reached after the 5th, 6th, and 7th tellings.
- Represent the number of customers reached with each telling as a numeric sequence. Then represent the sequence using a table of values.
- Identify the appropriate function family for the function. Then describe whether the function is continuous or discrete.

Review

1. For each scenario and graph:
   - Identify the appropriate function family.
   - Describe the domain based on the problem situation.
   - Identify the graphical behavior of the function as increasing, decreasing, or a combination.

a. A city discovers that its population has been tripling every year. The function graphed models the population (in thousands) after x years.

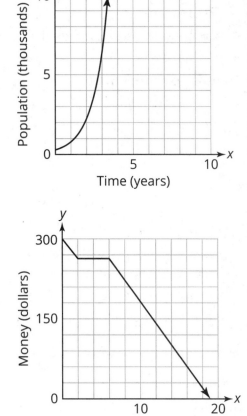

b. A vacationer has $300 to spend over the next 20 days. The first two days, she spends $20 on food each day. She visits with family members for the next four days and does not spend any money. She then spends $20 on transportation on each of the remaining days until she spends all of her money. The function graphed models the amount of money left after x days.

2. Determine whether each data set represents a function.
   a. {(−5, 8), (−6, 2), (−2, −6), (−1, 8), (4, 6)}

   b.

x	y
2	9
6	8
4	7
2	4
8	2

The Password Is: Operations

Arithmetic and Geometric Sequences

Warm Up

Write the next three terms in each sequence and explain how you generated each term.

1. −2, 4, −8, 16, . . .

2. 60, 53, 46, 39, 32, . . .

3. 1, 5, 17, 53, 161, 485, . . .

4. 4, 10, 16, 22, . . .

Learning Goals

- Determine the next term in a sequence.
- Recognize arithmetic sequences and geometric sequences.
- Determine the common difference or common ratio for a sequence.
- Graph arithmetic and geometric sequences.
- Recognize graphical behavior of sequences.
- Sort sequences that are represented graphically.

Key Terms

- arithmetic sequence
- common difference
- geometric sequence
- common ratio

You have represented patterns as sequences of numbers—a relationship between term numbers and term values. What patterns appear when sequences are represented as graphs?

What Comes Next, and How Do You Know?

Cut out Sequences A through P located at the end of the lesson.

1. **Determine the unknown terms of each sequence. Then describe the pattern under each sequence.**

2. **Sort the sequences into groups based on common characteristics. In the space provided, record the following information for each of your groups.**

   • **List the letters of the sequences in each group.**

   • **Provide a rationale as to why you created each group.**

3. **What mathematical operation(s) did you perform in order to determine the next terms of each sequence?**

Defining Arithmetic and Geometric Sequences

For some sequences, you can describe the pattern as adding a constant to each term to determine the next term. For other sequences, you can describe the pattern as multiplying each term by a constant to determine the next term. Still other sequences cannot be described either way.

An **arithmetic sequence** is a sequence of numbers in which the difference between any two consecutive terms is a constant. In other words, it is a sequence of numbers in which a constant is added to each term to produce the next term. This constant is called the **common difference**. The common difference is typically represented by the variable d.

The common difference of a sequence is positive if the same positive number is added to each term to produce the next term. The common difference of a sequence is negative if the same negative number is added to each term to produce the next term.

> **Remember:**
>
> When you add a negative number, it is the same as subtracting a positive number.

Worked Example

Consider the sequence shown.

$$11, 9, 7, 5, \ldots$$

The pattern is to add the same negative number, -2, to each term to determine the next term.

add -2 add -2 add -2

Sequence: __11__,   __9__,   __7__,   __5__, . . .

This sequence is arithmetic and the common difference d is -2.

---

1. Suppose a sequence has the same starting number as the sequence in the worked example, but its common difference is 4.

   a. How would the pattern change?

   b. Is the sequence still arithmetic? Why or why not?

   c. If possible, write the first 5 terms of the new sequence.

2. Analyze the sequences you cut out in the Getting Started.

   a. List the sequences that are arithmetic.

   b. Write the common difference of each arithmetic sequence you identified.

A **geometric sequence** is a sequence of numbers in which the ratio between any two consecutive terms is a constant. In other words, it is a sequence of numbers in which you multiply each term by a constant to determine the next term. This integer or fraction constant is called the common ratio. The **common ratio** is represented by the variable r.

Worked Example

Consider the sequence shown.

$$1, 2, 4, 8, \ldots$$

The pattern is to multiply each term by the same number, 2, to determine the next term.

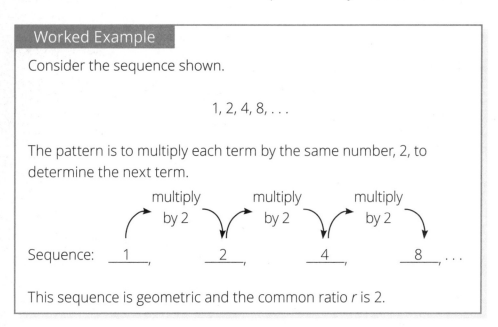

This sequence is geometric and the common ratio r is 2.

---

3. **Suppose a sequence has the same starting number as the sequence in the worked example, but its common ratio is 3.**

   a. **How would the pattern change?**

   b. **Is the sequence still geometric? Explain your reasoning.**

   c. **Write the first 5 terms of the new sequence.**

4. Suppose a sequence has the same starting number as the sequence in the worked example, but its common ratio is $\frac{1}{3}$.

   a. How would the pattern change?

   b. Is the sequence still geometric? Why or why not?

   c. Write the first 6 terms of the new sequence.

5. Suppose a sequence has the same starting number as the sequence in the worked example, but its common ratio is -2.

   a. How would the pattern change?

   b. Is the sequence still geometric? Explain your reasoning.

   c. Write the first 6 terms of the new sequence.

6. Consider the sequence shown.

$$270, 90, 30, 10, \ldots$$

Devon says that he can determine each term of this sequence by multiplying each term by $\frac{1}{3}$, so the common ratio is $\frac{1}{3}$. Chase says that he can determine each term of this sequence by dividing each term by 3, so the common ratio is 3. Who is correct? Explain your reasoning.

7. Consider the sequences you cut out in the Getting Started. List the sequences that are geometric. Then write the common ratio on each Sequence Card.

8. Consider the sequences that are neither arithmetic nor geometric. List these sequences. Explain why these sequences are neither arithmetic nor geometric.

9. Consider the first two terms of the sequence 3, 6, . . .

Dante says, "This is how I wrote the sequence for the given terms."

$$3, 6, 9, 12, \ldots$$

Kira says, "This is the sequence I wrote."

$$3, 6, 12, 24, \ldots$$

Who is correct? Explain your reasoning.

10. Using the terms given in Question 9, write a sequence that is neither arithmetic nor geometric. Then, have your partner tell you what the pattern is in your sequence.

11. How many terms did your partner need before the pattern was recognized?

12. Consider the sequence 2, 2, 2, 2, 2. . . Identify the type of sequence it is and describe the pattern.

13. Begin to complete the graphic organizers located at the end of the lesson to identify arithmetic and geometric sequences. Glue each arithmetic sequence and each geometric sequence to a separate graphic organizer according to its type. Discard all other sequences.

Matching Graphs and Sequences

As you have already discovered when studying functions, graphs can help you see trends of a sequence—and at times can help you predict the next term in a sequence.

1. **The graphs representing the arithmetic and geometric sequences from the previous activity are located at the end of this lesson. Cut out these graphs. Match each graph to its appropriate sequence and glue it into the Graph section of its graphic organizer.**

2. **What strategies did you use to match the graphs to their corresponding sequences?**

3. **How can you use the graphs to verify that all sequences are functions?**

TALK the TALK

Name That Sequence!

Write the first five terms of each sequence described and identify the sequence as arithmetic or geometric.

1. **The first term of the sequence is 8 and the common difference is 12.**

2. **The first term of the sequence is −9 and the common ratio is −2.**

3. **The first term of the sequence is 0 and the common difference is −6.**

4. **The first term of the sequence is −3 and the common ratio is $-\frac{1}{4}$.**

Sequence Cards

A

45, 90, 180, 360, _____, _____,

_____, . . .

B

−4, −2, 0, 2, _____, _____,

_____, . . .

C

−2, −6, −18, −54, _____, _____,

_____, . . .

D

2, 5, 10, 17, _____, _____,

_____, . . .

E

$4, \frac{7}{4}, -\frac{1}{2}, -\frac{11}{4}$ _____, _____,

_____, . . .

F

1234, 123.4, 12.34, 1.234, _____,

_____, _____, . . .

G

1, −2, 3, −4, 5 _____, _____,

_____, _____, . . .

H

−20, −16, −12, −8, −4, _____,

_____, _____, . . .

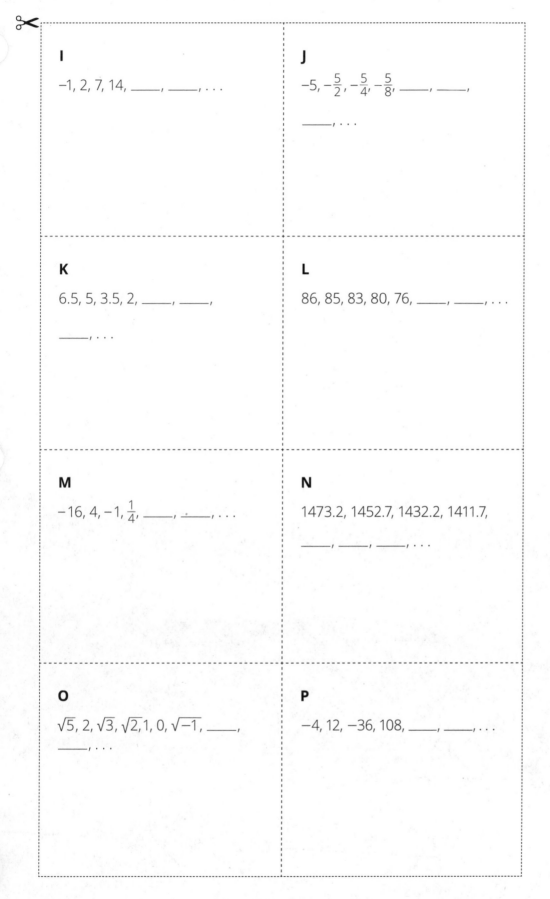

I

−1, 2, 7, 14, ____, ____, . . .

J

−5, −$\frac{5}{2}$, −$\frac{5}{4}$, −$\frac{5}{8}$, ____, ____,

____, . . .

K

6.5, 5, 3.5, 2, ____, ____,

____, . . .

L

86, 85, 83, 80, 76, ____, ____, . . .

M

−16, 4, −1, $\frac{1}{4}$, ____, ____, . . .

N

1473.2, 1452.7, 1432.2, 1411.7,

____, ____, ____, . . .

O

$\sqrt{5}$, 2, $\sqrt{3}$, $\sqrt{2}$, 1, 0, $\sqrt{-1}$, ____,

____, . . .

P

−4, 12, −36, 108, ____, ____, . . .

Graph Cards

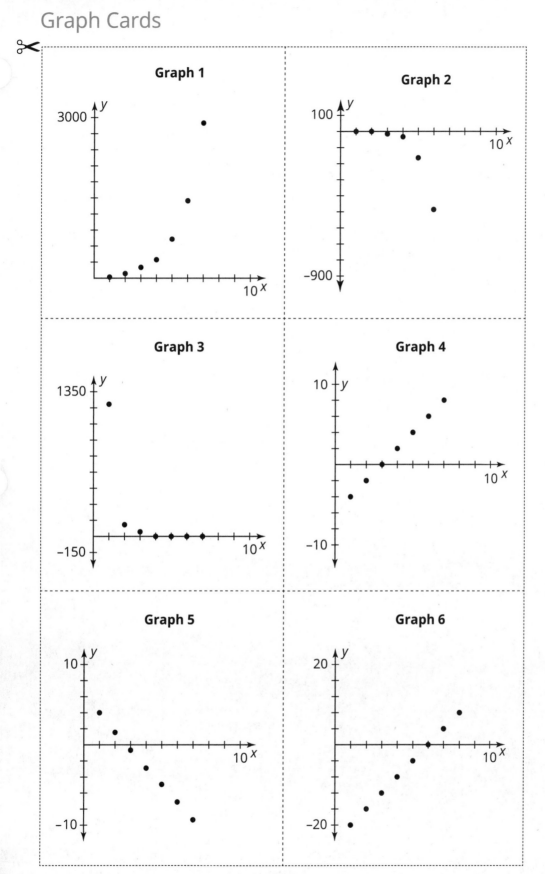

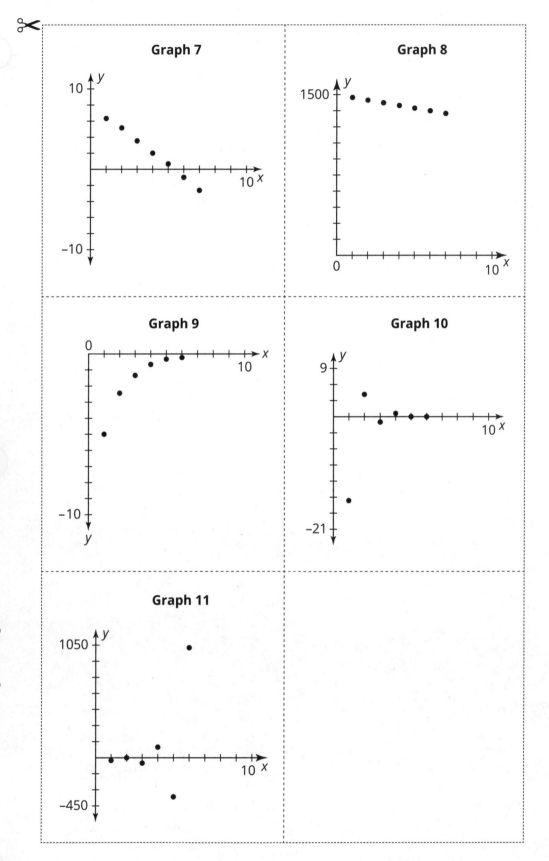

Graph 7

Graph 8

Graph 9

Graph 10

Graph 11

Sequence

Graph

Arithmetic Sequence

Recursive Formula

Explicit Formula

Sequence

Graph

Arithmetic Sequence

Recursive Formula

Explicit Formula

Sequence

Graph

Arithmetic Sequence

Recursive Formula

Explicit Formula

Sequence

Graph

Arithmetic Sequence

Recursive Formula

Explicit Formula

Sequence

Graph

Arithmetic Sequence

Recursive Formula

Explicit Formula

Sequence

Graph

Geometric Sequence

Recursive Formula

Explicit Formula

Sequence

Graph

Geometric Sequence

Recursive Formula

Explicit Formula

Sequence

Graph

Geometric Sequence

Recursive Formula

Explicit Formula

Sequence

Graph

Geometric Sequence

Recursive Formula

Explicit Formula

© Carnegie Learning, Inc.

Sequence

Graph

Geometric Sequence

Recursive Formula

Explicit Formula

Sequence

Graph

Geometric Sequence

Recursive Formula

Explicit Formula

© Carnegie Learning, Inc.

Sequence

Graph

Recursive Formula

Explicit Formula

Assignment

Write

Complete each sentence.

1. A sequence which terminates is called a(n)

   _____ .

2. A(n) _____ is an individual number, figure, or letter in a sequence.

3. A(n) _____ is a pattern involving an ordered arrangement of numbers, geometric figures, letters, or other objects.

4. A sequence which continues forever is called a(n) _____ .

Remember

An arithmetic sequence is a sequence of numbers in which the difference between any two consecutive terms is a constant.

A geometric sequence is a sequence of numbers in which the ratio between any two consecutive terms is a constant.

Practice

Consider the first 2 terms of the sequence 28, 14, . . .

1. Determine whether the sequence is arithmetic or geometric. Explain your reasoning.

2. Suppose the sequence 28, 14, . . . is arithmetic.
   a. Determine the common difference.
   b. List the next 3 terms in the sequence. Explain your reasoning.
   c. Determine whether the sequence is finite or infinite. Explain your reasoning.

3. Suppose the sequence 28, 14, . . . is geometric.
   a. Determine the common ratio.
   b. List the next 3 terms in the sequence. Explain your reasoning.
   c. Determine whether the sequence is finite or infinite. Explain your reasoning.

4. Using the first two terms 28 and 14, write the next 3 terms of a sequence that is neither arithmetic nor geometric.

Stretch

Consider the first 2 terms of the sequence −6, 18, . . .

1. Determine the next 5 terms in the sequence if the sequence is arithmetic. Then write a function to represent the arithmetic sequence.

2. Determine the next 5 terms in the sequence if the sequence is geometric. Then write a function to represent the geometric sequence.

Review

1. Juan updates his blog regularly with trivia questions for readers to answer. The month he started this, there were 8 trivia questions on his blog. The next month, there were 19 trivia questions on his blog. The month after that, there were 30 trivia questions on his blog.

   a. Think about the number of trivia questions on Juan's blog each month. Describe the pattern.

   b. Determine how many trivia questions will be on Juan's blog during months 4, 5, and 6.

   c. Represent the number of trivia questions on Juan's blog for the first 6 months as a numeric sequence. Then represent the sequence using a table of values.

2. Contestants on a popular game show have an opportunity to randomly select a cash prize in 6 hidden containers. The highest possible cash prize is $25,000. The next highest prize is $5000, and the one after that is $1000.

   a. Think about how the value of the prize changes from one container to the next. Describe the pattern.

   b. Determine the prize values in the remaining containers.

   c. Represent the prize values in all six containers as a numeric sequence. Then represent the sequence using a table of values.

3. Enter each function into your graphing calculator to determine the shape of its graph. Then complete the table based on the characteristics of the function family.

Function	Function Family	Increasing/ Decreasing	Absolute Maximum/ Minimum	Curve/ Line
$h(x) = 5 \cdot 2^x$				
$g(x) = 30x - 550$				

Did You Mean: *Recursion*?

Determining Recursive and Explicit Expressions from Contexts

Warm Up

The local bank has agreed to donate $250 to the annual turkey fund to help feed families in need. In addition, for every bank customer that donates $50, the bank will donate $25.

1. A sequence describes the relationship between the number of $50 donations and the amount of the bank's donation. Is the sequence arithmetic or geometric?
2. How can you calculate the 10th term based on the 9th term?
3. What is the 20th term?

Learning Goals

- Write recursive formulas for arithmetic and geometric sequences from contexts.
- Write explicit expressions for arithmetic and geometric sequences from contexts.
- Use formulas to determine unknown terms of a sequence.

Key Terms

- recursive formula
- explicit formula

You have learned that arithmetic and geometric sequences always describe functions. How can you write equations to represent these functions?

Can I Get a Formula?

Think about:

Notice that the 1st term in this sequence is the amount Rico donates if the team hits 0 home runs.

While a common ratio or a common difference can help you determine the next term in a sequence, how can they help you determine the thousandth term of a sequence? The ten-thousandth term of a sequence?

Consider the sequence represented in this situation.

Rico owns a sporting goods store. He has agreed to donate $125 to the Centipede Valley High School baseball team for their equipment fund. In addition, he will donate $18 for every home run the Centipedes hit during the season. The sequence shown represents the possible dollar amounts that Rico could donate for the season.

125, 143, 161, 179, . . .

Number of Home Runs	Term Number (n)	Donation Amount (dollars)
0	1	
1		
2		
3		
4		
5		
6		
7		
8		
9		

1. **Identify the sequence type. Describe how you know.**

2. **Determine the common difference or common ratio for the sequence.**

3. **Complete the table.**

4. **Explain how you can calculate the tenth term based on the ninth term.**

Writing Formulas for Arithmetic Sequences

A **recursive formula** expresses each new term of a sequence based on the preceding term in the sequence. The recursive formula to determine the nth term of an arithmetic sequence is:

nth term $\longrightarrow$ $a_n = \underbrace{a_{n-1}}_{\text{previous term}} + d$ $\longleftarrow$ common difference

> You only need to know the previous term and the common difference to use the recursive formula.

Worked Example

Consider the sequence $-2, -9, -16, -23, \ldots$
You can use the recursive formula to determine the 5th term.

$$a_n = a_{n-1} + d$$
$$a_5 = a_{5-1} + (-7)$$

The expression a_5 represents the 5th term. The previous term is -23, and the common difference is -7.

$$a_5 = a_4 + (-7)$$
$$a_5 = -23 + (-7)$$
$$a_5 = -30$$

The 5th term of the sequence is -30.

Consider the sequence showing Rico's contribution to the Centipedes baseball team in terms of the number of home runs hit.

1. **Use a recursive formula to determine the 11th term in the sequence. Explain what this value means in terms of this problem situation.**

2. **Is there a way to calculate the 20th term without first calculating the 19th term? If so, describe the strategy.**

You can determine the 93rd term of the sequence by calculating each term before it, and then adding 18 to the 92nd term, but this will probably take a while! A more efficient way to calculate any term of a sequence is to use an *explicit formula*.

An **explicit formula** of a sequence is a formula to calculate the nth term of a sequence using the term's position in the sequence. The explicit formula for determining the nth term of an arithmetic sequence is:

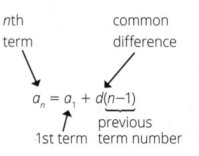

The 1st term in this sequence is the amount Rico donates if the team hits 0 home runs. So, the 93rd term represents the amount Rico donates if the team hits 92 home runs.

Worked Example

You can use the explicit formula to determine the 93rd term in this problem situation.

$$a_n = a_1 + d(n - 1)$$
$$a_{93} = 125 + 18(93 - 1)$$

The expression a_{93} represents the 93rd term. The first term is 125, and the common difference is 18.

$$a_{93} = 125 + 18(92)$$
$$a_{93} = 125 + 1656$$
$$a_{93} = 1781$$

The 93rd term of the sequence is 1781.

This means Rico will contribute a total of $1781 if the Centipedes hit 92 home runs.

3. **Use the explicit formula to determine the amount of money Rico will contribute for each number of home runs hit.**

    a. 35 home runs

    b. 48 home runs

    c. 86 home runs

    d. 214 home runs

Rico decides to increase his initial contribution and amount donated per home run hit. He decides to contribute $500 and will donate $75 for every home run the Centipedes hit.

4. **Write the first 5 terms of the sequence representing the new contribution Rico will donate to the Centipedes.**

5. **Determine Rico's contribution for each number of home runs hit.**

    a. 39 home runs

    b. 50 home runs

When it comes to bugs, bats, spiders, and—ugh, any other creepy crawlers—finding one in your house is finding one too many! Then again, when it comes to cells, the more the better. Animals, plants, fungi, slime, molds, and other living creatures are composed of eukaryotic cells. During growth, generally there is a cell called a "mother cell" that divides itself into two "daughter cells." Each of those daughter cells then divides into two more daughter cells, and so on.

1. **The sequence shown represents the growth of eukaryotic cells.**

   1, 2, 4, 8, 16, . . .

Notice that the 1st term in this sequence is the total number of cells after 0 divisions (that is, the mother cell).

   a. **Describe why this sequence is geometric and identify the common ratio.**

Number of Cell Divisions	Term Number (n)	Total Number of Cells
0	1	
1		
2		
3		
4		
5		
6		
7		
8		
9		

   b. **Complete the table of values. Use the number of cell divisions to identify the term number and the total number of cells after each division.**

   c. **Explain how you can calculate the tenth term based on the ninth term.**

The recursive formula to determine the nth term of a geometric sequence is:

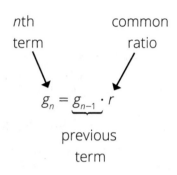

nth
term

common
ratio

$$g_n = \underbrace{g_{n-1}}_{\text{previous term}} \cdot r$$

Worked Example

Consider the sequence shown.

$$4, 12, 36, 108, \ldots$$

You can use the recursive formula to determine the 5th term.

$$g_n = g_{n-1} \cdot r$$
$$g_5 = g_{5-1} \cdot (3)$$

The expression g_5 represents the 5th term. The previous term is 108, and the common ratio is 3.

$$g_5 = g_4 \cdot (3)$$
$$g_5 = 108 \cdot (3)$$
$$g_5 = 324$$

The 5th term of the sequence is 324.

Consider the sequence of cell divisions and the total number of resulting cells.

2. **Write a recursive formula for the sequence and use the formula to determine the 12th term in the sequence. Explain what your result means in terms of this problem situation.**

The explicit formula to determine the nth term of a geometric sequence is:

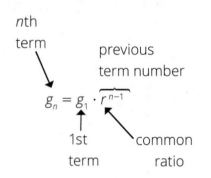

nth
term

previous
term number

$g_n = g_1 \cdot r^{n-1}$

1st
term

common
ratio

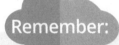

Remember:

The 1st term in this sequence is the total number of cells after 0 divisions. So, the 20th term represents the total number of cells after 19 divisions.

Worked Example

You can use the explicit formula to determine the 20th term in this problem situation.

$$g_n = g_1 \cdot r^{n-1}$$
$$g_{20} = 1 \cdot 2^{20-1}$$

The expression g_{20} represents the 20th term. The first term is 1, and the common ratio is 2.

$$g_{20} = 1 \cdot 2^{19}$$
$$g_{20} = 1 \cdot 524{,}288$$
$$g_{20} = 524{,}288$$

The 20th term of the sequence is 524,288.

This means that after 19 cell divisions, there are a total of 524,288 cells.

3. Use the explicit formula to determine the total number of cells for each number of divisions.

   a. 11 divisions

   b. 14 divisions

   c. 18 divisions

   d. 22 divisions

Suppose that a scientist has 5 eukaryotic cells in a petri dish. She wonders how the growth pattern would change if each mother cell divided into 3 daughter cells.

4. Write the first 5 terms of the sequence for the scientist's hypothesis.

5. Determine the total number of cells in the petri dish for each number of divisions.

   a. 13 divisions

   b. 16 divisions

ACTIVITY 3.3 Writing Recursive and Explicit Formulas

In the previous lesson you identified sequences as either arithmetic or geometric and then matched a corresponding graph.

1. Go back to the graphic organizers from the previous lesson. Write the recursive and explicit formulas for each sequence.

TALK the TALK

Pros and Cons

1. Explain the advantages and disadvantages of using a recursive formula.

2. Explain the advantages and disadvantages of using an explicit formula.

Assignment

Write

Explain the difference between a recursive formula and an explicit formula in your own words.

Remember

All sequences describe functions.

The explicit formula for an arithmetic sequence is $a_n = a_1 + d(n - 1)$, where n is the term number, a_1 is the first term in the sequence, a_n is the nth term in the sequence, and d is the common difference.

The explicit formula for a geometric sequence is $g_n = g_1 \cdot r^{(n - 1)}$ where n is the term number, g_1 is the first term in the sequence, g_n is the nth term in the sequence, and r is the common ratio.

Practice

1. Greta must volunteer 225 hours for a community service project. She plans to volunteer for 6 hours each week. The sequence shown represents the number of volunteer hours she has left after three weeks have passed.

   225, 219, 213, 207, . . .

   a. Describe this sequence.
   b. Use a formula to determine how many volunteer hours Greta has left to fulfill her requirement after 33 weeks have passed. Show your work.
   c. Which formula should you use to determine how many volunteer hours Greta has left to fulfill her requirement after 40 weeks have passed? Explain your reasoning.
   d. Calculate the number of volunteer hours Greta has left to fulfill her requirement after 40 weeks have passed. Explain what your answer means in terms of the problem situation.

2. The half-life of a substance is defined as the period of time it takes for the amount of the substance to decay by half. The sequence below shows the amount of a substance that will be left after a certain number of half-lives have elapsed.

   $1, \frac{1}{2}, \frac{1}{4}, \frac{1}{8}, \ldots$

   a. Describe this sequence.
   b. Calculate how much of the substance will be left after 21 half-lives have elapsed. Show your work. Does your answer make sense in this problem context? Why or why not?

Stretch

Consider the first two terms of this sequence $\frac{1}{16}, -\frac{3}{16}, \ldots$

- Determine the 63rd term if this is an arithmetic sequence. Write your answer as a reduced improper fraction.
- Determine the 63rd term if this is a geometric sequence. Write your answer in scientific notation.

Review

1. Determine whether each given sequence is arithmetic or geometric. Then write the next 3 terms of the sequence.

   a. 3, −12, 48, −192, . . .   b. 2.45, 3.86, 5.27, 6.68, . . .

2. Determine the independent and dependent quantities in each scenario. Include units when possible.

   a. A lamp manufacturing company produces 750 lamps per shift.

   b. A grocery store sells pears by the pound. A customer purchases 3 pounds for $5.07.

3. Determine the function family for each equation.

   a. $g(x) = -15|x - 2| + 430$ b. $h(x) = 3 \cdot (-5)^x - 17$

3 Pegs, N Discs

Modeling Using Sequences

Warm Up

Write an explicit formula for each arithmetic sequence.

1. {9, 8, 7, 6, 5, . . .}

2. {20, 40, 60, 80 . . .}

3. {1, $\frac{5}{2}$, 4, 5.5, 7, $\frac{17}{2}$ . . .}

Learning Goals

- Model situations using recursive and explicit formulas.
- Translate between recursive and explicit expressions of a mathematical model.
- Explore the process of mathematical modeling.

Key Term

- mathematical modeling

You have written recursive and explicit formulas for arithmetic and geometric sequences. How can you model a real-world situation using both recursive and explicit formulas for sequences?

Notice and Wonder

Mathematical modeling
is explaining patterns in the real world based on mathematical ideas.

In this lesson, you will explore the process of *mathematical modeling*. The first step in modeling a situation mathematically is to gather information, notice patterns, and formulate mathematical questions about what you notice.

Let's play a game.

The object of the game is to move an entire stack of discs or coins from the start circle to any of the other circles.

The rules of the game are simple:
- You can only move one disc at a time.
- You cannot put a larger disc on top of a smaller disc.

Let's first play with 3 discs. To begin, place a quarter, nickel, and dime on top of each other in that order in a stack in the Start circle. Or, use the cutout discs at the end of the lesson, stacked from largest to smallest inside the Start circle.

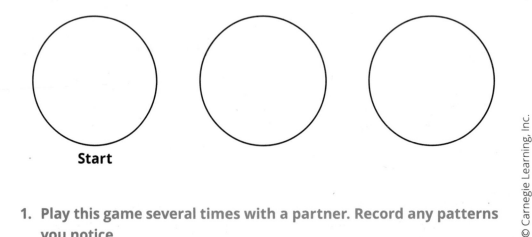

Start

Think about:

Is there a relationship between the number of discs and the number of moves it takes to complete the game?

1. **Play this game several times with a partner. Record any patterns you notice.**

ACTIVITY
4.1 Organize and Mathematize

The second step in the modeling process is to organize your information and represent it using mathematical notation.

Consider the question from the previous activity. Is there a relationship between the number of discs and the minimum number of moves?

1. Play the game again and record your results in the table.

Number of Discs	Minimum Number of Moves
1	
2	
3	

Ask yourself:

How do you know you did it in the least number of moves?

2. What pattern do you notice in your results?

3. Use mathematical notation to represent the pattern you have identified in your results. Explain your reasoning.

ACTIVITY
4.2 Predict and Analyze

Step 3 of the modeling process is to extend the patterns you created, complete operations, make predictions, and analyze the mathematical results.

1. **Use your results to extend the pattern in the table in the previous activity.**

2. **Write a recursive formula to represent the pattern shown in your table. What predictions does this formula make for the minimum number of moves required for 4 and 5 discs?**

3. **Write an explicit formula to represent the pattern shown in your table. What predictions does this formula make for the minimum number of moves required for 4 and 5 discs?**

The final step in the modeling process is to interpret your results and test your mathematical predictions in the real world. If your predictions are incorrect, you can revisit your mathematical work and make adjustments—or start all over!

1. **Play the game again to demonstrate that your prediction for 4 discs and 5 discs is accurate. Record your observations.**

2. **Construct a graph to represent your explicit formula. Describe the characteristics of the graph in terms of the situation.**

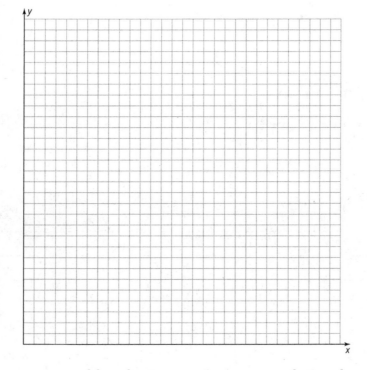

3. **Suppose you could make 1 move every second. How long would it take to complete a game with 25 discs? Show your work.**

Ask
yourself:

What is the level of accuracy appropriate for this situation?

TALK the TALK

A Modeling Process

In this lesson, you used a modeling process to figure out whether the number of moves in the disc game is related to the number of discs. The basic steps of the mathematical modeling process are summarized in the diagram.

Summarize what is involved in each phase of this modeling process.

Notice and Wonder

_____

_____

_____

Organize and Mathematize

_____

_____

_____

Predict and Analyze

_____

_____

_____

Test and Interpret

_____

_____

_____

The Modeling Process

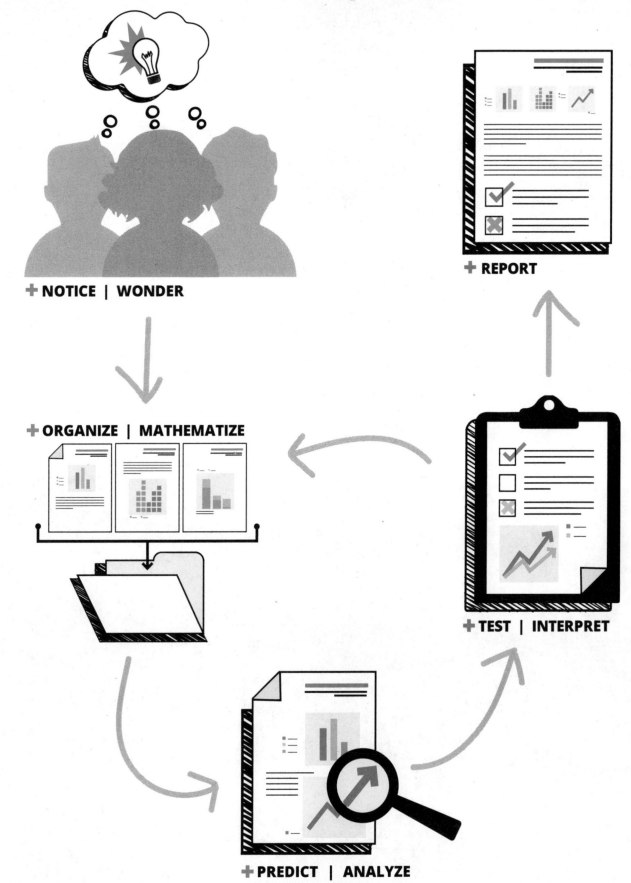

+ NOTICE | WONDER

+ ORGANIZE | MATHEMATIZE

+ PREDICT | ANALYZE

+ TEST | INTERPRET

+ REPORT

Discs

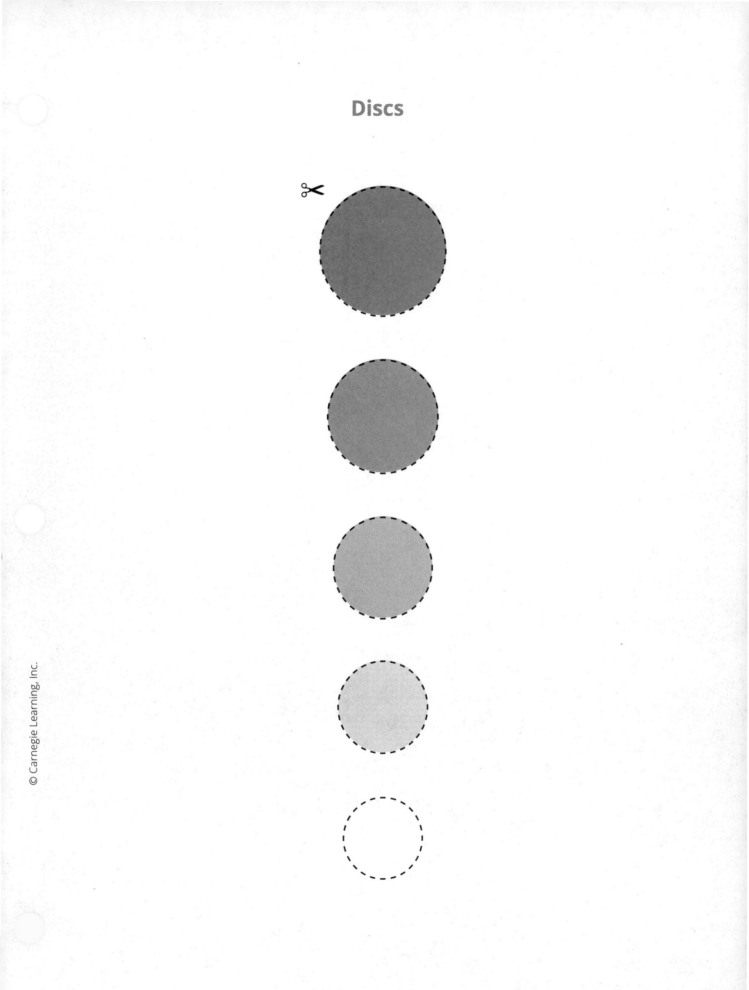

Assignment

Write

Explain why you might need to repeat steps in the Modeling Process.

Remember

The 4 steps of the mathematical modeling process are:
1. Notice and Wonder
2. Organize and Mathematize
3. Predict and Analyze
4. Test and Interpret

Practice

1. Triplets seem to run in the Tribiani family. Great-grandma Tribiani had triplets, each of her triplets had triplets and each of those triplets had triplets.

Step 1: Notice and Wonder

    a. What do you notice about the situation?

    b. Which of these is a mathematical question you can ask about the situation?
- Can triplets be represented by a function?
- How many children did Great-grandma Tribiani's siblings have?
- Is there a relationship between the generation and the number of triplets in that generation?

Step 2: Organize and Mathematize

    c. Represent the number of triplets in each generation as a numeric sequence with 4 terms. Then describe the sequence.

    d. Create a table of values using the first 4 terms of the sequence.

Step 3: Predict and Analyze

    e. Write an explicit formula to represent this sequence.

    f. Create a graph for the explicit formula you built.
Describe the characteristics of the graph in terms of the situation.

    g. Predict the number of descendants in the Tribiani family in 20 generations. Show your work.

Step 4: Test and Interpret

    h. Determine whether a discrete or continuous graph makes more sense in this scenario. Explain your reasoning.

    i. Describe the end behavior of your graph and explain what this means.

Stretch

Aaron just paid $7.40 for a new pair of sunglasses. His father told him that prices were different 10 years ago. Then his grandfather told him that 20 years ago, prices were even better. Aaron did some research and found that the prices did change, but not by much. Ten years ago, the average price for a generic pair of sunglasses was $6.80, and 20 years ago it was $6.20.

1. Describe a possible arithmetic relationship between the decade and the price in that decade. Represent the relationship with a table, an explicit formula, and a graph. Describe the characteristics of each.

2. Describe a possible geometric relationship between the decade and the price in that decade. Represent the relationship with a table, an explicit formula, and a graph. Describe the characteristics of each.

3. Predict the price of a pair of sunglasses in 5 decades using both sequences.

4. Which type of sequence better represents the situation? Explain your reason.

Review

1. Determine the 58th term of the sequence 540, 495, 450, . . .

2. Determine the 13th term of the sequence 0.4, −1.2, 3.6, . . .

3. Each pair of graphs has been grouped together. Use characteristics of the graphs to explain why they were likely grouped together.

a.

Graph A	Graph B

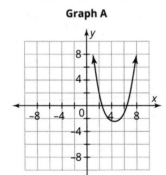
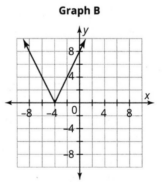

b.

Graph A	Graph B

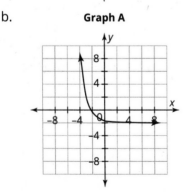
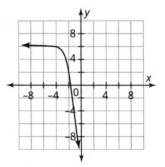

4. Determine the function family to which each equation belongs. Explain your reasoning.

a. $f(x) = 4 \cdot 9^x + 2$

b. $g(x) = |8x - 3|$

Sequences Summary

KEY TERMS

- sequence
- term of a sequence
- infinite sequence
- finite sequence
- arithmetic sequence
- common difference
- geometric difference
- common ratio
- recursive formula
- explicit formula
- mathematical modeling

LESSON 1

Is There a Pattern Here?

A **sequence** is a pattern involving an ordered arrangement of numbers, geometric figures, letters, or other objects. A **term in a sequence** is an individual number, figure, or letter in the sequence. Many different patterns can generate a sequence of numbers.

A sequence that continues on forever is called an **infinite sequence**. A sequence that terminates is called a **finite sequence**.

For example, consider the situation in which an album that can hold 275 baseball cards is filled with 15 baseball cards at the end of each week. A sequence to represent how many baseball cards can fit into the album after 6 weeks is 275 cards, 260 cards, 245 cards, 230 cards, 215 cards, and 200 cards. This sequence begins at 275 and decreases by 15 with each term. The pattern cannot continue forever since you cannot have a negative number of cards, so this is a finite sequence.

The Password Is: Operations

An **arithmetic sequence** is a sequence of numbers in which the difference between any two consecutive terms is a constant. This constant is called the **common difference** and is typically represented by the variable d. The common difference of a sequence is positive if the same positive number is added to each term to produce the next term. The common difference of a sequence is negative if the same negative number is added to each term to produce the next term.

For example, consider the sequence 14, $16\frac{1}{2}$, 19, $21\frac{1}{2}$, ... The pattern of this sequence is to add $2\frac{1}{2}$ to each term to produce the next term. This is an arithmetic sequence, and the common difference d is $2\frac{1}{2}$.

A **geometric sequence** is a sequence of numbers in which the ratio between any two consecutive terms is a constant. The constant, which is either an integer or a fraction, is called the **common ratio** and is typically represented by the variable r.

For example, consider the sequence 27, 9, 3, 1, $\frac{1}{3}$, $\frac{1}{9}$. The pattern is to multiply each term by the same number, $\frac{1}{3}$, to determine the next term. Therefore, this sequence is geometric and the common ratio r is $\frac{1}{3}$.

Did You Mean: *Recursion?*

A **recursive formula** expresses each new term of a sequence based on a preceding term of the sequence. The recursive formula to determine the nth term of an arithmetic sequence is $a_n = a_{n-1} + d$. The recursive formula to determine the nth term of a geometric sequence is $g_n = g_{n-1} \cdot r$. When using the recursive formula, it is not necessary to know the first term of the sequence.

For example, consider the geometric sequence 32, 8, 2, $\frac{1}{2}$, ... with a common ratio of $\frac{1}{4}$. The 5th term of the sequence can be determined using the recursive formula.

$$g_n = g_{n-1} \cdot r$$
$$g_5 = g_4 \cdot r$$
$$g_5 = \frac{1}{2} \cdot \frac{1}{4}$$
$$g_5 = \frac{1}{8}$$

The 5th term of the sequence is $\frac{1}{8}$.

An **explicit formula** for a sequence is a formula for calculating each term of the sequence using the index, which is a term's position in the sequence. The explicit formula to determine the nth term of an arithmetic sequence is $a_n = a_1 + d(n - 1)$. The explicit formula to determine the nth term of a geometric sequence is $g_n = g_1 \cdot r^{n-1}$.

For example, consider the situation of a cactus that is currently 3 inches tall and will grow $\frac{1}{4}$ inch every month. The explicit formula for arithmetic sequences can be used to determine how tall the cactus will be in 12 months.

$$a_n = a_1 + d(n - 1)$$
$$a_{12} = 3 + \frac{1}{4}(12 - 1)$$
$$a_{12} = 3 + \frac{1}{4}(11)$$
$$a_{12} = 5\frac{3}{4}$$

In 12 months, the cactus will be $5\frac{3}{4}$ inches tall.

LESSON 4

3 Pegs, N Discs

A process called **mathematical modeling** involves explaining patterns in the real world based on mathematical ideas. The four basic steps of the mathematical modeling process are Notice and Wonder, Organize and Mathematize, Predict and Analyze, and Test and Interpret.

For example, consider a theater that has 25 rows of seats. The first three rows have 16, 18, and 20 seats, respectively. The ushers working at this theater need to know how many seats their sections have when they are directing people.

The first step of the modeling process, Notice and Wonder, is to gather information, look for patterns, and formulate mathematical questions about what you notice. In the example, each row seems to have 2 more seats than the previous row.

The second step of the modeling process, Organize and Mathematize, is to organize the information and express any patterns you notice using mathematical notation. A table can be used to represent the given information about the first three rows in the theater. The recursive pattern shown in the table can be expressed as $S_n = S_{n-1} + 2$.

Row	Number of Seats
1	16
2	18
3	20

The third step of the modeling process, Predict and Analyze, is to analyze the mathematical notation and make predictions. The fourth row will have 22 seats and the fifth row will have 24 seats. The pattern can be expressed using the explicit formula $S_n = 16 + 2(n - 1)$.

The fourth and final step of the modeling process, Test and Interpret, is to test and interpret the information. A graph can be constructed for the explicit formula. The graph is discrete because rows and seats are integer values.

This information can be used to determine that an usher working in rows 15 and 16 will have 44 and 46 seats, respectively.

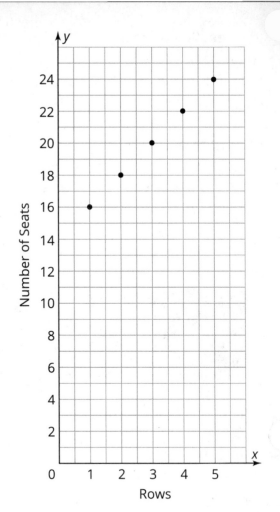

TOPIC 3
Linear Regressions

The Milky Way looks two-dimensional from this point of view. Its line of best fit would have a negative slope.

Module 1: Searching for Patterns

TOPIC 3: LINEAR REGRESSIONS

In this topic, students focus on the patterns that are evident in certain data sets and use linear functions to model those patterns. Using the informal knowledge of lines of best fit that was built in previous grades, students advance their statistical methods to make predictions about real-world phenomena. They differentiate between correlation and causation, recognizing that a correlation between two quantities does not necessarily mean that there is also a causal relationship. And, at the end of this topic, students will synthesize what they have learned to decide whether a linear model is appropriate.

Where have we been?

Students have analyzed the shape of data, informally fit lines of best fit to model data sets, determined the equations of those lines, interpreted the slopes and *y*-intercepts of the lines, and used the equations to make and judge the reasonableness of predictions about the data. Students have also examined linear relationships and recognized that the slope of a line defines its steepness and direction.

Where are we going?

Using and analyzing linear regressions to model data is an important bridge between the first two topics in the first module of this course and the concepts students will encounter in the next module, **Exploring Constant Change**. As students continue in this course and in high school mathematics, they will determine and analyze more complicated regressions, including exponential and quadratic regressions.

Regression Lines

Real-world data points never fit neatly on a line. But you can model the data points using a line, which represents a linear function.

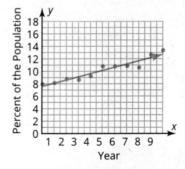

There are an infinite number of lines that can pass through the collection of data points. But there is just one line that models the data with the minimum distances between the data points and the line.

Now Hiring

According to a report published in 2017, the demand for data scientists, data developers, and data engineers will grow nearly 40% over the next few years, paying an average starting salary of over $80,000 per year.

Currently, approximately 88% of data scientists have a master's degree and 46% have a Ph.D. in math, statistics, computer science, or engineering.

Talking Points

Regressions can be an important topic to know about for college admissions tests.

Here is a sample question:

The data in the table show test scores after certain amounts of study time. Use a linear regression to estimate the score associated with a study time of 20 minutes.

Score	Time (min)
86	45
70	15
90	40
78	35

Time is the independent variable, so the time values must be entered as x's and score values as y's in a graphing calculator.

This yields a linear regression equation of $y = 0.61x + 60.51$. A study time of 20 minutes would yield an estimated score of $y = 0.61(20) + 60.51$, or 72.71.

Key Terms

regression line
For a scatter plot of data, the regression line is a mathematical model that can be used to predict the values of a dependent variable based upon the values of an independent variable.

interpolation
Using a linear regression to make predictions within the data set is called interpolation.

extrapolation
To make predictions for values that are outside of the data set is called extrapolation.

correlation
A measure of how well a regression fits a set of data is called correlation.

Like a Glove

Least Squares Regressions

Warm Up

Use the slope formula to write an equation for each.

1. A line that passes through the point (2, 5) with a slope of 5

2. A line that passes through the points (5, 2) and (3, 8)

Learning Goals

- Create a graph of data points with and without technology.
- Determine an equation for a line of best fit by visual approximation of a hand-drawn line.
- Determine a linear regression equation using technology.
- Make predictions about data using a linear regression equation.
- Explain the calculations involved in the Least Squares Method.
- Choose a level of accuracy appropriate when reporting quantities.

Key Terms

- Least Squares Method
- centroid
- regression line
- interpolation
- extrapolation

You have searched for patterns in graphs and sequences of numbers. How can you use what you know to identify patterns in sets of data?

Frozen Yogurt...When It's Freezing?

Mr. Templeton's Future Business Leaders Club (FBLC) is helping a frozen yogurt shop located near the school analyze how the business is affected by the weather. The owner is wondering whether there is a relationship between the temperature and the number of customers that buy yogurt during the 2 hours immediately after school. The FBLC collected this data.

Temperature (°F)	Number of Customers
45	97
25	55
60	85
15	37
100	100

1. **Construct a scatter plot of the collected data.**

   a. **Plot the first data point. Is there a pattern? Use a piece of spaghetti to approximate a line that models the data.**

   b. **Add the second data point to the graph. Is there a pattern? Adjust the piece of spaghetti to approximate a line that models the data with the additional point.**

   c. **Add the third data point to the graph. Describe the pattern that you see. Approximate the line by using the spaghetti.**

   d. **Continue this process until all five data points are plotted and recorded in the table.**

2. **Use your linear model to describe the relationship between the temperature outside and the number of customers at the frozen yogurt shop.**

You have approximated the line that best represents the data with each additional data point.

1. **Use the full data set and the line that you approximated to write an equation that you think best represents the data.**

2. **Based on your equation, predict the number of customers to visit the frozen yogurt shop in the two hours after school for each given temperature.**

    a. **85°F**   b. **115°F**

    c. **10°F**

3. **Compare your predictions with your classmates. Did your predictions differ from the other groups? Explain why or why not.**

You have noticed that estimating a line of best fit can give different predictions. Fortunately, with technology you can create prediction equations as well as a scatter plots from tables of data. You just need to build a data table that has an independent variable and a dependent variable.

4. **Identify the independent and dependent variable. What is the significance of those designations?**

5. **Use the data table and a graphing calculator to generate a line of best fit. What is the slope and *y*-intercept of the line and what do they represent?**

6. **Use the new line of best fit to predict the number of customers at the frozen yogurt shop immediately after school for each given temperature.**

   a. **85°F**   b. **115°F**

   c. **10°F**

7. **How do your predictions compare to the predictions from the other groups?**

The equation that your calculator uses to give you the line of best fit is called the **Least Squares Method**. This is a method that creates a line of best fit for a scatter plot that has two basic requirements:

- The line must contain the *centroid* of the data set. The **centroid** is a point whose *x*-value is the mean of all the *x*-values of the points on the scatter plot and its *y*-value is the mean of all the *y*-values of the points on the scatter plot.
- Even though infinitely many lines can pass through the centroid, the **regression line** has the smallest possible vertical distances from each given data point to the regression line. The sum of the *squares* of those distances are at a minimum with this line.

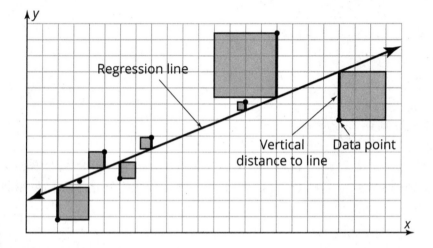

8. **Consider the graph of the sample regression line.**

   a. **What do the vertical lines in bold represent?**

   b. **What do the shaded squares represent? How do they relate to the Least Squares Method?**

9. Alysse and Bonito each draw a regression line to model a set of data. They both record the vertical distances between each point and the regression line.

Alysse

Vertical Distances: 2, 2, 2, 2, 2

Bonito

Vertical Distances: 1, 1, 1, 1, 6

Both students believe they drew the least square regression line. Who's correct? Justify your choice.

10. How does your decision in Question 9 inform you about the placement of a line of best fit using the Least Squares Method?

ACTIVITY 1.2

Making Predictions

The table shown lists the average global temperature in 5-year spans from 1957 to 2016.

1. **What is the range of the data set?**

2. **Identify the independent and dependent quantities and their units of measure.**

3. **Do the data itself represent a function? Does it appear that there is a specific function that could model this data set? If so, describe the function. If not, state why not.**

4. **Use technology to graph a scatter plot demonstrating the relationship between time spans and temperature. What association do you notice?**

Years	Span	Average Temperature (°F)
1957–1961	1	57.250
1962–1966	2	57.121
1967–1971	3	57.196
1972–1976	4	57.189
1977–1981	5	57.495
1982–1986	6	57.445
1987–1991	7	57.780
1992–1996	8	57.700
1997–2001	9	58.053
2002–2006	10	58.262
2007–2011	11	58.244
2012–2016	12	58.448

5. **Between which consecutive spans was there a decrease in average global temperature?**

6. **Use your graphing technology to determine the regression equation for the average global temperature data. Then sketch the data points and the line of best fit that you see.**

7. **What is the relationship between the equation for the line of best fit and any association you notice in the graph? Do you think that this line fits the data well?**

8. **For each expression from your linear regression equation about global temperatures, write an appropriate unit of measure and describe the contextual meaning. Then, choose a term from the word box to describe the mathematical meaning of each part.**

Word Box
- input value
- output value
- rate of change
- y-intercept

Expression	Unit	What it Means	
		Contextual Meaning	Mathematical Meaning
$f(x)$			
0.1259			
x			
56.863			

9. **Use your linear regression equation to predict the average global temperature for the years 2032–2036.**

Making Predictions Within and Outside a Data Set

The music industry is constantly changing how it delivers music to its listeners. The table shows the percent of total U.S. music sales revenues from streaming.

Year	2010	2011	2012	2013	2014	2015
Percent of Total U.S. Music Sales Revenue From Streaming	7	9	15	21	27	34

1. **Use graphing technology to determine the linear regression equation for the data.**

2. **Interpret the equation of the line in terms of this problem situation.**

Ask yourself:

What is an appropriate level of accuracy needed throughout this situation?

If there is a linear association between the independent and dependent variables of a data set, you can use a linear regression to make predictions within the data set. Using a linear regression to make predictions within the data set is called **interpolation**.

3. **Use your equation to predict the percent of streaming revenues in 2013. Compare the predicted value percent in 2013 with the actual value.**

4. **Compute the predicted value percent for 2011 and compare it with the actual value.**

5. **Do you think a prediction made using interpolation will always be close to the actual value? Explain your reasoning.**

To make predictions for values of *x* that are outside of the data set is called **extrapolation**.

6. **Use the equation to predict the percent of streaming revenues:**

   a. **in 2040.**   b. **in 2004.**

7. **Are these predictions reasonable? Explain your reasoning.**

TALK the TALK

Tell Me Ev-ery-thing

You have used technology to determine linear regression equations. You have then used those linear regression equations to predict unknown values within and without a data set.

1. **Why is the linear regression line generated using technology more accurate than the line of best fit that can be written using two points?**

2. **Why are predictions made by extrapolation more likely to be less accurate than predictions made by interpolation?**

© Carnegie Learning, Inc.

Assignment

Write

Complete each sentence with the appropriate vocabulary term.

1. A _____ can be used to organize and display the values of two variables in a data set.
2. _____ models the relationship between two variables in a data set by producing a line of best fit.
3. A(n) _____ is a line that best approximates the linear relationship between two variables in a data set.
4. The _____ is used to approximate a line of best fit by minimizing the squares of the distances of the points from the line.
5. _____ is using a linear regression to make predictions within the data set.
6. Using a linear regression to make predictions outside of the data set is _____.
7. After a scatter plot is created, the _____ is a point with an *x*-value that is the mean of all the *x*-values of the points on the plot and a *y*-value that is the mean of all the *y*-values of the points on the plot.

Remember

Patterns in data can be modeled with lines of best fit. The Least Squares Method is one way to create a linear regression equation, and it is the method that graphing calculators tend to use.

Practice

1. One of the jobs of the National Center for Education Statistics is to gather information about public high schools and their dropout rates. This includes anyone who leaves school without a high school diploma or an equivalent credential. The table shows the average percent of high school dropouts from the year 2002 through the year 2014.

   a. Create a scatter plot of the high school dropout data. What information can you gather about the dropout rates from the scatter plot?

   b. Use the data table and graphing technology to generate a line of best fit.

   c. Interpret the slope and *y*-intercept of the linear regression equation. What do these values represent in terms of the problem situation?

   d. Determine the dropout rate for the year 2010. Is this the same as the dropout rate recorded in the table? If not, explain the difference.

Year	High School Dropout Rate (percent)
2002	3.5
2003	4.0
2004	4.7
2005	3.8
2006	3.8
2007	3.5
2008	3.5
2009	3.4
2010	3.0
2011	3.4
2012	3.4
2013	4.7
2014	5.2

2. Mr. Li is a math teacher at Pinkston High School and is preparing his students to take the SAT test. He collected data from 10 students who took the test last year and presented this information to the students in a table. The highest math SAT score a student can achieve is 800. Analyze the data in the table.

Time Spent Studying (hours)	Math SAT Score
1	350
22	780
12	600
14	700
4	380
10	650
9	580
3	400
7	530
4	410

a. Construct a scatter plot of the data and describe any patterns you see in the data.

b. Determine the equation of a line passing through (14, 700) and (7, 530). Then determine the equation of a line passing through (22, 780) and (4, 380). Graph both lines on the same graph as the scatter plot.

c. Which line seems to best fit the data? Would you use either one of these lines to make predictions about a student's math SAT score based on the amount of studying they do? Why or why not?

d. Use graphing technology to determine the regression equation.

e. Interpret the least squares regression equation in terms of the problem situation.

f. Use the regression line to predict the math SAT score for a student who studies for 17 hours. Did you use interpolation or extrapolation to make this prediction? Is this prediction reasonable for this problem situation? Explain your reasoning.

g. Use the line of best fit to predict the math SAT score for a student who studies for 40 hours. Did you use interpolation or extrapolation to make this prediction? Is this prediction reasonable for this problem situation? Explain your reasoning.

h. One of Mr. Li's students comes back to him the following year and says that he studied for 15 hours for the math SAT and got a score of 610. He argues that the equation predicted that he would have scored a 682. What do you think explains the discrepancy?

Stretch

Consider the two sets of data shown in the graphs.

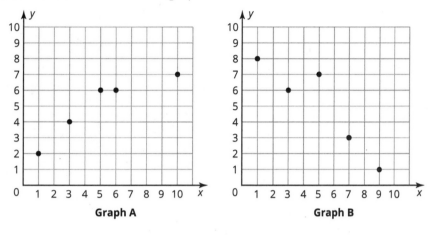

Graph A

Graph B

1. Calculate the mean of the *x*-values, $\bar{x}$, and the mean of the *y*-values, $\bar{y}$, for each graph.

2. Complete the tables for each graph.

Graph A				
x	$x - \bar{x}$	*y*	$y - \bar{y}$	$(x - \bar{x})(y - \bar{y})$
1	−4	2	−3	12
3		4		
5		6		
6		6		
10		7		
			SUM =	

Graph B				
x	$x - \bar{x}$	*y*	$y - \bar{y}$	$(x - \bar{x})(y - \bar{y})$
1	−4	8	3	−12
3		6		
5		7		
7		3		
9		1		
			SUM =	

3. Compare the two sums in the last column of each table. Determine if there seems to be a connection between the sums and the graphs of the data set.

Review

1. A maintenance worker in a factory notices that a water tank is leaking. She records the amount of water in the tank each day in a table.

   a. Write a recursive formula to represent the pattern shown in the table. What predictions does this formula make for the amount of water in the tank on the 5th day?

   b. Write an explicit formula to represent the pattern shown in the table. What predictions does this formula make for the amount of water in the tank on the 10th day?

Day	Volume of Water (L)
1	16,000
2	12,000
3	9,000
4	6,750

2. The graph represents a linear relationship between x and y.

   a. Describe whether the graph is increasing or decreasing. Justify your reasoning.

   b. Determine the x- and y-intercept.

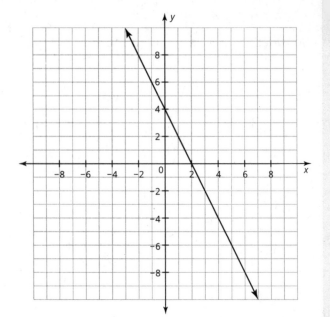

Gotta Keep It Correlatin'

Correlation

Warm Up

Describe a possible flaw in the reasoning for each situation.

1. If I wash my hands regularly, I will not get sick.

2. If I practice my guitar every day, I will be a rock star.

3. If I wear my favorite football jersey to support the team, they will win the game.

4. If I am a good driver, I will not have an accident.

Learning Goals

- Determine the correlation coefficient using technology.
- Interpret the correlation coefficient for a set of data.
- Understand the difference between r and r^2.
- Understand the difference between correlation and causation.
- Understand necessary conditions.
- Understand sufficient conditions.
- Choose a level of accuracy appropriate when reporting quantities.

Key Terms

- correlation
- correlation coefficient
- coefficient of determination
- causation
- necessary condition
- sufficient condition
- common response
- confounding variable

You have learned how to write a line of best fit using the Least Squares Method. How do you know if that line actually produces valid, useable results? Is there a way to measure the strength of the relationship between the variables?

Associate, Formulate, Correlate!

Consider each relationship shown.

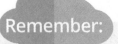

Remember:

Data comparing two variables can show a positive association, negative association, or no association.

1. **Describe any associations between the independent and dependent variables, and then draw a line of best fit, if possible.**

a.

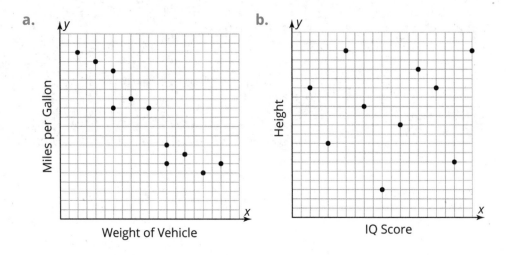
Weight of Vehicle — Miles per Gallon

b.
IQ Score — Height

c.

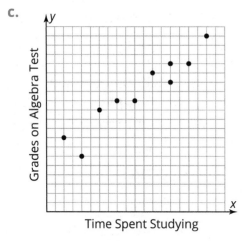
Time Spent Studying — Grades on Algebra Test

A measure of how well a regression fits a set of data is called **correlation**. The **correlation coefficient** is a value between −1 and 1, which indicates how close the data are to the graph of the regression equation. The closer the correlation coefficient is to 1 or −1, the stronger the relationship is between the two variables. The variable r is used to represent the correlation coefficient.

> The correlation coefficient falls between −1 and 0 if the data show a negative association or between 0 and 1 if the data show a positive association.

1. **Determine whether the points in each scatter plot have a positive correlation, a negative correlation, or no correlation. Four possible r-values are given. Circle the r-value you think is most appropriate. Explain your reasoning for each.**

a.
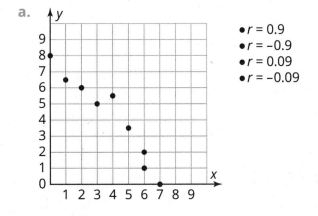

- $r = 0.9$
- $r = -0.9$
- $r = 0.09$
- $r = -0.09$

> The closer the r-value gets to 0, the less of a linear relationship there is in the data.

b.
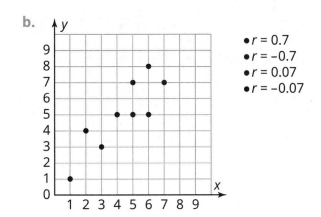

- $r = 0.7$
- $r = -0.7$
- $r = 0.07$
- $r = -0.07$

© Carnegie Learning, Inc.

c.

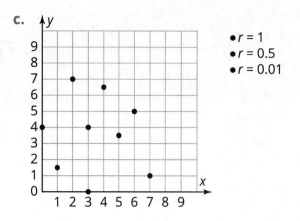

- $r = 1$
- $r = 0.5$
- $r = 0.01$

You can calculate the correlation coefficient of a data set using the formula:

$$r = \frac{\sum_{i=1}^{n}(x_i - \bar{x})(y_i - \bar{y})}{\sqrt{\sum_{i=1}^{n}(x_i - \bar{x})^2}\sqrt{\sum_{i=1}^{n}(y_i - \bar{y})^2}}$$

Fortunately your graphing calculator can do this arithmetic. Previously you used a graphing calculator to determine the linear regression using the Least Squares Method. Along with calculating the equation for the line, the calculator also calculated the value r, the correlation coefficient.

Let's use technology to compute the value of the correlation coefficient.

2. **Consider the data set (23, 23), (1, 2), and (3, 4).**

   a. **Use technology to compute the correlation coefficient.**

   b. **Interpret the correlation coefficient of the data set.**

A group of friends completed a survey about their monthly income and how much they pay for rent each month. The table shows the results.

Monthly Net Income (dollars)	Monthly Rent (dollars)
1400	450
1550	505
2000	545
2600	715
3000	930
3400	1000

1. **Identify the independent and dependent quantities in this problem situation.**

2. **Construct a scatter plot of the data using technology.**

   a. **Sketch and label the scatter plot.**

   b. **Do you think a linear regression equation would best describe this situation? Explain your reasoning.**

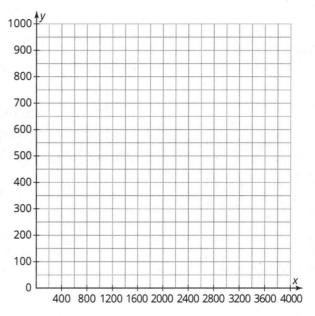

Ask yourself:

What is the appropriate level of accuracy needed for this linear regression equation?

3. Use technology to determine whether a line of best fit is appropriate for these data.

   a. Determine and interpret the linear regression equation.

   b. Compute the correlation coefficient.

4. Would a line of best fit be appropriate for this data set? Explain your reasoning.

The correlation coefficient, r, indicates the type (positive or negative) and strength of the relationship that may exist for a given set of data points. The **coefficient of determination**, r^2, measures how well the graph of the regression fits the data. It represents the percentage of variation of the observed values of the data points from their predicted values.

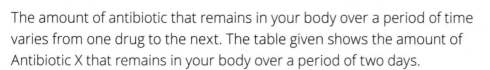

The amount of antibiotic that remains in your body over a period of time varies from one drug to the next. The table given shows the amount of Antibiotic X that remains in your body over a period of two days.

Time (hours)	Amount of Antibiotic X in Body (mg)
0	60
6	36
12	22
18	13
24	7.8
30	4.7
36	2.8
42	1.7
48	1

1. **Determine and interpret a linear regression equation for this data set.**

2. **Compute and interpret both the correlation coefficient and coefficient of determination of this data set.**

3. **Does it seem appropriate to use a line of best fit? If no, explain your reasoning.**

4. **Sketch a scatter plot of the data.**

5. **Look at the graph of the data. Do you still agree with your answer to Question 3? Explain your reasoning.**

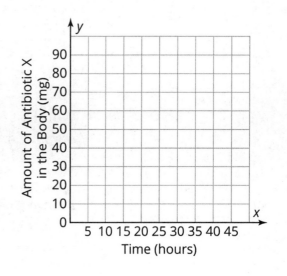

ACTIVITY
2.4   Correlation Vs. Causation

Does correlation mean causation? What do you think causation means?
That is a question that statisticians are always trying to determine.

Read the three true statements that Alonzo and Richard are given by their Algebra I teacher. She asks them to decide what conclusions they can draw from the data. Do you agree with them? If so, why? If not, why not?

1. **The number of smartphones sold in the United States has increased every year since 2005. The number of flat screen televisions sold in the United States has also increased during the same period of time.**

   Alonzo and Richard reached the conclusion that owning a cell phone causes a person to buy a flat screen television.

2. **Since 2004, the average salary of an NFL football player has increased every year. The average weight of an NFL player has also increased yearly since 2004.**

   After much discussion, Alonzo and Richard reached the conclusion that higher salaries cause the players to gain weight.

3. **Worldwide, the number of automobiles sold annually has steadily increased since 1920. Gasoline production has also steadily increased since 1920.**

   Alonzo and Richard concluded that the increase in the number of automobiles sold caused an increase in the amount of gasoline produced.

Proving causation is challenging. The scenarios Alonzo and Richard analyzed demonstrate that even though two quantities are correlated, this does not mean that one quantity caused the other. This is one of the most misunderstood and misapplied uses of statistics.

Causation is when one event effects the outcome of a second event. A correlation is a **necessary condition** for causation, but a correlation is not a **sufficient condition** for causation. While determining a correlation is straightforward, using statistics to establish causation is very difficult.

4. **Many medical studies have tried to prove that smoking causes lung cancer.**

   a. **Is smoking a necessary condition for lung cancer? Why or why not?**

   b. **Is smoking a sufficient condition for lung cancer? Why or why not?**

   c. **Is there a correlation between people who smoke and people who get lung cancer? Explain your reasoning.**

   d. **Is it true that smoking causes lung cancer? If so, how was it proven?**

5. It is often said that teenage drivers cause automobile accidents.

   a. Is being a teenage driver a necessary condition to have an automobile accident? Why or why not?

   b. Is being a teenage driver a sufficient condition to have an automobile accident? Why or why not?

   c. Is there a correlation between teenage drivers and automobile accidents? Explain your reasoning.

   d. Is it true that teenage drivers cause automobile accidents? Explain your reasoning.

Does school absenteeism cause poor performance in school? A correlation between the independent variable of days absent to the dependent variable of grades makes sense. However, this alone does not prove causation.

6. In order to prove that the number of days that a student is absent causes the student to get poor grades, we would need to conduct more controlled experiments.

   a. List several ways that you could design experiments to attempt to prove this assertion.

   b. Will any of these experiments prove the assertion? Explain your reasoning.

There are two relationships that are often mistaken for causation. A **common response** is when some other reason may cause the same result. A **confounding variable** is when there are other variables that are unknown or unobserved.

7. **Consider each relationship. List two or more common responses that could also cause this result.**

    a. **In North Carolina, the number of shark attacks increases when the temperature increases. Therefore, a temperature increase appears to cause sharks to attack.**

    b. **A company claims that their weight loss pill caused people to lose 20 pounds when following the accompanying exercise program.**

TALK the TALK

Correlations R Us

Consider the given data sets.

Set A

x	y
0	24
2	19
5	12
10	6
20	0

Set B

x	y
8	13
10	4
14	15
15	14
19	73

1. **Determine the linear regression for each set.**

2. **Compare the correlation coefficient and the coefficient of determination of each data set. Describe which regression equation is the better fit and why.**

Write

Complete each sentence.

1. A correlation is a _____ for causation, but a correlation is not a _____ for causation.
2. A _____ is when some other reason may cause the same result.
3. _____ is when one event causes a second event.
4. A _____ is when there are other variables that are unknown or unobserved.
5. The _____ is a value between −1 and 1 that indicates how close the data are to form a straight line.
6. The percentage of variation of the observed values of the data points from their predicted values is represented by the _____.

Remember

Sets of data can frequently be modeled by using a linear function called a regression equation. A value called the correlation coefficient can also be calculated to assist in determining how well the regression equation fits the data.

Practice

1. The table shows the percent of the United States population who did not receive needed dental care services due to cost.

Year	1999	2000	2001	2002	2003	2004	2005	2006	2007	2008	2009
Percent	7.9	8.1	8.7	8.6	9.2	10.7	10.7	10.8	10.5	12.6	13.3

a. Do you think a linear regression equation would best describe this situation? Why or why not?
b. Determine the linear regression equation for these data. Interpret the equation in terms of this problem situation.
c. Compute and interpret the correlation coefficient of this data set. Does it seem appropriate to use a line of best fit? Explain your reasoning.
d. Sketch a scatter plot of the data. Then, plot the equation of the regression line on the same grid. Do you still think a linear regression is appropriate? Explain your answer.

2. A teacher claims that students who study will receive good grades.
   a. Do you think that studying is a necessary condition for a student to receive good grades?
   b. Do you think that studying is a sufficient condition for a student to receive good grades?
   c. Do you think that there is a correlation between students who study and students who receive good grades?
   d. Do you think that it is true that studying will cause a student to receive good grades?
   e. List two or more confounding variables that could have an effect on this claim.
3. For each situation, decide whether the correlation implies causation. List reasons why or why not.
   a. The number of violent video games sold in the U.S. is highly correlated to crime rates in real life.
   b. The number of newspapers sold in a city is highly correlated to the number of runs scored by the city's professional baseball team.
   c. The number of mouse traps found in a person's house is highly correlated to the number of mice found in their house.

Stretch

Consider the points: (1, 2), (2, 3), (3, 2), (4, 5), (5, 2.5), (6, 6), (7, 3), (8, 7). The line of best fit for the graph of the points is $y = 0.5x + 1.4$.

1. Complete the table to determine the predicted values of y for each value of x using the line of best fit, and the values of the differences between the observed y-values from the points and the predicted values of y from the line of best fit.

x	Observed Value of y	Predicted Value of y	Observed Value of y − Predicted Value of y
1	2	1.9	0.1
2	3		
3	2		
4	5		
5	2.5		
6	6		
7	3		
8	7		

2. Determine whether there is a pattern in the differences between the y-values from the completed table. Explain what this might indicate about using the line of best fit to make predictions.

Review

1. The table shows the highest maximum temperature for the month of October in Philadelphia, Pennsylvania, over ten years.

Year	2008	2009	2010	2011	2012	2013	2014	2015	2016	2017
Highest Maximum Temperature (°F)	64.9	53.1	61	54	63	68	61	57.9	64.9	66.9

   a. Identify the independent and dependent quantities and their units of measure.
   b. Use the data table and graphing technology to generate a line of best fit. What is the slope and *y*-intercept of the line and what do they represent?

2. Harrison draws a rectangle, and then in each successive figure he splits the rectangles into two rectangles as shown.

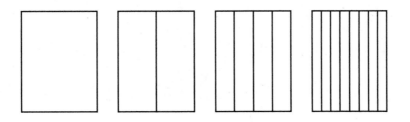

   a. Analyze the number of rectangles in each figure. Describe the pattern.
   b. Write the number of rectangles in each of the first six figures as a numeric sequence.

3. Determine the slope, *x*-intercept, and *y*-intercept of the graph.

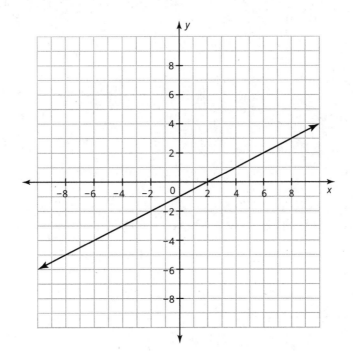

The Residual Effect

Creating Residual Plots

Warm Up

Determine the distance between each pair of points.

1. $A(10, 12)$ and $B(10, 17)$

2. $A(10, 12)$ and $C(10, 7)$

3. Is point A closer to point B or point C?

4. Can the distance between two points be represented by a negative value? Explain your reasoning.

Learning Goals

- Create residual plots.
- Analyze the shapes of residual plots.

Key Terms

- residual
- residual plot

You have used the correlation coefficient, r, to indicate the strength of the linear relationship for a given set of data points. How can you determine whether another function type would better fit the data?

Hit the Brakes!

You have used the shape of data in a scatter plot and the correlation coefficient to help you determine whether a linear model is an appropriate model for a data set. For some data sets, these measures may not provide enough information to determine if a linear model is most appropriate.

In order to be a safe driver, there are a lot of things to consider. For example, you have to leave enough distance between your car and the car in front of you in case you need to stop suddenly. The table shows the braking distance for a particular car when traveling at different speeds.

1. **Construct a scatter plot of the data. Then calculate the line of best fit.**

Speed (mph)	Braking Distance (feet)
30	48
40	80
50	120
60	180
70	240
80	320

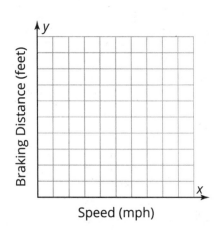

2. **Determine and interpret the correlation coefficient.**

yourself:

Do you think a linear model is appropriate?

3. **Write a function to represent the braking distance, *d(s)*, given the speed of a car, *s*. Interpret the function in terms of this problem situation.**

In addition to the shape of the scatter plot and the correlation coefficient, one additional method to determine whether a linear model is appropriate for the data is to analyze the *residuals*. A **residual** is the vertical distance between an observed data value and its predicted value using the regression equation.

1. **Complete the table to determine the residuals for the braking distance data.**

Speed (mph)	Observed Braking Distance (feet)	Predicted Braking Distance (feet)	Residual Value Observed Value − Predicted Value
30	48		
40	80		
50	120		
60	180		
70	240		
80	320		

Now, let's analyze the relationship between the observed braking distances and the predicted braking distances using graphs. The graph of the line of best fit for the observed braking distances is shown.

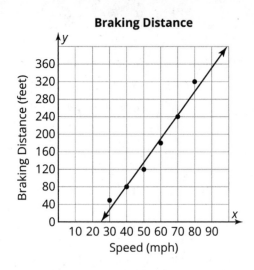

Braking Distance

2. **Examine the scatter plot and the residual values.**

   a. **Show the residual values on the scatter plot by connecting each observed value to its predicted value using a vertical line segment.**

   b. **When does a residual have a positive value?**

   c. **When does a residual have a negative value?**

The residual data can now be used to create a *residual plot*.
A **residual plot** is a scatter plot of the independent variable on the *x*-axis and the residuals on the *y*-axis.

3. **Construct a residual plot of the speed and braking distance data.**

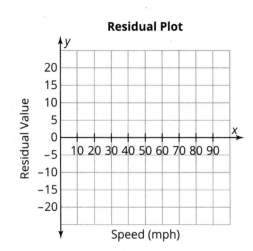

Residual Plot

4. Interpret each residual in the context of the problem situation.

- At 30 mph, the braking distance is _____.

- At 40 mph, the braking distance is _____.

- At 50 mph, the braking distance is _____.

- At 60 mph, the braking distance is _____.

- At 70 mph, the braking distance is _____.

- At 80 mph, the braking distance is _____.

5. What pattern, if any, do you notice in the residuals?

The shape of the residual plot can be useful to determine whether there may be a more appropriate model other than a linear model for a data set.

If a residual plot results in no identifiable pattern or a flat pattern, then the data may be linearly related. If there is a pattern in the residual plot, the data may not be linearly related. Even if the data are not linearly related, the data may still have some other type of nonlinear relationship.

Residual Plots Indicating a Possible Linear Relationship

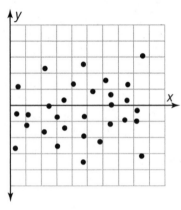

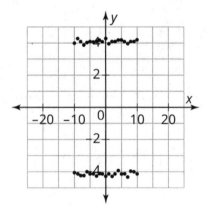

There is no pattern in the residual plot. The data may be linearly related.

There is a flat pattern in the residual plot. The data may be linearly related.

Residual Plots Indicating a Nonlinear Relationship

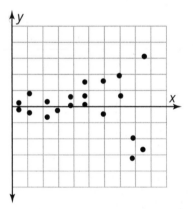

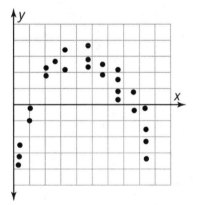

There is a pattern in the residual plot. As the x-value increases, the residuals become more spread out. The data may not be linearly related.

There is a pattern in the residual plot. The residuals form a curved pattern. The data may not be linearly related.

6. Interpret the residual plot for the braking distance data.

7. Anita thinks the residual plot looks like it forms a curve. She says that this means the data must be more quadratic than linear. Is Anita correct? Why or why not?

8. Is the regression line you determined in the Getting Started a good fit for this data set? Explain your reasoning.

Think about:

Keep in mind that this represents only a portion of the entire data set.

Attendance Matters

Over the last semester, Mr. Finch kept track of the number of student absences. Now that the semester is over, he wants to see if there is a linear relationship between the number of absences and a student's grade for the semester. The data he collected are given in the table.

Student	Number of Absences	Grade (percent)
James	0	95
Tiona	5	73
Mikala	3	84
Paul	1	92
Danasia	2	92
Erik	3	80
Rachael	10	65
Cheyanne	0	90
Chen	6	70
Javier	1	88

1. Construct a scatter plot of the data.

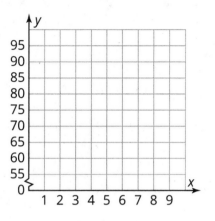

2. Describe the association shown in the scatter plot.

3. Determine the equation of the least squares regression line. Interpret the equation for this problem situation.

4. Compute and interpret the correlation coefficient.

5. Determine the residuals for the data. Interpret each residual.

Student	Number of Absences	Algebra Grade (percent)	Predicted Value	Residual	Interpretation
James	0	95	92.6	2.4	For 0 absences the actual grade is 2.4% greater than predicted.
Tiona	5	73			
Mikala	3	84			
Paul	1	92			
Danasia	2	92			
Erik	3	80			
Rachael	10	65			
Cheyanne	0	90			
Chen	6	70			
Javier	1	88			

6. Construct and interpret a residual plot of the data.

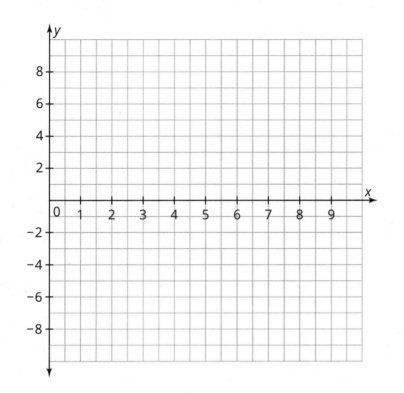

Remember:

When determining the fit of a curve, you need to look at the pattern of the scatter plot, correlation coefficient, and residuals.

TALK the TALK

The Shape Beyond the Shape!

1. **Explain what you can conclude from each residual plot about whether a linear model is appropriate.**

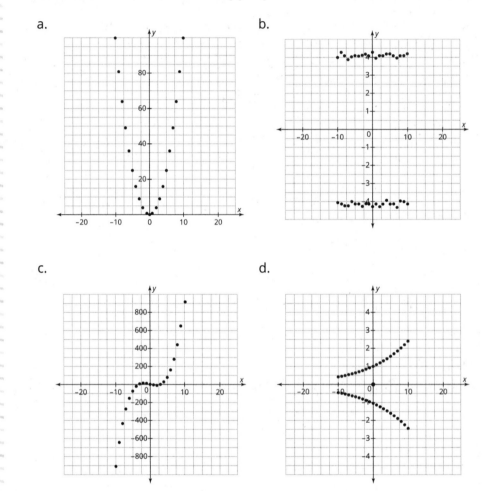

a.

b.

c.

d.

2. **How would you describe the difference between the line of best fit and the most appropriate model?**

Assignment

Write

Write a definition for each term.

1. residual
2. residual plot

Remember

A residual plot of a linear regression equation is an important tool when determining its appropriateness. The pattern in the residual data indicates whether or not there may be a linear relationship.

Practice

1. A manager of a telemarketing firm is trying to increase his employees' productivity. The table shown indicates the number of months the employees have been working and the number of calls they successfully complete with customers per day.

   a. Construct a scatter plot of the data.

   b. Based on the shape of the scatter plot, is a linear regression appropriate? What type of correlation appears to be present?

   c. Write a function $c(m)$ to represent the line of best fit. Then interpret the function in terms of the problem situation.

   d. Compute and interpret the correlation coefficient.

   e. Calculate the residuals for the data and create a residual plot of the data.

   f. Based on the residual plot, is a linear model appropriate for the data? Explain your reasoning.

Employee	Number of Months of Employment	Observed Number of Successful Calls
A	10	19
B	11	22
C	14	23
D	15	25
E	17	27
F	18	28
G	21	31
H	22	32
I	25	33
J	29	33

   g. Should the manager use a linear regression equation to predict how many successful calls an employee will make if they have been employed for 36 months? Explain your reasoning.

Stretch

1. A table of values is given.

   a. Generate a line of best fit using the data in the table.

   b. Determine the residuals for the data.

   c. Plot the residuals (dependent variable) versus the x-values (independent variable) on one graph, and the residuals (dependent variable) versus the predicted y-values (independent variable) on another graph.

   d. Compare the shape of the two graphs from part (c).

Point	x	y
A	3	1
B	4	3
C	7	5
D	10	9
E	11	9
F	14	12
G	17	14

Review

1. Determine whether the points in the scatter plot have a positive correlation, a negative correlation, or no correlation. Four possible r-values are given. Determine which r-value is most appropriate. Explain your reasoning.

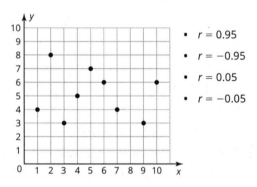

- $r = 0.95$
- $r = -0.95$
- $r = 0.05$
- $r = -0.05$

2. Stefan has been drinking protein shakes to try to improve his performance in basketball. In the last five games, Stefan's percentage of successful shooting attempts has increased. Stefan concludes that protein shakes have caused him to shoot better. Determine if Stefan reached a valid conclusion. Explain your reasoning.

3. Consider the geometric sequence 5, −15, 45, −135, . . .

   Determine the common ratio and write the next 3 terms of the sequence.

4. Determine the slope, x-intercept, and y-intercept for each linear representation.

   a.

   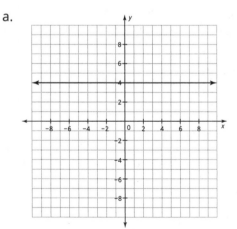

   b.

x	y
−20	8
−10	10
0	12
10	14
20	16

To Fit or Not To Fit? That Is The Question!

Using Residual Plots

Warm Up

What information can you gain from each representation for any given scenario?

1. A table of values listing data points

2. A scatter plot composed of the original data values

3. A regression equation

4. A table of values listing the residuals

5. A residual plot

Learning Goals

- Use scatter plots and correlation coefficients to determine whether a linear regression is a good fit for data.
- Use residual plots to help determine whether a linear regression is the best fit for data.
- Choose a level of accuracy appropriate when reporting quantities.

You have learned about correlation coefficients and residual plots. How can you use these measures to determine if a linear model is a good fit for a data set?

What Aren't You Telling Me?

1. For each data set determine the regression equation and the value of *r*.

Francis J. Anscombe published a paper titled *Graphs in Statistical Analysis* in which he talked about the dangers of just relying on the analytic side of statistics without looking at the graphical side to help draw appropriate conclusions.

Set 1		Set 2		Set 3		Set 4	
x	*y*	*x*	*y*	*x*	*y*	*x*	*y*
10	8.04	10	9.14	10	7.46	8	6.58
8	6.95	8	8.14	8	6.77	8	5.76
13	7.58	13	8.74	13	12.74	8	7.71
9	8.81	9	8.77	9	7.11	8	8.84
11	8.33	11	9.26	11	7.81	8	8.47
14	9.96	14	8.10	14	8.84	8	7.04
6	7.24	6	6.13	6	6.08	8	5.25
4	4.26	4	3.10	4	5.39	19	12.50
12	10.84	12	9.13	12	8.15	8	5.56
7	4.82	7	7.26	7	6.42	8	7.91
5	5.68	5	4.74	5	5.73	8	6.89

2. **Calculate the average of the *x* values in each data set. Then calculate the average of the *y* values in each data set.**

3. What does all this data tell you about the similarities between the four data sets? What does the data tell you about the differences between the four data sets? Explain your reasoning.

4. Construct a scatter plot for each of the data sets. What does each scatter plot tell you about the data sets?

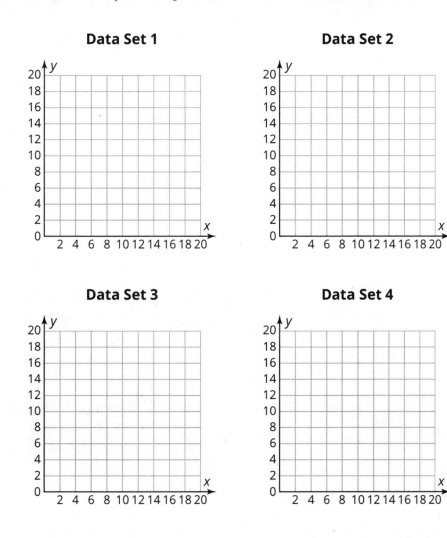

Data Set 1

Data Set 2

Data Set 3

Data Set 4

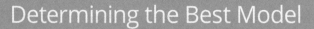

ACTIVITY
4.1   Determining the Best Model

Think

about:

What does this table
tell you?

The table shows the number of CDs sold in the United States since 2000.
Sandy wants to know if the relationship between the time since 2000 and
the number of CDs sold can be best modeled with a linear function.

Time Since 2000	Number of CDs Sold (millions)
0	13,215
2	12,044
4	11,447
6	9,373
8	5,471
10	3,389
12	2,486
14	1,829
16	1,172

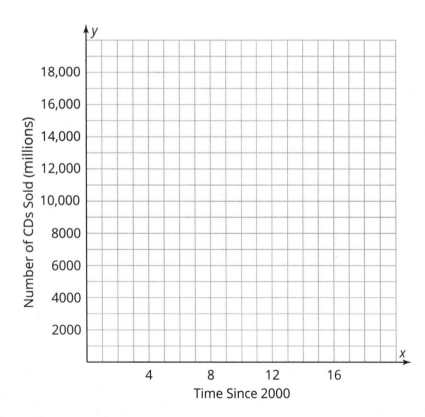

1. **Construct a scatter plot of the data on the coordinate plane shown.**

2. **Based on the shape of the scatter plot, do you think a linear model is a good fit for the data? Why or why not?**

© Carnegie Learning, Inc.

3. Calculate the line of best fit for the data. Write a function to represent the number of CDs sold, $c(t)$, given the time since 2000, t. Interpret the line of best fit in terms of this problem situation. Then, graph the line of best fit on the same coordinate plane as the scatter plot.

Ask yourself:

What is the appropriate level of accuracy needed for the linear regression equation?

4. Compute and interpret the correlation coefficient.

5. Based on the correlation coefficient, do you think a linear model is a good fit for the data? Why or why not?

6. Use the line of best fit to predict the number of CDs sold in each year.

   a. 2007

   b. 2015

   c. 2025

Think about:

Don't always trust what you see. A little more analysis is in order!

7. Calculate and interpret the residuals for the data.

Time Since 2000	Number of CDs Sold (millions)	Predicted Value	Residual	Interpretation
0	13,215			
2	12,044			
4	11,447			
6	9,373			
8	5,471			
10	3,389			
12	2,486			
14	1,829			
16	1,172			

8. Create a residual plot of the data on the coordinate plane shown.

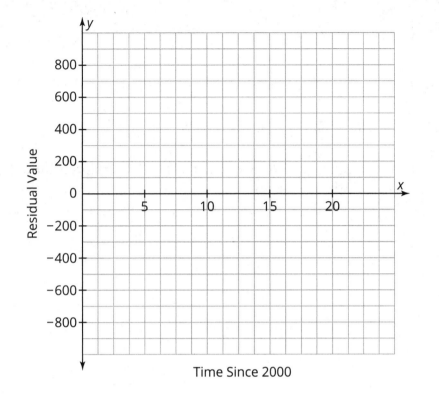

Time Since 2000

Remember:

A residual plot can't tell you whether a linear model is appropriate. It can only tell you that there may be something better.

9. Based on the residual plot, do you think a linear model is a good fit for the data? Why or why not?

You used the shape of the scatter plot, the correlation coefficient, and the residual plot to determine whether a linear model was a good fit for the data. Let's consider a different function family.

1. **Use technology to graph the scatter plot of the relationship between the number of CDs sold and the time since 2000. Then graph the function $q(t) = 7.7x^3 - 168.2x^2 - 8.9x + 13{,}153.7$. Sketch the curve of $q(t)$ on the graph shown.**

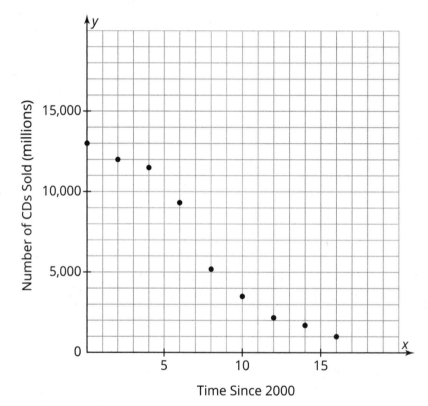

Time Since 2000

2. **Do you think the function $q(t)$ is a better fit for the data than the line of best fit? Explain your reasoning.**

3. Use the function $q(t)$ to predict the number of CDs sold in each year.

a. 2005

b. 2015

c. 2025

4. Compare the predictions using the line of best fit $c(t)$ and the predictions using the function $q(t)$. What do you notice?

© Carnegie Learning, Inc.

TALK the TALK

Does it Really Fit?

1. Explain how you can use each representation to help determine whether a linear model is an appropriate fit for a data set.

   a. shape of scatter plot

   b. correlation coefficient

   c. residual plot

2. Why is it important to use more than one measure to determine whether a linear model is a good fit for a data set?

3. Do you think determining the best fit for a data set is more important for interpolation or extrapolation? Explain your reasoning.

Assignment

Write

Describe the analytic and graphic representations you can use to determine whether a linear model is an appropriate fit for a data set.

Remember

When determining a line of best fit for a set of data, you must consider the graph, the correlation coefficient (r), and the residual plot. These three work together to help you assess the appropriate model of best fit.

Practice

1. The value of a new car starts to depreciate the minute a new owner drives it off the lot. The table shows the values of 15 used cars and their ages.

   a. Construct a scatter plot of the data.

   b. Write a function $P(x)$ to represent the line of best fit for the data. Graph and then interpret the line of best fit in terms of the problem situation.

   c. Does the line of best fit appear to be a good model for this data set? Explain your reasoning.

   d. Calculate the residuals for the data to the nearest whole number and create a residual plot of the data.

Age of Car (years)	Price (dollars)
1	11,500
2	10,500
3	9100
4	8000
5	7500
6	5100
9	3000
11	3000
11	2900
13	2500

   e. Based on the residual plot, do you think a linear model is a good fit for the data? Why or why not?

   f. The quadratic function $f(x) = 63.2x^2 - 1666.6x + 13{,}455.8$ also represents this data set. Graph this function on the same graph as the scatter plot and line of best fit. Does it appear to fit the data better than the line of best fit?

   g. Calculate the residuals for the function $f(x)$ and create a residual plot of the data. What does the residual plot tell you about the quadratic model used for the data?

Stretch

1. The table shows the population of Lakewood over an eight year period.

   a. Construct a scatter plot of the data.

   b. Based on the shape of the scatter plot, determine if a linear model is a good fit for the data.

   c. Determine the type of model that you would use if the population in 2017 is 27,500. Explain your reasoning.

   d. Determine the model that you would use if the population in 2017 is 29,876.

   e. Based on your answers to parts (c) and (d), discuss the influence of one point on determining a model of a data set.

Year	Population
2009	16,450
2010	17,220
2011	18,490
2012	19,222
2013	21,365
2014	22,161
2015	24,987
2016	27,001

Review

1. Students collected data on the earnings of teenagers aged 13 through 18 who work outside of school, and the number of hours they work in a week. The line of best of fit, $y = 8.25x + 35.7$, where x represents the number of hours worked, and y represents the earnings in dollars, was calculated for the data. One teenager in the study works 15 hours a week and earns $119.95. Determine the residual for the data point and explain the meaning in words.

2. Consider the residual plot.

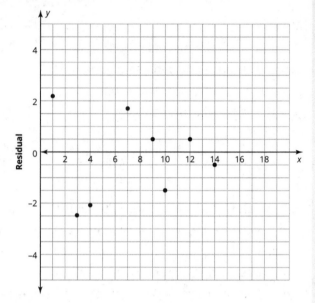

Determine whether the plot indicates that there is a possible linear relationship between the data. Explain your reasoning.

3. The population of a sunflower field is initially 60 plants. Each year the population grows 14%. Use the explicit formula to determine how many sunflower plants will be in the field in 6 years.

4. The graph shows two different lines. Which line has the steeper slope? Explain your reasoning.

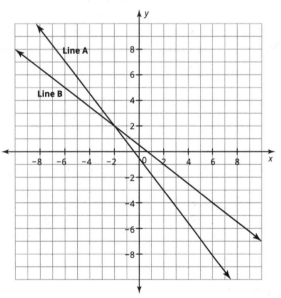

5. Determine the slope and y-intercept of the graph shown.

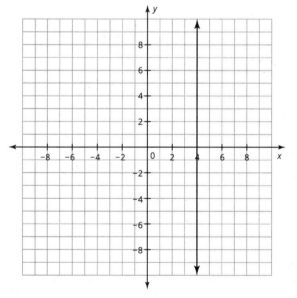

Linear Regressions Summary

KEY TERMS

- Least Squares Method
- centroid
- regression line
- interpolation
- extrapolation
- correlation
- correlation coefficient
- coefficient of determination
- causation
- necessary condition
- sufficient condition
- common response
- confounding variable
- residual
- residual plot

<table>
<tr><td>**LESSON**
1</td><td>Like a Glove</td></tr>
</table>

Technology calculates the line of best fit of data on a scatter plot using the **Least Squares Method**. The line includes the **centroid**, or point whose *x* value is the mean of all *x* values and whose *y* value is the mean of all *y* values. The **regression line** has the smallest possible vertical distances from each given data point to the line. The sum of the squares of those distances is at a minimum with the regression line.

If there is a linear association between the independent and dependent variables, a linear regression can be used to make predictions within the data set. Using a linear regression to make predictions within the data set is called **interpolation**. To make predictions outside the data set is called **extrapolation**.

For example, consider the situation of Nina selling charms to her classmates. The table records the sales of her charms over the months since she began selling them.

Month	Charms Sold
1	3
2	7
3	8
4	12
5	17
6	24

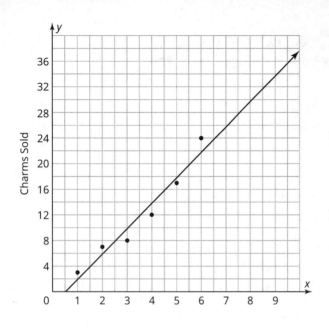

The regression line modeling the situation is graphed on the scatter plot shown.

The linear regression equation is $y = 3.97x - 2.07$.

Using the equation to interpolate, Nina should sell about 14 charms in the fourth month.

$y = 3.97(4) - 2.07.$
$\quad = 13.81$

Using the equation to extrapolate, Nina should sell about 30 charms in the eighth month.

$y = 3.97(8) - 2.07.$
$\quad = 29.69$

LESSON

2

Gotta Keep It Correlatin'

A measure of how well a regression fits a set of data is called **correlation**. When dealing with regression equations, the variable r is used to represent a value called the **correlation coefficient**. The correlation coefficient indicates how close the data are to the graph of the regression equation. The correlation coefficient either falls between -1 and 0 if the data show a negative association or between 0 and 1 if the data show a positive association. The closer the r-value is to 1 or -1, the stronger the relationship is between the two. The coefficient of determination, r^2, measures how well the regression line fits the data. It represents the percentage of variation of the observed values of the data points from their predicted values.

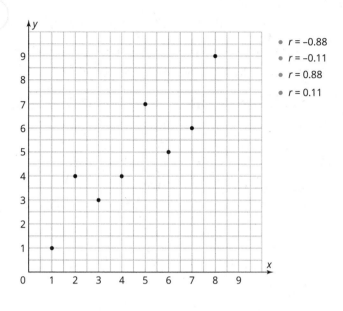

For example, consider the possible *r*-values for a linear regression given for the data graphed in the scatter plot.

● *r* = −0.88
● *r* = −0.11
● *r* = 0.88
● *r* = 0.11

The data has a positive correlation. Because of this, the value of *r* must be positive. Also, the data are fairly close to forming a straight line, so of the choices, *r* = 0.88 would be the most accurate. Technology can be used to verify the correlation coefficient. The coefficient of determination for this data set is 0.7744.

When interpreting the correlation between two variables, you are looking at the association between the variables. While an association may exist, that does not mean there is causation between the variables. **Causation** is when one event causes a second event. A correlation is a **necessary condition** for causation, but a correlation is not a **sufficient condition** for causation. Correlation may be due to either a **common response**, which is when another reason may cause the same result, or a **confounding variable**, which is when other variables are either unknown or unobserved.

For example, consider an experiment conducted by a group of college students that found that more class absences correlated to rainy days. The group concluded that rain causes students to be sick. However, this correlation does not imply causation. Rain is neither a necessary condition (because students can get sick on days that do not rain) nor a sufficient condition (because not every student who is absent is necessarily sick) for students being sick.

An additional method used to determine if a linear model is appropriate for a data set is to analyze the residuals. A **residual** is the distance between an observed data value and its predicted value using the regression equation. Once residuals are determined, this residual data can be used to create a residual plot. A **residual plot** is a scatter plot of the independent variable on the x-axis and the residuals on the y-axis.

For example, consider the data collected relating minutes spent exercising per day and resting heart rate in beats per minute.

Time Exercised per Day (minutes)	Resting Heart Rate (beats per minute)	Predicted Resting Heart Rate (beats per minute)	Residual Value Observed Value − Predicted Value
10	90	$y = -0.26(10) + 86.23 = 83.63$	$90 - 83.63 = 6.37$
20	75	$y = -0.26(20) + 86.23 = 81.03$	$75 - 81.03 = -6.03$
30	80	$y = -0.26(30) + 86.23 = 78.43$	$80 - 78.43 = 1.57$
60	65	$y = -0.26(60) + 86.23 = 70.63$	$65 - 70.63 = -5.63$
90	67	$y = -0.26(90) + 86.23 = 62.83$	$67 - 62.83 = 4.17$

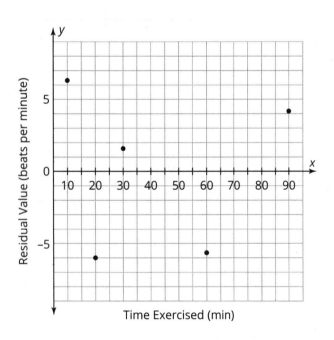

The residual plot for the data set is shown.

The shape of a residual plot can be useful when determining the most appropriate model for a data set. If a residual plot results in no identifiable pattern or a flat pattern, then the data may be linearly related. If there is a pattern in the residual plot, the data may not be linearly related. Even if the data are not linearly related, the data may still have some other type of non-linear relationship.

Residual Plots Indicating a Possible Linear Relationship

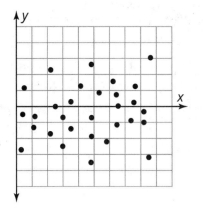

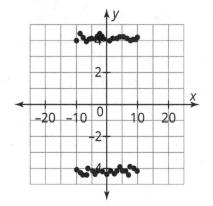

There is no pattern in the residual plot.
The data may be linearly related.

There is a flat pattern in the residual plot.
The data may be linearly related.

Residual Plots Indicating a Nonlinear Relationship

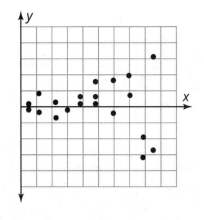

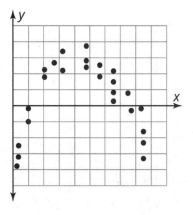

There is a pattern in the residual plot. As
the x-value increases, the residuals become
more spread out. The data may not be
linearly related.

There is a pattern in the residual plot.
The residuals form a curved pattern. The data
may not be linearly related.

To Fit or Not To Fit? That Is the Question!

To determine whether a linear model is an appropriate fit for a data set, consider the shape of the scatter plot, the correlation coefficient, or the residual plot. It is always a good idea to look at the data in multiple ways because one measure may show you something that isn't obvious with another measure. If the points on a scatter plot appear to lie along a line, then a linear model may be appropriate. A correlation coefficient close to −1 or 1 indicates that a linear model may be appropriate. If the residual plot is curved, then a linear model may not be the most appropriate model for the data.

For example, consider the scatter plot of a data set shown.

The linear regression equation is $y = 0.836x - 2$ and the r-value is 0.837. From the scatter plot and the r-value, it seems like the regression equation is a good fit for the data.

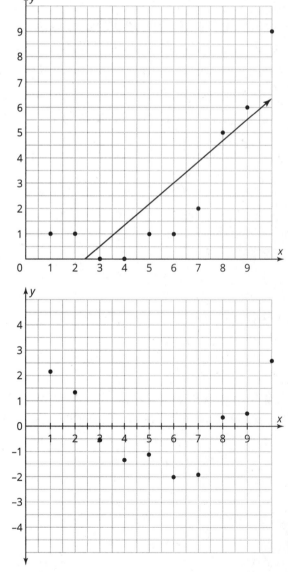

Now consider the residual plot of the same data set.

The residual plot indicates that a linear model may not be the best fit for the data because the residual plot is not flat.

EXPLORING

Constant

Change

The lessons in this module build on your experiences with arithmetic sequences and deepen your understanding of linear functions. You will use your knowledge of rigid motion from middle school to investigate transformations of functions. You will learn a new strategy to solve a system of linear equations and consider a system of linear inequalities. In the last topic, you will use what you know about linear equations to verify and determine properties of shapes on the coordinate plane.

Linear Functions

A set of points in a straight line can be modeled by a linear function.

Module 2: Exploring Constant Change

TOPIC 1: LINEAR FUNCTIONS

In this topic, students begin where they left off with arithmetic sequences. They move from an arithmetic sequence and its explicit formula to a linear function, examining and comparing the structures of the sequence and the function. They prove that the common difference of an arithmetic sequence and the slope of the corresponding linear function are both constant and equal. Students are introduced to function transformations, using vertical dilations and horizontal and vertical translations. Students use translations to prove that the slopes of parallel lines are the same; they use rotations to prove that the slopes of perpendicular lines are negative reciprocals. Understanding the rules of transformations for linear functions lays the groundwork for students to transform any function type.

Where have we been?

Throughout middle school, students have had extensive experience with linear relationships. They have represented relationships using tables, graphs, and equations. They understand slope as a unit rate of change and as the steepness and direction of a graph.

Where are we going?

From this topic, students should understand the key and defining characteristics of a linear function represented in situations, tables, equations, and graphs. This prepares students for the remaining topics in this module, where students will explore equations as the most specific representation for linear functions. By solving equations using horizontal lines on the graph, this lesson lays the foundation for solving systems of linear equations as well as the more complicated nonlinear equations that they will encounter throughout high school.

Transformation Notation

The graph of the function $f(x) = x$ is a straight diagonal line that passes through the origin. If a constant D is added, $f'(x) = x + D$, the graph shifts up or down vertically. If the function is multiplied by a constant, $f'(x) = A \cdot x$, the graph is stretched or compressed vertically.

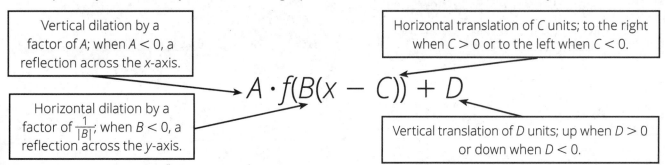

Vertical dilation by a factor of A; when $A < 0$, a reflection across the x-axis.

Horizontal translation of C units; to the right when $C > 0$ or to the left when $C < 0$.

Horizontal dilation by a factor of $\frac{1}{|B|}$; when $B < 0$, a reflection across the y-axis.

$$A \cdot f(B(x - C)) + D$$

Vertical translation of D units; up when $D > 0$ or down when $D < 0$.

The effects on a function of the constants B and C will be explored in future lessons.

A Fly on the Ceiling

You've worked with coordinate planes before, but you may not know how they were invented. As one story goes, the 16th-century French mathematician and philosopher René Descartes (pronounced day-KART) was suffering through a bout of insomnia. While attempting to fall asleep, he spotted a fly walking on the tiled ceiling above his head. At this sight, his mind began to wander and a question popped in his head: Could he describe the fly's path without tracing the actual path?

From that question came the revolutionary invention of the coordinate system—an invention that makes it possible to link algebra and geometry.

Talking Points

Linear functions can be an important topic to know about for college admissions tests.

Here is a sample question:

x	0	1	2	3
$f(x)$	−2	3	8	13

What equation could represent $f(x)$?

Students may recognize that since the x-values increase by 1s, they can use *first differences* to determine the slope.

$$3 - (-2) = 5 \qquad 8 - 3 = 5 \qquad 13 - 8 = 5$$

The constant difference is 5, so the slope is 5. The y-intercept is (0, −2), so the equation that represents the function is $y = 5x - 2$.

Key Terms

first differences

First differences are the values determined by subtracting consecutive output values when the input values have an interval of 1. If the first differences of a table of values are constant, the relationship is linear.

average rate of change

Another name for the slope of a linear function is average rate of change.

degree

The degree of a polynomial is the greatest exponent of a variable term in an expression.

zero of a function

A zero of a function is a real number that makes the value of the function equal to zero, or $f(x) = 0$.

Connecting the Dots

Making Connections Between Arithmetic Sequences and Linear Functions

Warm Up

Use what you know about arithmetic sequences to complete each task.

1. Write the first 5 terms of the sequence generated by $a_n = 10 - 3(n - 1)$.

2. Given the function $f(x) = -3x + 10$, calculate $f(1)$, $f(2)$, $f(3)$, $f(4)$, and $f(5)$.

Learning Goals

- Use algebraic properties to prove the explicit formula for an arithmetic sequence is equivalent to the equation of a linear function.
- Relate the defining characteristics of an arithmetic sequence, the first term and common difference, and the defining characteristics of a linear function, the y-intercept and slope.
- Connect the slope of a line to the average rate of change of a function.

Key Terms

- conjecture
- first differences
- average rate of change

You know that all sequences are functions. What type of function is an arithmetic sequence?

Line Up in Sequential Order

Kenyatta counts the number of new flowers that are blooming in her garden each day in the spring. Sequence A represents the number of new flowers on day 1, day 2, etc.

Sequence A: 3, 6, 12, 24, 48

She also measures the height of the first sunflower that has started blooming. Sequence B represents the height in centimeters of the sunflower on day 1, day 2, etc.

Sequence B: 3, 6, 9, 12, 15

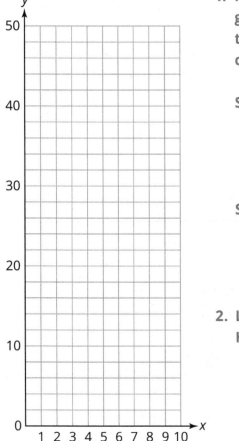

1. **For each sequence, determine whether it is arithmetic or geometric and write the explicit formula that generates the sequence. Then graph and label each on the coordinate plane.**

   Sequence A:

   Sequence B:

2. **List at least three common characteristics of the graphs. How do the two sequences compare?**

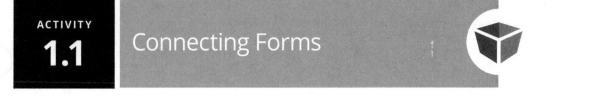

Consider the four explicit formulas, each representing a different arithmetic sequence.

- $a_n = 2 - 4(n - 1)$
- $a_n = -4 + 2(n - 1)$
- $a_n = 2 + 4(n - 1)$
- $a_n = 4 + 2(n - 1)$

1. **Match each explicit formula with its graph. Describe the strategies you used.**

Ask yourself:

How do you know by the form of the explicit formula that it represents an arithmetic sequence?

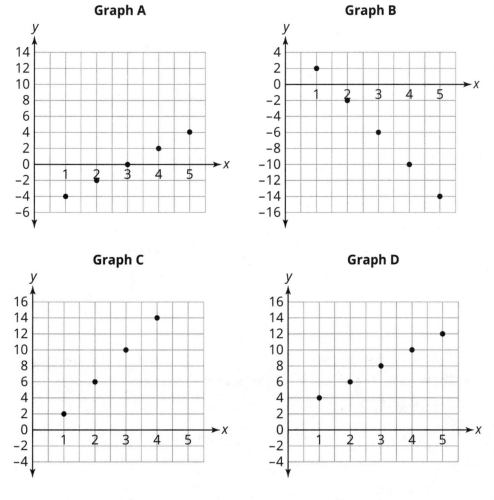

Graph A

Graph B

Graph C

Graph D

2. **Consider the set of graphs and identify the function family represented. Based on these formulas and graphs, do you think that all arithmetic sequences belong to this function family? Explain your *conjecture*.**

A **conjecture** is a mathematical statement that appears to be true, but has not been formally proven.

© Carnegie Learning, Inc.

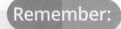

Remember:

An arithmetic sequence is a sequence of numbers in which the differences between any two consecutive terms is constant. The explicit formula is of the form $a_n = a_1 + d(n - 1)$.

Let's take a closer look at the relationship between arithmetic sequences and the family of linear functions. You know a lot about each relationship.

The explicit formula and the table of values that represents Graph C are shown.

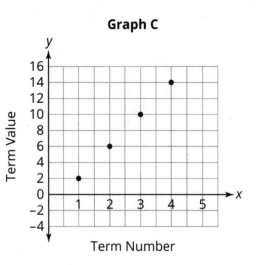

Graph C

$$a_n = 2 + 4(n - 1)$$

Term Number n	Term Value a_n	
1	a_1	2
2	a_2	6
3	a_3	10
4	a_4	14

3. **Describe the domain of the sequence.**

4. **Identify the common difference in each representation.**

5. **Draw a line to model the linear relationship seen in the graph. Then write the equation to represent your line. Describe your strategy.**

6. **Describe the domain of the graph of the linear model.**

An explicit formula is one equation that you can use to model an arithmetic sequence. You can rewrite the explicit formula for the arithmetic sequence $a_n = 2 + 4(n - 1)$ in function notation.

A linear function written in general form is $f(x) = ax + b$, where a and b are real numbers. In this form a represents the slope and b represents the y-intercept.

Worked Example

You can represent a_n using function notation.

$$a_n = 2 + 4(n - 1)$$
$$f(n) = 2 + 4(n - 1)$$

Next, rewrite the expression $2 + 4(n - 1)$.

$f(n) = 2 + 4n - 4$	Distributive Property
$= 4n + 2 - 4$	Commutative Property
$= 4n - 2$	Combine Like Terms

So, $a_n = 2 + 4(n - 1)$ written in function notation is $f(n) = 4n - 2$.

7. **Compare the equation you wrote to model the graph of the arithmetic sequence to the explicit formula written in function form. What do you notice?**

8. **Compare the common difference with the slope. What do you notice?**

9. **Explain why Hank's reasoning is not correct.**

Hank

The y-intercept of a linear function is the same as the first term of an arithmetic sequence.

ACTIVITY
1.2

Connecting Constant
Difference and Slope

At the end of the last show, stagehands at the community theater stack the audience chairs and place them in storage. The height of one chair is 34 inches, and as each additional chair is stacked, the height increases by 8 inches.

1. Write an equation using the explicit formula to represent this scenario.

2. Rewrite the explicit formula in function form and define your variables.

3. Compare the two algebraic representations of this scenario.

   a. How is the value of d in the explicit formula related to the value of a in function form? How are d and a represented in the scenario? Be sure to include units of measure.

   b. How is the value of a_1 from the explicit formula related to b in function form? How are a_1 and b represented in the scenario?

   c. If a_1 represents the first term of a sequence, what does a_0 represent? How can you rewrite the arithmetic sequence using a_0?

   $a_n = $ _____

In this stacked chair scenario, both d and a represent the additional 8 inches of height per one chair, or the unit rate of change. The common difference, d, of the explicit formula is the same as the slope, a, of a general linear function. They both represent constant change.

In a sequence, the common, or constant, difference is the difference in term values between consecutive terms.	In a linear function, the slope describes the direction and steepness of the line. It is the difference in output values divided by the difference in corresponding input values.

The slope formula is $\frac{y_2 - y_1}{x_2 - x_1}$.

When you see a graph or rewrite an explicit formula for an arithmetic sequence, it is apparent that it represents a linear function. However, the structure of a table requires other strategies to determine whether it represents a linear function.

One strategy is to examine *first differences*. **First differences** are the values determined by subtracting consecutive output values when the input values have an interval of 1. If the first differences of a table of values are constant, the relationship is linear.

The tables that represent the explicit formula and function form of the stacking chairs scenario are shown.

n	a_n
1	34
2	42
3	50
4	58

x	$y = f(x)$
0	26
1	34
2	42
3	50

4. **Determine the first differences in each table to verify they both represent a linear relationship.**

The expression $y = f(x)$ means that the value of y depends on the value of x. That is, for different values of x, there is a function f which determines the value of y.

© Carnegie Learning, Inc.

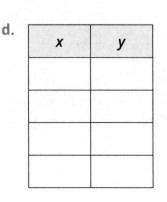

5. Parks and Eva Cate agree that the table shown represents a linear relationship because there is a constant difference between consecutive points. Parks claims the slope is 5 and Eva Cate claims the slope is −5.
   Who's correct? Explain your reasoning.

Ask yourself:

What does slope describe?

x	y
1	22
2	17
3	12
4	7

$22 - 17 = 5$

$17 - 12 = 5$

$12 - 7 = 5$

6. Use first differences to determine whether each table represents a linear function. Then, create your own table to represent a linear function. Describe your strategy.

a.

x	y
5	12
6	15
7	21
8	30

b.

x	y
−2	18
−1	14
0	10
1	6

c.

x	y
10	1
11	4
12	9
13	16

d.

x	y

ACTIVITY

1.3

Connecting Constant Difference, Slope, and Average Rate of Change

In the previous activity, you determined that the constant difference of the chair heights and the slope of the line are both equal to 8 inches per chair. Is the slope of a linear function always equal to the constant difference of the corresponding arithmetic sequence?

Consider the graph of the arithmetic sequence represented by the general linear function $f(x) = ax + b$.

1. **Identify the constant difference of the sequence in the graph.**

2. **Complete the table for consecutive values of the input.**

Term Number	Term Value	
n	$f(n)$	$a(n) + b$
$n + 1$	$f(n + 1)$	$a(n + 1) + b$
$n + 2$		
$n + 3$		

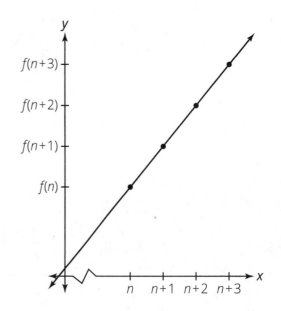

3. **Select any two consecutive input values in the sequence. Use the expressions for the term values to determine the constant difference of the sequence.**

Recall that the slope of a line is constant between any two points on the line, not just consecutive points.

4. Use the table and graph from Question 2 to complete each task.

   a. Identify the slope of the function on the graph.

   b. Select two non-consecutive points in the table and determine the slope between those two points.

The slope, a, is equal to the constant difference. Another name for the slope of a linear function is **average rate of change**. The formula for the average rate of change is $\frac{f(t)-f(s)}{t-s}$. This represents the change in the output as the input changes from s to t.

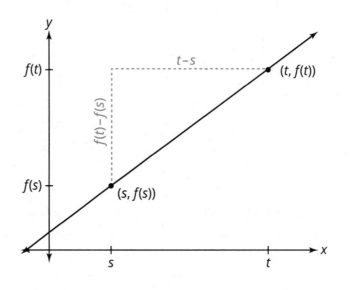

5. Show that the slope formula and the average rate of change formula represent the same ratio.

Verifying that Common Differences and Slopes are the Same

The remaining explicit formulas and graphs from Activity 1 are shown.

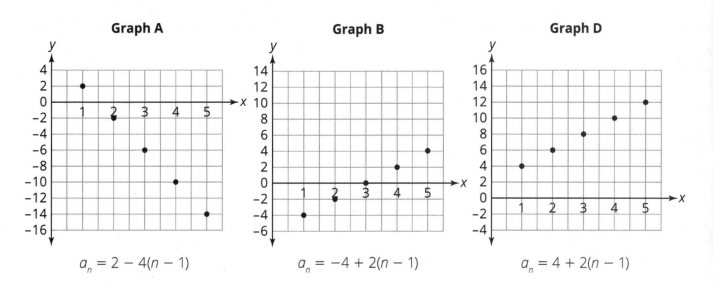

Graph A

$a_n = 2 - 4(n - 1)$

Graph B

$a_n = -4 + 2(n - 1)$

Graph D

$a_n = 4 + 2(n - 1)$

1. **For each graph and arithmetic sequence, complete each task.**

   a. **Identify the constant difference in the explicit formula and on the graph.**

   b. **Rewrite each explicit formula in function notation.**

   c. **Verify that the constant difference is the same as the slope of the linear function.**

   d. **Describe how the first term in the explicit formula is related to the *y*-intercept of the function.**

Kenyatta's cat loves to knock over flowerpots. Each morning, she counts the number of flowerpots her cat knocked over during the night before she uprights them again. Sequence C represents the number of flowerpots knocked over on day 1, day, 2, etc.

Sequence C: 3, 3, 3, 3, 3

1. **Determine the constant difference and write the explicit formula to represent Sequence C. Then create a table of values and graph it.**

Term Number (n)	Term Value (a_n)

2. **Use function notation to write an equation representing the relationship between the number of days, x, and the number of new flowerpots, C. Interpret the function in terms of the context.**

3. **Prove that the slope of C(x) is equal to the common difference of Sequence C.**

Consider a similar sequence.

Sequence D: −5, −5, −5, −5, −5

4. **Write the function, $D(x)$, to model this sequence.**

5. **Prove $D(x)$ is a constant function.**

> **Remember:**
>
> If the values of the dependent variable of a function remain constant over the entire domain, then the function is called a constant function.

TALK the TALK

Making It Plain and Clear

You have proven that all arithmetic sequences can be represented by linear functions.

1. **Complete the graphic organizer to summarize the connections between arithmetic sequences and linear functions. Then describe how you can tell a linear relationship exists given a table of values or a graph.**

Equation

Arithmetic Sequence $a_n = a_1 + d(n - 1)$	Linear Function $f(x) = ax + b$	Mathematical Meaning
a_n		
d		
n		
$a_1 - d$		

CHARACTERISTICS AND REPRESENTATIONS OF LINEAR FUNCTIONS

Table of Values

Graph

Assignment

Write

Describe how the terms *constant difference, slope,* and *average rate of change* are related.

Remember

The explicit formula of an arithmetic sequence can be rewritten as a linear function in the general form $f(x) = ax + b$, where a and b are real numbers, using algebraic properties. The constant difference of an arithmetic sequence is always equal to the slope of the corresponding linear function.

Practice

1. Rakesha claims that the equation $f(n) = 5n - 7$ is the function notation for the sequence that is represented by the explicit formula $a_n = -2 + 5(n - 1)$. James doesn't understand how this can be the case.

   a. Help James by listing the steps to write the explicit formula of the given sequence in function notation. Provide a rationale for each step.

   b. Graph the function. Label the first 5 values of the sequence on the graph.

2. Determine whether each table of values represents a linear function. For those that represent linear functions, write the function. For those that do not, explain why not.

a.

x	f(x)
3	14
4	18
5	23
6	29

b.

x	f(x)
0	2
1	−1
2	−4
3	−7

c.

x	f(x)
1	11
2	16
3	21
4	26

3. Calculate the average rate of change for each linear function using the formula. Show your work.

a.

x	f(x)
3	−4
7	4
9	8
12	14

b.

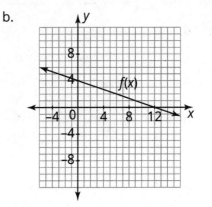

Stretch

Craig left his house at noon and drove 50 miles per hour until 3 PM. Then he drove the next 5 hours at 70 miles per hour. Graph Craig's driving trip and calculate the average rate of change for the entire trip.

Review

Evaluate each function for the given values.

1. $f(x) = 3x - 10$
   a. $f(0)$
   b. $f(5)$

2. $f(x) = 6$
   a. $f(0)$
   b. $f(-2)$

3. $f(x) = 9x + 7 - 3x$
   a. $f(0)$
   b. $f(0.5)$

4. The linear regression equation for the given data is $y = -x + 19.7$. Complete the table for the linear regression equation, rounding your answers to the nearest tenth. Then construct and interpret a residual plot.

x	y	Predicted Value	Residual Value
2	17		
4	16		
6	15		
8	12		
10	9		
12	8		

5. The linear regression equation for the given data is $y = 3.93x - 11.33$, $r = 0.8241$. Consider the scatterplot, the correlation coefficient, and the corresponding residual plot. State whether a linear model is appropriate for the data.

x	2	4	6	8	10	12
y	9	2	1	12	25	48

Scatter Plot and Line of Best Fit   Residual Plot

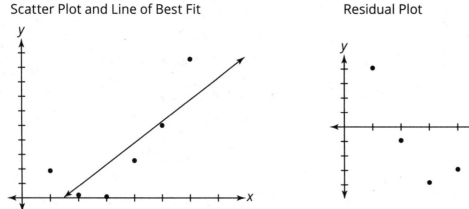

Fun with Functions, Linear Ones

Making Sense of Different Representations of a Linear Function

Warm Up

Determine the slope of the line between each pair of points.

1. (0, 10) and (3, 12)

2. (−1, 4.5) and (1, −4.5)

3. (−1, 0) and (0, 12)

Learning Goals

- Determine whether a scenario, equation, table, or graph represents a linear relationship.
- Calculate the average rate of change from a table.
- Write functions given a table of values.
- Interpret expressions that represent different quantities in terms of a context and a graph.
- Compare different equation representations of linear functions.

Key Terms

- polynomial
- degree
- leading coefficient
- zero of a function

© Carnegie Learning, Inc.

You know how to determine whether a relationship represents a linear function, and you know how to write an equation for the function. How can you use the structure of the equation to identify characteristics of the function?

Well, Are Ya or Aren't Ya?

1. Determine whether each representation models a linear or nonlinear function. Explain your reasoning.

Scenario A
A tree grows 3.5 inches each year.

Scenario B
The strength of a medication decreases by 50% each hour it is in the patient's system.

Scenario C
The area of a square depends on its side length.

Equation A
$y = 14 - 9x$

Equation B
$y = 2^x + 1$

Equation C
$y = \frac{1}{4}(x + 7) - 1$

Table A

x	y
1	3
1	4
1	5

Table B

x	y
3	1
4	1
5	1

Table C

x	y
−9	45
−8	30
−7	15

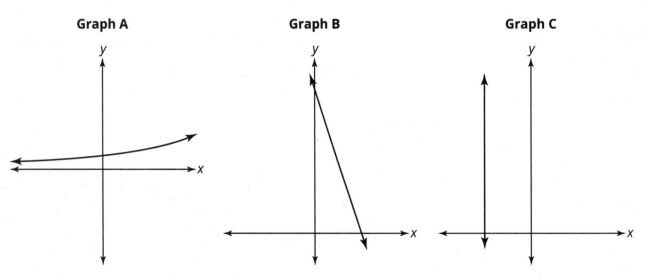

Graph A

Graph B

Graph C

Interpreting Linear Functions

Each table of values in the previous activity had consecutive input values. Tables in that format allow you to use differences to determine whether the representation is linear. Often, input values are in intervals other than 1, and sometimes the input values are in random order. To determine whether these tables represent linear functions, you need to make sure the slope, or average rate of change, is constant between all given points.

1. **Determine whether each table represents a linear function. If so, write the function.**

a.

x	y
−2	5.5
1	4.75
4	4
7	3.25

b.

x	y
0	5
2	13
4	21
8	29

Ask

yourself:

Is there a pattern in the input values?

Analyze each situation represented as a table of values.

2. **Dillan sells pretzels at festivals on weekends. The table shown is a record of past sales.**

Number of Pretzels Sold	Amount of Money Earned (dollars)
15	37.5
42	105
58	145
29	72.5

   a. **What does this table tell you about his sales?**

   b. **How much money would Dillan earn if he sold 75 pretzels?**

3. Delany and her friends recently went to the community fair. They had to pay an entrance fee and then purchase 1 ticket for each ride. Dakota is going to the fair tomorrow and wants to know the cost of each ride ticket. Delany and her friends help Dakota by writing down how much money they spent and the number of tickets they purchased.

Number of Ride Tickets	Amount of Money Spent (dollars)
2	7.5
4	9
6	10.5
11	14.25

a. What does this table tell you about the cost to go to the fair and ride the rides?

b. If Dakota has $20 to spend, how many ride tickets can she buy?

4. The local pet store has a fish tank on display at the community fair. Darren is responsible for draining the tank at the end of the fair. The pet store manager provides him with this information from when they drained the tank at the end of the fair last year.

Time (hours)	Amount of Water Remaining (gallons)
$\frac{1}{4}$	169
$\frac{1}{2}$	163
$\frac{3}{4}$	157
1	151

a. How many gallons did the fish tank hold?

b. When will the tank be empty?

Marilynn sells silk screened T-shirts for her mom at local festivals. After each festival, she returns whatever money she earns to her mom. The graph shown represents her potential earnings based on the number of T-shirts she sells.

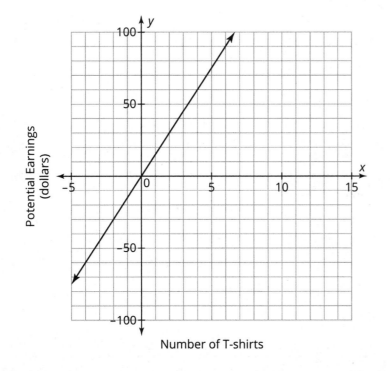

Number of T-shirts

© Carnegie Learning, Inc.

1. **Analyze and interpret the graph. List as many facts as you can about the scenario based on what you see in the graph and describe how they relate to the scenario.**

2. **Interpret the meaning of the origin.**

3. **Write a function, *E*(*t*), to model Marilynn's potential earnings given the number of T-shirts she sells.**

Ask yourself:

What is the meaning of the slope, *x*- and *y*-intercepts, domain, and range in terms of this situation?

4. What does $(t, E(t))$ represent in terms of the function and the graph?

5. Evaluate each and interpret the meaning in terms of the equation, the graph, and the scenario.

   a. $E(2)$ b. $E(5)$ c. $E(2.75)$

Marilynn has a goal to earn $100 at the festival. Let's consider how to determine the number of T-shirts she needs to sell to meet her goal.

Worked Example

To determine the number of T-shirt sales it takes to earn $100 using the function, $E(t) = 15t$, substitute 100 for $E(t)$ and solve.

$$E(t) = 15t$$
$$100 = 15t$$
$$\frac{100}{15} = t$$
$$6.67 = t$$

6. Consider the worked example.

   a. Interpret the meaning of $t = 6.67$.

   b. Why can you substitute 100 for $E(t)$?

You can also use the graph to determine the number of T-shirts Marilynn needs to sell to earn $100.

> ### Worked Example
>
> To determine the number of T-shirts sales it takes to earn $100 using your graph, you need to determine the intersection of the two lines represented by the equation $100 = 15t$.
>
> First, graph the function defined by each side of the equation, and then determine the intersection point of the two graphs.
>
>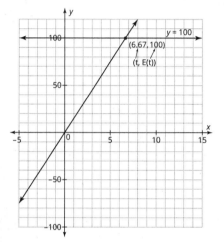
>
> $$h(t) = 15t$$
> $$100 = 15t$$
>
> $y = 100 \qquad y = 15x$
>
> Solution: (6.67, 100)
>
> In terms of the graph, Marilynn needs to sell 6.67 T-shirts to earn $100. In terms of the context, she needs to sell 7 T-shirts.

7. **Consider the equation and graphical representations. What are the limitations of using each to answer questions about the number of T-shirts sold or the amount of money earned?**

   a. **equation**

   b. **graph**

Interpreting Changes to the Graph of a Linear Function

For the next festival, Marilynn's mom suggests that she still sells each T-shirt for $15, but should give away 3 T-shirts in a raffle. This new relationship, $G(t)$, is shown on the graph.

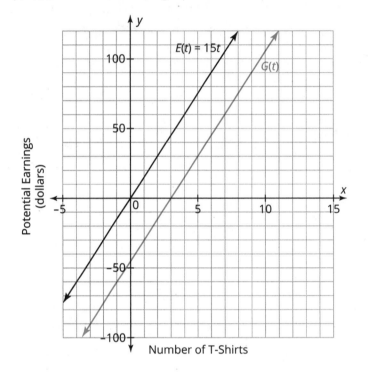

1. **Compare the two graphs. What do you notice?**

   a. **How do the graphs show the selling price per T-shirt remains the same?**

   b. **Determine and interpret the meaning of $y = G(0)$ in terms of the graph and this scenario. Label the point on the graph.**

   c. **Determine and interpret the meaning of $G(t) = 0$ in terms of the graph and this scenario. Label the point on the graph.**

Michelle and Myra each wrote an equation to describe the effect of giving away three T-shirts.

Michelle 👍
Marilynn is giving away 3 T-shirts, so she has 3 fewer shirts to sell.
$$G(t) = 15(t - 3)$$

Myra 👍
The cost of giving away three shirts is $45.
$$G(t) = 15t - 45$$

2. Verify the two equation representations are equivalent.

3. How many T-shirts will Marilynn need to sell to earn $100? Use the graph and an equation.

4. Consider the expressions in the first two rows that define the quantities of the function and then the parts of each equation written by Michelle and Myra to complete the table. First, determine the unit of measure for each expression. Then describe the contextual meaning and the mathematical meaning of each part of the function.

Expression	Unit	What It Means	
		Contextual Meaning	**Mathematical Meaning**
t			
$G(t)$			
15			
$(t - 3)$			
$15t$			
-45			

The linear functions that Michelle and Myra each wrote are equivalent; however, they are written in different forms. The linear function $G(t) = 15(t - 3)$ is written in factored form and $G(t) = 15t - 45$ is written in general form.

A linear function can also be referred to as a *polynomial* function. A **polynomial** is a mathematical expression involving the sum of powers in one or more variables multiplied by coefficients. The **degree** of a polynomial is the greatest variable exponent in the expression. The **leading coefficient** of a polynomial is the numeric coefficient of the term with the greatest power.

Polynomial comes from *poly-* meaning "many" and *-nomial* meaning "term," so it means "many terms."

When you graph a polynomial the degree tells you the maximum number of times the graph can cross the *x*-axis.

Worked Example

A few examples of polynomial functions.

	Polynomial Functions		Degree
Constant		$P(x) = 7$	0
Linear		$P(x) = 2x - 5$	1
Quadratic		$P(x) = 3x^2 - 2x + 4$	2
Cubic		$P(x) = 4x^3 - 2$	3

The structure of each linear function tells you important information about the graph. Let's consider the general form of a linear function, $f(x) = ax + b$, where a and b are real numbers and $a \neq 0$. In this form, the a-value is the leading coefficient, which describes the steepness and direction of the line. The b-value describes the y-intercept.

The variables used to represent any real number in the general linear form are irrelevant. Think about the position of the number as either the leading coefficient or a constant and the potential effect on the function.

You know the form $y = mx + b$ as slope-intercept form, where m represents the slope and b represents the y-intercept. Notice that the general form has the same structure. The general form shows that a linear equation is a polynomial of degree 1. You will learn more about polynomials as you progress through high school mathematics.

5. Consider the general form of the linear function $G(t)$.

   a. Label a on the graph.

   b. Label b on the graph.

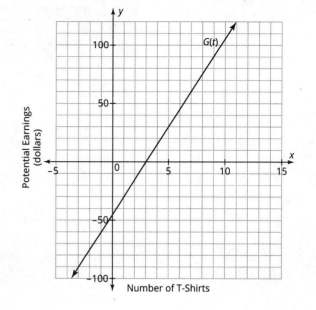

Next, consider the factored form of a linear function, $f(x) = a(x - c)$, where a and c are real numbers and $a \neq 0$. When a polynomial is in factored form, the value of x that makes the factor $(x - c)$ equal to zero is the x-intercept. This value is called the *zero of the function*. A **zero of a function** is a real number that makes the value of the function equal to zero, or $f(x) = 0$.

You can set $(x - c)$ equal to zero and determine the point where the graph crosses the x-axis.

6. Consider the factored form of the linear function $G(t)$.

   a. Label a on the graph.

   b. Label c on the graph.

7. What is the zero of $G(t)$? Explain your reasoning.

Interpreting More Changes to the Graph of a Linear Function

The next festival that Marilynn is attending charges a $35 fee to rent a booth. She is still selling her mom's T-shirts for $15 each and giving 3 away in a raffle. The graph shows this new relationship, $F(t)$.

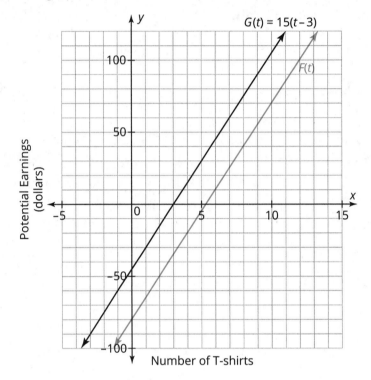

1. **Consider the relationship between graphs of $G(t)$ and $F(t)$.**

   a. **How do the graphs show that the selling price per T-shirt remains the same?**

   b. **How did the new booth fee of $35 change the graph?**

c. How many T-shirts will Marilynn need to sell before she will have any money to return to her mom? Explain your reasoning.

d. How many T-shirts will Marilynn need to sell to earn $100?

2. Consider the relationship between the equations of $G(t)$ and $F(t)$.

   a. Write the function $F(t)$ in terms of $G(t)$.

   b. Rewrite $F(t)$ in general form. Then describe how the a- and b-values are represented on the graph.

   > The general form of a linear function is $f(x) = ax + b$.

   c. Rewrite $F(t)$ in factored form. Use a fraction to represent the c-value. Then describe how the a- and c-values are represented on the graph.

   > The factored form of a linear function is $f(x) = a(x - c)$.

   > The values a, b, and c are real numbers and $a \neq 0$.

TALK the TALK

Reading Between the Lines

Complete each "I can" sentence using *always*, *sometimes*, or *never*.

1. **Suppose you are given a dependent value and need to calculate an independent value of a linear function.**

   a. **I can** _____ **use a table to determine an** *approximate* **value.**

   b. **I can** _____ **use a table to calculate an** *exact* **value.**

   c. **I can** _____ **use a graph to determine an** *approximate* **value.**

   d. **I can** _____ **use a graph to calculate an** *exact* **value.**

   e. **I can** _____ **use an equation to determine an** *approximate* **value.**

   f. **I can** _____ **use an equation to calculate an** *exact* **value.**

2. **Write the function that models each table of values. Then evaluate the function for each independent and dependent value.**

   a.

x	1	2	3	4	5
f(x)	−20	5	30	55	80

   $f(x) =$

   $f(12) =$

   $f(x) = -145$

b.

x	1	3	5	7	9
g(x)	18	6	−6	−18	−30

g(x) =

g(−9) =

g(x) = −54

3. Complete the graphic organizer located at the end of this lesson for the linear function $f(x) = 2x - 8$.

a. Write $f(x)$ in general form. Then describe the information given in this form.

b. Write $f(x)$ in factored form. Then describe the information given in this form.

c. Graph $f(x)$. Describe how you know this graph can cross the x-axis only one time.

d. Create a table of values for $f(x)$.

Graphic Organizer

General Form

$f(x) = ax + b$, where a and b are real numbers and $a \neq 0$

Factored Form

$f(x) = a(x - c)$, where a and c are real numbers and $a \neq 0$

$f(x) = 2x - 8$

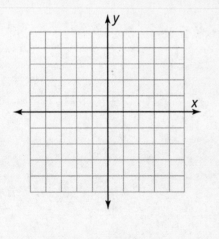

Graph

x	y

Table

Assignment

Write
Describe a zero of a function in your own words.

Remember
The general form of a linear function is $f(x) = ax + b$, where a and b are real numbers and $a \neq 0$. In this form, the a-value is the leading coefficient which describes the steepness and direction of the line. The b-value describes the y-intercept.

The factored form of a linear function is $f(x) = a(x - c)$, where a and c are real numbers and $a \neq 0$. In this form, the a-value is the slope and the value of x that makes the factor $(x - c)$ equal to zero is the x-intercept.

Practice
Determine whether the table of values represents a linear function. If so, write the function.

1.

x	y
−2	$5\frac{2}{3}$
0	5
2	$4\frac{1}{3}$
4	$3\frac{2}{3}$

2.

x	y
−5	−27
0	−2
5	20
10	48

For each scenario, write a linear function in factored form and in general form. Then sketch a graph and label the x- and y-intercepts. Finally, answer each question.

3. Carlos prints and sells T-shirts for $14.99 each. Each month 5 T-shirts are misprinted and cannot be sold. How much money will he earn if he prints 22 T-shirts? How many T-shirts will he need to sell to earn $200?

4. Mei paints and sells ceramic vases for $35 each. Each month she typically breaks 3 vases in the kiln. How much money will she earn if she sells 17 ceramic vases? How many ceramic vases will she need to sell to earn $600?

5. Emilio builds and sells homemade wooden toys for $12 each. The festival he is attending charges $50 to set up his booth. How much money will he earn if sells 35 wooden toys? How many wooden toys will he need to sell to earn $250?

Stretch

A pretzel manufacturer has two production lines. Line A produces a variety of pretzel that is sold for $2.40 per bag. Line A typically produces 3 bags per day that do not meet company standards and cannot be sold. Line B produces a variety of pretzel that is sold for $3.60 per bag. Line B typically produces 4 bags per day that do not meet company standards and cannot be sold. Line A produces 3 times as many bags as Line B each day.

Write a linear function that represents the total number of bags the lines can produce combined.

Review

1. Determine whether each relationship shows a constant difference. If so, write the linear function that represents the relationship.

a.

x	y
2	9
3	11
4	13
5	15

b.

x	y
1	2
2	1
3	$\frac{1}{2}$
4	$\frac{7}{2}$

2. Determine whether the points in each scatter plot have a positive association, a negative association, or no association. Explain your reasoning.

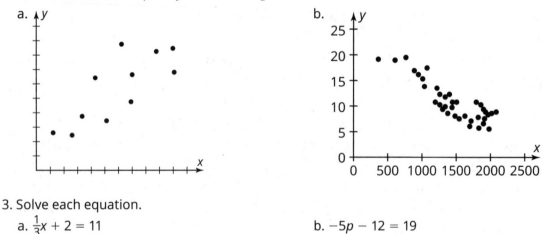

a.

b.

3. Solve each equation.

a. $\frac{1}{3}x + 2 = 11$

b. $-5p - 12 = 19$

Move It!

Transforming Linear Functions

Warm Up

Determine each value, given the function $h(x) = -2x - 5$.

1. $h(3)$

2. $2 \cdot h(-2)$

3. $-1 \cdot h(1) + 5$

4. $5 \cdot h(0) + 5$

Learning Goals

- Determine the effects on the graph of a linear function when $f(x)$ is replaced by $f(x) + D$ or $A \cdot f(x)$.
- Graph linear function transformations expressed symbolically and show intercepts.
- Identify key characteristics of the graphs of linear functions, such as slope and y-intercept, in terms of quantities from a verbal description.
- Prove that a translated line and its pre-image have the same slope and are therefore parallel.
- Write equations of parallel lines.

Key Term

- basic function

You have learned about linear functions and their characteristics, including slope and y-intercept. How can you transform a function? What effects do different transformations have on the characteristics of linear functions?

Returning to Transformation Station

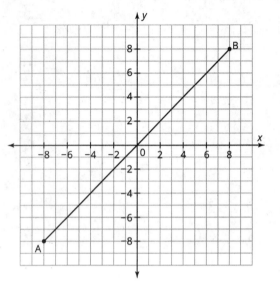

Consider $\overline{AB}$ with coordinates A (−8, −8) and B (8, 8).

Follow your teacher's instructions to copy this line segment on a coordinate plane on the floor of your classroom, with different students standing at different points of the line segment.

1. **Move on the coordinate plane to translate the entire line segment up 4 units and then down 4 units. Describe how the student "points" move.**

2. **How do the translations affect the coordinates of the figure?**

Original Point	4 Units Up	4 Units Down
(x, y)		

3. **Draw $\overline{CD}$ on the coordinate plane so that it is a vertical translation of $\overline{AB}$ up 4 units. Compare the two line segments. Describe how they are related.**

4. Move back to where you started. Then, multiply all the
   y-coordinates by 2 and then by −2. Describe how the student
   "points" move.

5. Draw $\overline{EF}$ on the coordinate plane by multiplying all the
   y-coordinates of $\overline{AB}$ by 2. Compare the two line segments.
   Describe how they are related.

6. Draw $\overline{GH}$ on the coordinate plane by multiplying all the
   y-coordinates of $\overline{AB}$ by −2. Compare the two line segments.
   Describe how they are related.

Vertical Translations of Functions

Let's determine how translations impact the graph of the linear function $f(x) = x$. The function $f(x) = x$ is the *basic function* for the linear function family. A **basic function** is the simplest function of its type.

© Carnegie Learning, Inc.

Worked Example

You can translate the graph of $f(x)$ down 5 units by moving each point 5 units down. The transformed graph is labeled as $m(x)$.

To translate the point $(-2, -2)$ on $f(x)$, subtract 5 units from the output value, or y-value. The input value, or x-value, remains unchanged. The coordinates of the translated point on $m(x)$ are $(-2, -7)$. The coordinates of four additional points on $f(x)$ are translated for you.

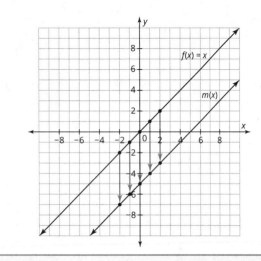

Original Graph	
x	**$f(x)$**
−2	−2
−1	−1
0	0
1	1
2	2

Transformed Graph	
x	**$m(x)$**
−2	−7
−1	−6
0	−5
1	−4
2	−3

For the family of linear functions having the general form $f(x) = ax + b$, where a and b are any real numbers, the function $f(x) = x$, where $a = 1$ and $b = 0$, is the basic function. It is the simplest linear function.

1. **Consider the translated function, $m(x)$. Identify the slope and y-intercept of the graph of the function. Then, write the equation for the function in general form.**

2. **Translate $f(x)$ again to create a new function, $p(x)$.**

   a. **Translate the graph of $f(x)$ up 5 units. Label your graph as $p(x)$. Complete the table of corresponding points on $p(x)$.**

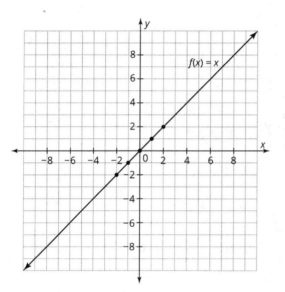

Original Graph		Transformed Graph	
x	f(x)	x	p(x)
−2	−2		
−1	−1		
0	0		
1	1		
2	2		

   b. **Identify the slope and y-intercept of the graph of the function. Then, write the equation for the function in general form.**

For the basic function $f(x) = x$, the transformed function $y = f(x) + D$ shows a vertical translation of the function. This translation affects the output values, or y-values, of the function. For $D > 0$, the resulting graph vertically shifts up. For $D < 0$, the resulting graph vertically shifts down. The distance the graph is shifted is the absolute value of D, or $|D|$.

3. **Compare the values of $f(2)$ and $p(2)$. How did the transformation of the function affect the value of the function at $x = 2$?**

4. Consider the graph of $j(x) = 2x - 1$.

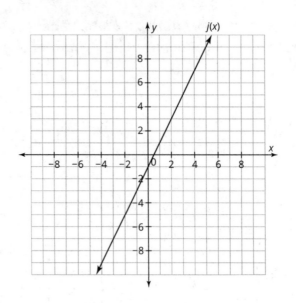

a. Translate the graph of $j(x)$ up 4 units. Label the graph as $q(x)$. Then, write an equation for $q(x)$ in terms of $j(x)$.

b. Translate the graph of $j(x)$ down 4 units. Label the graph as $r(x)$. Then, write an equation for $r(x)$ in terms of $j(x)$.

c. Rewrite $q(x)$ and $r(x)$ in terms of $j(x)$.

d. Compare the equations and graphs of $j(x)$, $q(x)$, and $r(x)$. What do you notice?

Ask yourself:

Will the graphs of $j(x)$, $q(x)$, and $r(x)$ ever intersect?

In the previous activity you translated the function $j(x) = 2x - 1$ up 4 units to create $q(x) = 2x + 3$.

1. **Will the graphs of $j(x)$ and $q(x)$ ever intersect? Explain your reasoning.**

You can algebraically prove that a line and its translation are parallel to each other.

2. **Line AB was translated a units up to create line $A'B'$.**

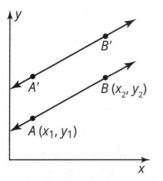

a. **Identify the x- and y-coordinates of each corresponding point on the image.**

b. **Use the slope formula to calculate the slope of the pre-image.**

c. **Use the slope formula to calculate the slope of the image.**

> **Remember:**
>
> The original figure is the pre-image and the transformation of the figure is the image.

d. How does the slope of the image compare to the slope of the pre-image?

e. How would you describe the relationship between the graph of the image and the graph of the pre-image?

Jillian and Ramses each write the equation of a line that is parallel to $y = \frac{1}{2}x + 3$ and passes through the point (2, 9).

Jillian 👍

I know that since the lines are parallel, the new line is a translation of $y = \frac{1}{2}x + 3$. I can substitute the x-value from (2, 9) into $y = \frac{1}{2}x + 3$ to determine the corresponding point on the pre-image.

$$y = \frac{1}{2}(2) + 3 = 4$$

The point that corresponds to the point (2, 9) on $y = \frac{1}{2}x + 3$ is (2, 4). Going from (2, 4) to (2, 9) is a translation up five units. Since

$$y = (\tfrac{1}{2}x + 3) + 5 = \tfrac{1}{2}x + 8,$$

the equation of the parallel line is $y = \frac{1}{2}x + 8$.

Ramses 👍

To write the equation of the line, all I need to know is the slope formula, $m = \dfrac{y_2 - y_1}{x_2 - x_1}$.

I used $m = \frac{1}{2}$ and (2, 9) for (x, y).

$$\frac{1}{2} = \frac{y - 9}{x - 2}.$$

Then, I rearranged the equation to write it in general form.

$$2(y - 9) = x - 2$$
$$y - 9 = \tfrac{1}{2}(x - 2)$$
$$y = \tfrac{1}{2}(x - 2) + 9$$
$$y = \tfrac{1}{2}x - 1 + 9$$
$$y = \tfrac{1}{2}x + 8$$

3. Which student's method do you prefer and why?

4. Write the equation of a line that is parallel to $y = -3x - 1$ and passes through the point (−1, 5).

In this activity, let's consider how dilations impact the graph of the linear function $f(x) = x$.

1. **Suppose the output values of $f(x)$ are changed by a factor of 4 to create $a(x)$.**

   a. **Sketch the graph of $a(x)$ and complete the table of values.**

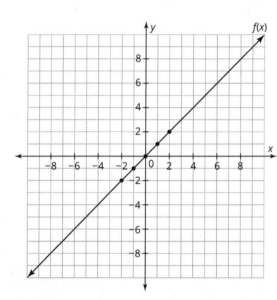

Original Graph		Transformed Graph	
x	**f(x)**	**x**	**a(x)**
−2	−2	−2	
−1	−1	−1	
0	0	0	
1	1	1	
2	2	2	

   b. **Identify the slope and y-intercept of the function $a(x)$. Then, write the equation for the function $a(x)$ in general form.**

2. **Suppose the output values of $f(x)$ are changed by a factor of $\frac{2}{3}$ to create $b(x)$.**

   a. **Sketch the graph of $b(x)$ and complete the table of values.**

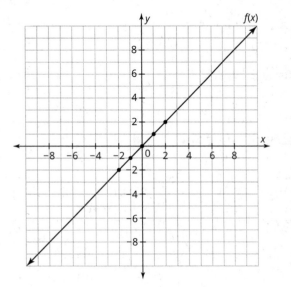

Original Graph		Transformed Graph	
x	**f(x)**	**x**	**b(x)**
−2	−2	−2	
−1	−1	−1	
0	0	0	
1	1	1	
2	2	2	

   b. **Identify the slope and y-intercept of the function $b(x)$. Then, write the equation for the function $b(x)$ in general form.**

3. Suppose the output values of $f(x)$ are changed by a factor of -4 to create $c(x)$.

   a. Sketch the graph of $c(x)$ and complete the table of values.

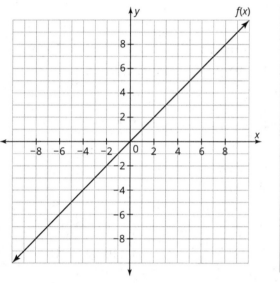

Original Graph	
x	**f(x)**
−2	−2
−1	−1
0	0
1	1
2	2

Transformed Graph	
x	**c(x)**
−2	
−1	
0	
1	
2	

   b. Identify the slope and y-intercept of the function $c(x)$. Then, write the equation for the function $c(x)$ in general form.

For the basic function $f(x) = x$, the transformed function $y = A \cdot f(x)$ shows a vertical dilation of the function. This dilation affects the output values, or y-values, of the function. For $|A| > 1$, the resulting graph vertically stretches by a factor of A units. For $0 < |A| < 1$, the resulting graph vertically compresses by a factor of A units. For $A < 0$, the resulting graph is vertically stretched or compressed and is reflected across the x-axis.

4. Compare the values $f(-1)$ and $c(-1)$. How did the transformation of the function affect the value of the function at $x = -1$?

ACTIVITY

3.4

Vertical Dilations and Vertical Translations of Functions

Let's consider more transformations of the basic function $f(x) = x$.

1. **Describe the transformations performed on $f(x)$ to produce $g(x)$. Then, graph $g(x)$. Write the function equation in general form.**

a. $g(x) = 2 \cdot f(x) + 7$

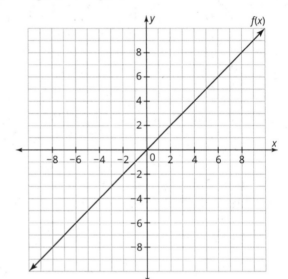

b. $g(x) = 3 \cdot f(x) - 1$

c. $g(x) = \frac{1}{3} \cdot f(x) + 2$

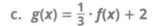
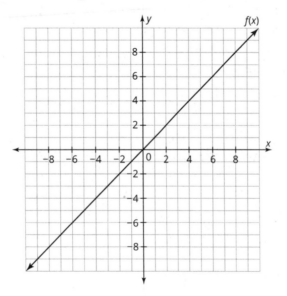

d. $g(x) = \frac{1}{2} \cdot f(x) - 3$

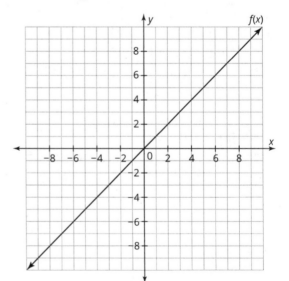

e. $g(x) = -1 \cdot f(x) - 4$ **f.** $g(x) = -\frac{2}{3} \cdot f(x) + 5$

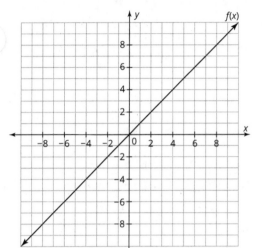

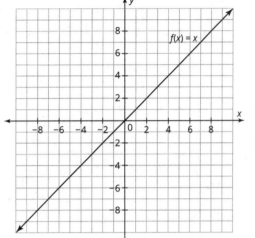

When a function is both translated and stretched vertically, the resulting function can be written in the form $A \cdot f(x) + D$, where D represents the vertical translation of $f(x)$ and A represents the vertical dilation of $f(x)$.

2. **Consider the function $g(x) = A \cdot f(x) + D$.**

    a. **How does changing the A-value affect the slope of the function? The y-intercept of the function?**

    b. **How does changing the D-value affect the slope of the function? The y-intercept of the function?**

Applying Linear Function Transformations

Your company is developing a new video game for kids, which involves scoring points by shooting targets with a cannon.

The cannon starts at the origin of a coordinate system as shown. By default it shoots along the line $f(x) = x$. Players can move the cannon up and down the y-axis and also change the angle of the cannon. When a player shoots the cannon, the game program determines the values of A and D for the linear function $A \cdot f(x) + D$. If the target is on that line, the program will show an animation of the cannonball hitting the target.

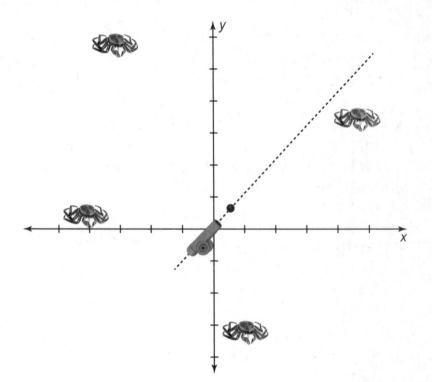

1. **Test the program. Determine values for _A_ and _D_ for 4 linear functions that should hit the targets shown.**

Ask
yourself:

The cannon can shoot in only one direction. Does that affect the domain or range of the linear function?

2. **Identify the domain on which each graph hits the target.**

The game developer is also testing two other versions of the game, with different abilities for the cannon.

Version B

The cannon can only shoot along a line parallel to $f(x) = x$ or $f(x) = -x$. It can move up and down the _y_-axis.

Version C

The cannon can change angles, but remains fixed at the origin.

3. **Determine values for _A_ and _D_, along with their corresponding domains, for 4 linear functions that can hit the targets in each version of the game. Show your work.**

TALK the TALK

Function Matching

The graph shows the linear function $f(x) = x$ and four transformations of $f(x)$.

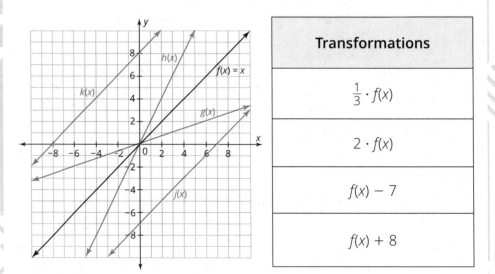

Transformations
$\frac{1}{3} \cdot f(x)$
$2 \cdot f(x)$
$f(x) - 7$
$f(x) + 8$

Match each transformed graph to one of the transformations in the table. Explain your reasoning.

1. $k(x) = $ _____

2. $h(x) = $ _____

3. $g(x) = $ _____

4. $j(x) = $ _____

Assignment

Write

Describe the term *basic function* in the context of transformations using your own words.

Remember

For the basic function $f(x) = x$, the transformed function $y = f(x) + D$ shows a vertical translation of the function. For $D > 0$, the resulting graph vertically shifts up. For $D < 0$, the resulting graph vertically shifts down. The basic function and the resulting graph are parallel because they have the same slope but different y-intercepts.

The transformed function $y = Af(x)$ shows a vertical dilation of the function. For $|A| > 1$, the resulting graph vertically stretches by a factor of A units. For $0 < |A| < 1$, the resulting graph vertically compresses by a factor of A units. For $A < 0$, the resulting graph is vertically stretched or compressed and is reflected across the x-axis.

Practice

1. Given $w(x) = 4x$.
   a. Graph $r(x) = \frac{1}{2} \cdot w(x)$. Then complete the table of corresponding points on $r(x)$.

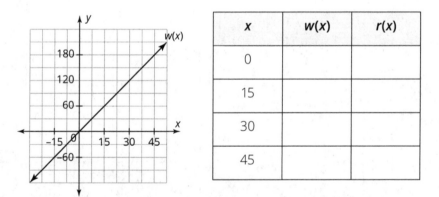

x	w(x)	r(x)
0		
15		
30		
45		

   b. Describe the transformation performed on $w(x)$ to produce $r(x)$.
   c. Write the equation for the function $r(x)$ in general form.

2. Write the equation of a line parallel to the line $y = 2x$ that passes through the given points.
   a. (0, 4) b. (−2, −1) c. (2, 0)

3. Given $f(x) = 50x$.

   a. Graph $b(x) = f(x) - 150$. Then complete the table of corresponding points on $b(x)$.

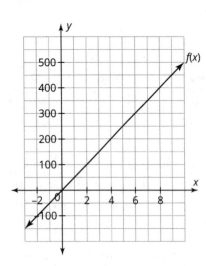

x	f(x)	b(x)
2		
4		
6		
8		

   b. Write the equation for the function $b(x)$ in general form.

   c. Describe the transformation performed on $f(x)$ to produce $b(x)$.

Stretch

The functions $f(x)$ and $g(x)$ are shown on the graph. Write an equation for each function in general form. Then write an equation for $g(x)$ in terms of $f(x)$.

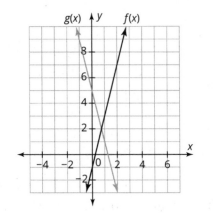

Review

1. Brody works as a fly-fishing guide. The table indicates the number of fish caught on each expedition he guided in a week and the amount of the tip he received for each expedition.

Number of Fish Caught	Amount of Tip ($)
22	125
19	80
25	130
26	150
21	100
18	75
27	150

   a. Construct a scatter plot of the data.
   b. Based on the shape of the scatter plot, is a linear regression appropriate? What type of correlation appears to be present?
   c. Use technology to write a function to represent the line of best fit.
   d. Compute and interpret the correlation coefficient.

2. Determine whether each table of values represents a linear function. If so, write the function. If not, explain why.

   a.

x	y
2	3
4	4
6	5
8	6

   b.

x	y
−4	−17
−2	−9
2	7
4	17

Amirite?

Determining Slopes of Perpendicular Lines

Warm Up

Determine the reciprocal of each value.

1. 3

2. −10

3. $\frac{1}{5}$

4. $-\frac{5}{4}$

5. $-c$

6. $\frac{a}{b}$

Learning Goals

- Identify and write the equations of lines perpendicular to given lines.
- Identify and write the equations of horizontal and vertical lines.

You have translated the graphs of linear equations to determine the slopes of parallel lines. How can you rotate the graphs of linear equations to determine the slopes of perpendicular lines?

Coordinate Rotation

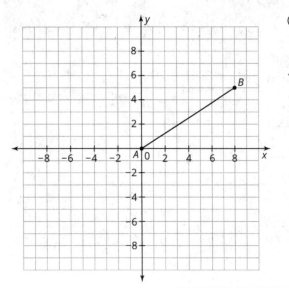

Consider $\overline{AB}$ with coordinates A (0, 0) and B (8, 5).

1. **Suppose the line segment is rotated through an angle with the origin as the center of rotation. Complete the table with the coordinates of the rotated figure.**

Original Line Segment	90° Counterclockwise	180°	270° Counterclockwise
$\overline{AB}$	$\overline{A'B'}$	$\overline{A''B''}$	$\overline{A'''B'''}$
A (0, 0)			
B (8, 5)			

2. **What do you notice about the coordinates of the endpoints of each rotated figure?**

3. **Determine the slope of each line segment.**

   a. $\overline{AB}$

   b. $\overline{A'B'}$

   c. $\overline{A''B''}$

   d. $\overline{A'''B'''}$

4. **Describe any patterns you notice in the slopes of the figures.**

Recall that perpendicular lines or lines segments form a right angle at the point of intersection.

Consider the three graphs shown. Each shows a line and its rotation 90° about a point, which is also the point of intersection.

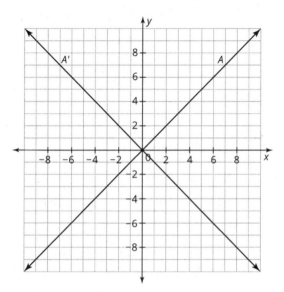

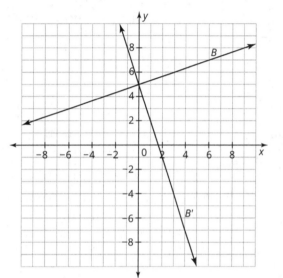

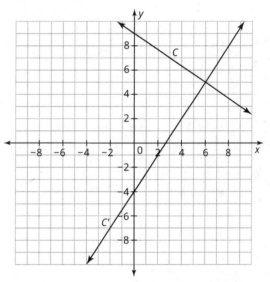

1. **Are the lines in each graph perpendicular? Explain your reasoning.**

2. **Write the equation for each line and its transformation. What do you notice?**

Remember:

The reciprocal of a number $\frac{a}{b}$ is the number $\frac{b}{a}$, where a and b are nonzero numbers. Because the product of a number and its reciprocal is one, reciprocal numbers are also known as multiplicative inverses.

Consider the theorem.

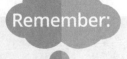
Worked Example

Theorem: If two lines are perpendicular, their slopes are negative reciprocals.

Use the graph and the proof shown to analyze the validity of the theorem.

Given: $p \perp q$

Let m_1 = slope of line p and let m_2 = slope of line q.

Point R lies on line p.

Prove: $m_1 = -\dfrac{1}{m_2}$

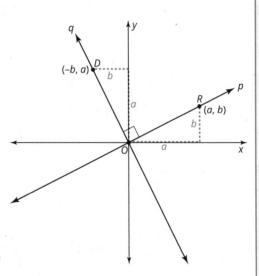

Rotate point R 90° counterclockwise using point O as the center of rotation. Since p and q are perpendicular, the image (point D) will lie on line q under this 90° rotation.

Since this rotation maps the positive x-axis to the positive y-axis, and the positive y-axis to the negative x-axis, then the coordinates of $R(a, b)$ are transformed into the coordinates of $D(-b, a)$. Graphically, you can see the movement of lengths a and b under the rotation.

The graph shows the slope of line p, $m_1 = \dfrac{b}{a}$, and the slope of line $q, m_2 = \dfrac{a}{-b}$.

Using these slopes, you can demonstrate that $m_1 = -\dfrac{1}{m_2}$.

$$\frac{b}{a} = -\frac{1}{\frac{a}{-b}}$$
$$= -1 \cdot \frac{-b}{a}$$
$$= \frac{b}{a}$$

The slope of line q is the negative reciprocal of the slope of line p.

The product of the slopes of perpendicular lines is −1.

The proof shown is a paragraph proof. You will learn different formats of proof as you investigate more properties of lines and figures.

© Carnegie Learning, Inc.

There is often more than one way to prove a theorem. Suppose that point R is rotated 90° clockwise using point O as the center of rotation.

3. **Rewrite the proof using the clockwise rotation of point R.**

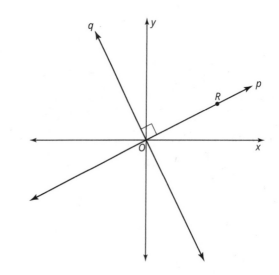

4. **Line j and line k are perpendicular. Given each slope of line j, determine the slope of line k.**

a. $m = \frac{2}{3}$ b. $m = -\frac{4}{5}$ c. $m = -3$

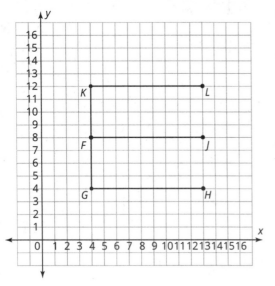

Consider the graph shown.

1. Use a straightedge to extend $\overline{GK}$ to create line p, extend $\overline{GH}$ to create line q, extend $\overline{FJ}$ to create line r, and extend $\overline{KL}$ to create line s.

2. Consider the three horizontal lines you drew for Question 1. For any horizontal line, if x increases by one unit, by how many units does y change?

3. Describe the slope of any horizontal line. Explain your reasoning.

4. Consider the vertical line you drew in Question 1. Suppose that y increases by one unit. By how many units does x change?

5. Describe the slope of any vertical line. Explain your reasoning.

6. Determine whether each of the given statements is always, sometimes, or never true. Explain your reasoning.

   a. All vertical lines are parallel.

   b. All horizontal lines are parallel.

7. Describe the relationship between any vertical line and any horizontal line.

8. Write an equation for a horizontal line and an equation for a vertical line that pass through the point (2, −1).

9. Write an equation for a line that is perpendicular to the line given by $x = 5$ and passes through the point (1, 0).

10. Write an equation for a line that is perpendicular to the line given by $y = -2$ and passes through the point (5, 6).

Writing Equations of Perpendicular Lines

Remember:

You can use the slope formula to write an equation for any line if you know its slope and one point on that line.

In the previous lesson you wrote the equation of a line parallel to a given line that passes through a given point. You can write the equation of a perpendicular line using what you know about the slope of that line and any point on that line.

1. **Write the equation of the line perpendicular to $y = 2x + 1$ that passes through the point (6, 2).**

2. **Write the equation of the line perpendicular to $y = -\frac{3}{4}x$ that passes through the point (3, −8).**

3. **Write the equation of the line that passes through the point (6, 2) and is perpendicular to a line that passes through the points (−5, 3) and (−1, −9).**

4. Write the equation of a line that passes through the point (−2, 7) and is perpendicular to a line that passes through the points (−6, 1) and (0, 4).

5. A pair of perpendicular lines intersect at the point (5, 9). Write the equation of the line that is perpendicular to the line that also passes through point (−4, 4).

TALK the TALK

Things Aren't Always What They Seem

Consider the graphs of six linear equations shown.

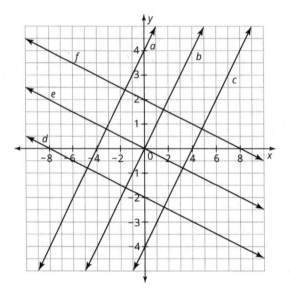

1. **Rosalva says lines *a*, *b*, and *c* are parallel to each other and perpendicular to lines *d*, *e*, and *f*. Felino agrees that lines *a*, *b*, and *c* are parallel to each other but says they are not perpendicular to lines *d*, *e*, and *f*. Who is correct? Justify your reasoning.**

Assignment

Write

Explain in your own words why the slope of a vertical line is undefined.

Remember

The slopes of perpendicular lines are negative reciprocals. Any vertical line is perpendicular to any horizontal line.

Practice

Christopher is a developer and plans to build a new development. Use the grid to help Christopher create a map for his development. Each gridline represents one block.

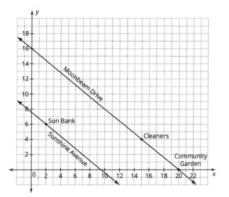

1. There are two main roads that pass through the development, Moonbeam Drive and Sunshine Avenue. Are these two roads parallel to each other? Explain your reasoning.

2. Christopher wants to build a road named Stargazer Boulevard that will be parallel to Moonbeam Drive. On this road, he will build a diner located 7 blocks north of the community garden. Determine the equation of the line that represents Stargazer Boulevard. Show your work. Then draw and label Stargazer Boulevard on the coordinate plane.

3. Christopher wants to build a road named Rocket Drive that connects Sun Bank to Moonbeam Drive. He wants this road to be as short as possible. Determine the equation of the line that represents Rocket Drive. Show your work. Then draw and label Rocket Drive on the coordinate plane.

4. Two office buildings are to be located at the points (8, 4) and (12, 10). Would the shortest road between the two office buildings be a line that is perpendicular to Moonbeam Drive? Explain your reasoning.

5. A straight road named Planet Drive is planned that will connect the diner and the community garden. What is the equation of the line that represents Planet Drive? Show your work. Draw and label Planet Drive on the coordinate plane.

6. Christopher decides that another road to be named Saturn Avenue is needed that will go past the cleaners and be perpendicular to Planet Drive. Determine the equation of the line that represents Saturn Avenue. Show your work. Draw and label Saturn Avenue on the coordinate plane.

Stretch

Triangle *ABC* is located on three lines such that the vertices occur at the points of intersection of pairs of the lines, as shown on the graph.

If △*ABC* is rotated 90° counterclockwise around the origin to form △*A'B'C'*, determine the equations of the lines that would contain △*A'B'C'*. Explain your reasoning. Then draw the three lines that contain △*A'BC'* and label △*A'B'C'*.

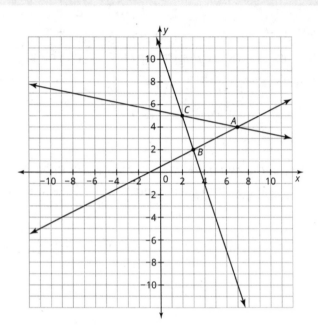

Review

1. Graph the estimated line of best fit for the set of points: (−2, −6), (−3, −2), (2, 4), (6, 3). Determine the estimated linear regression equation for the line.

2. Determine whether the points on the scatter plot have a positive correlation, a negative correlation, or no correlation. Then determine which *r*-value is most accurate.

   a. $r = 0.005$

   b. $r = -0.865$

   c. $r = -0.045$

   d. $r = 0.905$

   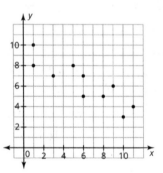

3. Write the equation of a line parallel to the line $2x - 3y = 6$ that passes through the given points.

   a. (0, 3)   b. (−4, −1)

4. Write a recursive and explicit formula for the arithmetic sequence shown.

   4, 8, 12, 16, 20 .....

5. Write a recursive and explicit formula for the geometric sequence shown.

   9, −3, 1, $-\frac{1}{3}, \frac{1}{9}$ ...

Making a Connection

Comparing Linear Functions in Different Forms

Warm Up

Determine whether each set of ordered pairs represents a function. Explain your reasoning.

1. {(−1, −1), (0, 0) (1, 1), (2, 2)}

2. {(−1, −2), (0, 0) (1, 2), (2, 4)}

3. {(−1, −1), (0, −1) (1, −1), (2, −1)}

4. {(−1, −1), (−1, 0) (−1, 1), (−1, 2)}

Learning Goals

- Compare linear functions represented algebraically, graphically, in tables, or with verbal descriptions.
- Choose and interpret appropriate units to represent independent and dependent quantities in situations modeled by linear functions.
- Choose and interpret appropriate scales and origins for graphs of linear functions.

You have represented linear functions in a variety of different ways. How does each linear function representation compare with the others?

Odd One Out

1. **Choose the function that does not belong with the others and justify your choice.**

Function A

x	y
−5	10
−1.5	3
0	0
2.5	−5

Function B

During one year at Bellefield High School, the ratio of boys to girls was 1 : 1.

Function C

$$c(x) = \frac{1}{5}x$$

Function D

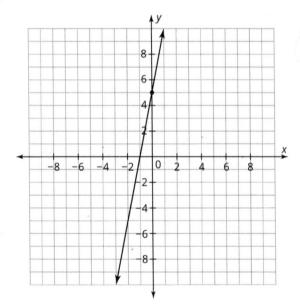

Consider the line that represents the equation $y = 4x - 3$.

1. **Determine whether the graph of each linear relationship is parallel, perpendicular, or neither parallel nor perpendicular to the graph of $y = 4x - 3$.**

a.

x	y
−2.5	−6
0	4
0.5	6
3	16

b. **An elevator descends 4 feet every second.**

c. $y = \frac{1}{4}x + 5$

d.

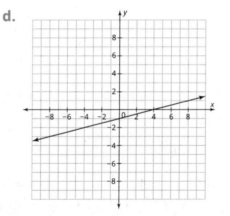

e.

x	y
−4	3
0	2
2	1.5
8	0

f. **For every hour Chiletso bakes, she makes 4 dozen cookies.**

© Carnegie Learning, Inc.

Large recycling centers pay out different amounts per ton of cardboard recycled. Washington County Recycling Center lists its payout amounts in a table, and Jackson County uses a graph to advertise its payout amounts. The two centers' payout amounts are close but not equal.

Washington County Recycling

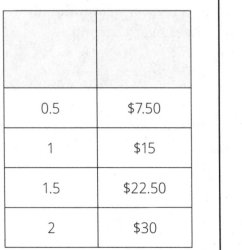

0.5	$7.50
1	$15
1.5	$22.50
2	$30

Jackson County Recycling

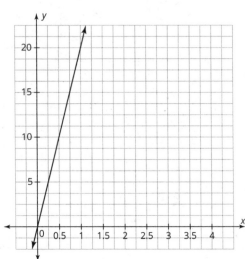

1. **Each representation shows a functional relationship between quantities. Label the quantities and their units in the table and on the graph.**

2. **Let w(x) represent the function for Washington County, and let j(x) represent the function for Jackson County. Use >, <, or = to complete each statement.**

   a. w(0.5) _____ j(0.5)   b. w(1) _____ j(1)   c. w(3) _____ j(3)

3. **Compare the y-intercepts of each relationship. What does each y-intercept mean in terms of the relationship between the quantities?**

4. **Which recycling center would you choose? Provide evidence to justify your choice.**

Josh and Greg are friends who live in different countries. When they chat online and talk about the weather, one of them always uses temperature in degrees Celsius while the other talks about temperature using degrees Fahrenheit.

Josh uses an equation to convert Greg's temperatures, and Greg looks at a table to convert Josh's temperatures. The equation and part of the table are shown.

Remember:

$0°C = 32°F$

Greg's Table

10	−12.2
30	−1.1
50	10
75	23.9

Josh's Equation

$$J(x) = \frac{9}{5}x + 32$$

1. **Identify quantities in the table and equation. Who is converting from °C to °F, and who is converting from °F to °C? Explain your reasoning.**

2. **Compare the given characteristics for each function in terms of the quantities.**

   a. slope

   b. *y*-intercept

Think

about:

The units of the quantities are very important.

Michelle and D'Andre both opened bank accounts at the same time. D'Andre's account balance is shown in the graph. He started with $0 and deposited the same amount each month. In the 4th month, he had $80 saved. Michelle opened her bank account on September 1st with $25 and continues to deposit $25 each month.

D'Andre

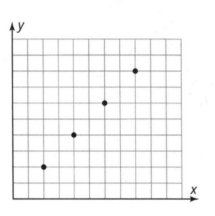

Michelle

Michelle opened her bank account on September 1st with $25 and continues to deposit $25 each month.

1. **Use what you know about D'Andre's account to determine the scale of each axis and interpret the origin on the graph. Explain your reasoning.**

2. **Compare the given characteristics for each function in terms of the quantities.**

   a. slope   **b. y-intercept**

TALK the TALK

Function Maker Space

Consider the table of values.

x	−10	10	20	25
y	0	5	7.5	8.75

1. **Create a situation to represent the table of values shown.**

2. **Write an equation that has a slope that is less steep than the relationship in the table.**

3. **How does the slope of the graph shown compare to the slope from the table of values and your equation?**

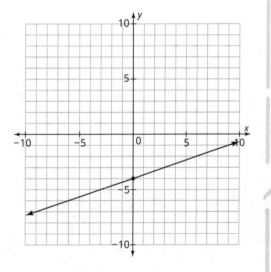

4. **What strategies did you use to create your linear functions and to compare the slopes?**

Assignment

Write

Describe how to compare the slopes and *y*-intercepts of two linear functions if one is represented as a graph and one is represented as a table.

Remember

A linear function can be represented using an equation, a table, a graph, or with a verbal description. Characteristics of linear functions, such as slope, *y*-intercepts, and independent and dependent quantities can be understood from different representations of functions.

Practice

1. Bookstores specializing in selling used books award different amounts of points to customers who supply them with used books. The points are used toward the purchase of other books in the store. BookTraders lists its point values in a table, and Round the Block Books uses a graph to post its point values.

BookTraders Reward Points

2	12
4	24
6	36
8	48

Round the Block Books Reward Points

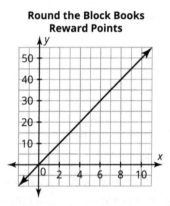

a. Label each column of values in the table and label the *x*-axis and *y*-axis on the graph with the appropriate variable quantities.

b. Compare the slope of each function and explain what each represents in context.

c. Compare the *y*-intercepts of each function and explain what each represents in context.

2. Sherry and Chris live in different cities. They are planning to meet in Nashville, but each will need to drive several days to get there. They have each calculated the distance to Nashville from their homes, but one calculated the distance in miles and the other calculated the distance in kilometers.

Sherry uses an equation to convert the distances Chris plans to drive each day, and Chris uses a table to convert the distances Sherry plans to drive each day. The equation and part of the table are shown.

Chris's Table

300	482.80
382	614.77
426	685.58
475	764.44

Sherry's Equation

$$y = 0.6214x$$

a. Label each column of quantities in the table and identify the meaning of x and y in Sherry's equation. Who is converting from miles to kilometers and who is converting from kilometers to miles? Explain your reasoning.

b. Compare the slope for each function. Explain what each represents in context.

c. Compare the y-intercepts of each function and explain what each represents in context.

3. Alejandro and Maria collect movies. Maria's movie collection is shown in the graph. She started with 0 movies and added the same number of movies to her collection each month. In the 5th month, she had 15 movies. Alejandro's movie collection is given by a description.

Maria

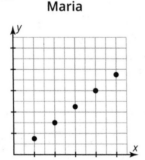

Alejandro

Alejandro started his collection with 27 movies he inherited from his uncle and continues to buy 2 movies each month.

a. Use what you know about Maria's movie collection to determine the scale of her graph. Label the x- and y-axis, the origin, and the intervals on both axes. Explain your reasoning.

b. Compare the slope for each function. Explain what each represents in context.

c. Compare the y-intercepts of each function and explain what each represents in context.

Stretch

1. Tim and Tom are twins. Their parents track their height every year between the ages of 5 and 15. Tim's height is given by the equation, and Tom's height is shown in the graph.
    a. Label the x- and y-axis, the origin, and the intervals on both axes. Explain your reasoning.
    b. Which twin is growing faster? Justify your answer.
    c. At what age does one twin surpass the other in height? Explain your reasoning.

Tim

$$y = 3.1x + 40.6$$

Tom

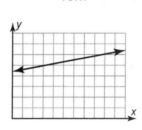

Review

1. For each situation decide whether the correlation implies causation. List reasons why or why not.
    a. The number of winter coats sold at department stores is highly correlated to average low temperatures in the area.
    b. The number of concessions sold at a concert is highly correlated to the number of people in attendance at the concert.

2. The graph represents the basic function $f(x) = x$. The equation for the transformed function $g(x)$ is $g(x) = \frac{2}{3} \cdot f(x) - 2$.
    a. Describe the transformations performed on $f(x)$ to produce $g(x)$.
    b. Graph $g(x)$.
    c. Write the equation of $g(x)$ in general form and identify the slope and y-intercept.

3. Write a recursive formula for each sequence.
    a. 3, −6, 12, −24, 48, ...   b. 180, 160, 140, 120, 100, ...

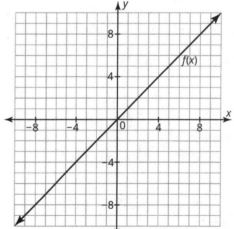

Linear Functions Summary

KEY TERMS

- conjecture
- first differences
- average rate of change
- polynomial

- degree
- leading coefficient
- zero of a function
- basic function

LESSON 1	Connecting the Dots

You can make a conjecture that the graphs of arithmetic sequences represent linear functions. A **conjecture** is a mathematical statement that appears to be true, but has not been formally proven. An explicit formula for an arithmetic sequence can be rewritten in function notation to prove your conjecture.

For example, to write the explicit formula $a_n = 2 + 4(n - 1)$ as a linear function in general form, first use function notation to represent a_n.

$$a_n = 2 + 4(n - 1)$$
$$f(n) = 2 + 4(n - 1)$$

Next, rewrite the expression $2 + 4(n - 1)$.

$f(n) = 2 + 4n - 4$	Distributive Property
$= 4n + 2 - 4$	Commutative Property
$= 4n - 2$	Combine like terms.

So, $a_n = 2 + 4(n - 1)$ written in function notation is $f(n) = 4n - 2$.

One strategy to determine if a table of values represents a linear function is to examine first differences. **First differences** are the values determined by subtracting consecutive output values when the input values have an interval of 1. If the first differences of a table of values are constant, the relationship is linear.

x	y	
1	22	$17 - 22 = -5$
2	17	$12 - 17 = -5$
3	12	$7 - 12 = -5$
4	7	

For example, the first differences of the table shown are constant, so the relationship is linear.

The slope, a, of a linear function is equal to the constant difference of an arithmetic sequence. Another name for the slope of a linear function is **average rate of change**. The formula for the average rate of change is $\frac{f(t) - f(s)}{t - s}$. This represents the change in the output as the input changes from s to t.

<table>
<tr><td>LESSON
2</td><td>Fun with Functions, Linear Ones</td></tr>
</table>

To determine whether a table of values represents a linear function, the slope, or average rate of change, needs to be constant between all given points.

You can use substitution or a graph to determine the output for a given input of a function.

For example, consider the function $E(t) = 15t$ which models the amount of money Marilynn earns for selling t T-shirts. To determine the number of shirts she needs to sell to earn $100, substitute $100 for $E(t)$ and solve.

$E(t) = 15t$
$100 = 15t$
$6.67 = t$

Or you can determine the intersection of the graphs of the two lines represented by the equation $100 = 15x$.

Marilynn needs to sell 6.67 T-shirts to earn $100. In terms of the context, she needs to sell 7 T-shirts.

A linear function can also be referred to as a polynomial function. A **polynomial** is a mathematical expression involving the sum of powers in one or more variables multiplied by coefficients. The **degree** of a polynomial is the greatest variable exponent in the expression. The **leading coefficient** of a polynomial is the numeric coefficient of the term with the greatest power.

The chart shows a few examples of polynomial functions.

Polynomial Function		Degree
Constant	$P(x) = 7$	0
Linear	$P(x) = 2x - 5$	1
Quadratic	$P(x) = 3x^2 - 2x + 4$	2
Cubic	$P(x) = 4x^3 - 2$	3

The structure of each linear function provides important information about the graph. The general form of a linear function is $f(x) = ax + b$, where a and b are real numbers and $a \neq 0$. In this form, the a-value is the leading coefficient, which describes the steepness and direction of the line. The b-value describes the y-intercept.

When you graph a polynomial, the degree indicates the maximum number of times the graph can cross the x-axis. A linear function has a degree of 1, so it crosses the x-axis at most one time.

The factored form of a linear function is $f(x) = a(x - c)$, where a and c are real numbers and $a \neq 0$. When a linear function is in factored form, the value of x that makes the factor $(x - c)$ equal to zero is the x-intercept. This value is called the zero of the function. A **zero of a function** is a real number that makes the value of the function equal to zero, $f(x) = 0$.

You can set the factor $(x - c)$ equal to zero to determine the point where the graph crosses the x-axis.

For example, the linear function $f(x) = 4x + 8$ in factored form is $f(x) = 4(x + 2)$. Set the factor $x + 2$ equal to zero and then solve for x to determine the zero of the function, which is the point at which the graph of the function will cross the x-axis.

$$x + 2 = 0$$
$$x = -2$$

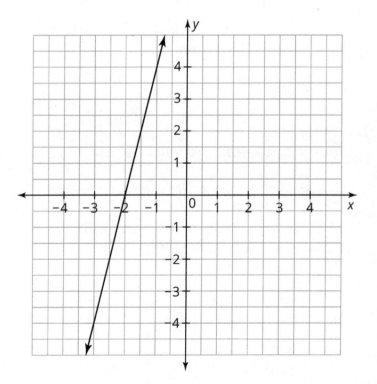

A **basic function** is the simplest function of its type. For example, $f(x) = x$ is the simplest linear function. It is in the form $f(x) = ax + b$, where $a = 1$ and $b = 0$.

For the basic function $f(x) = x$, the transformed function $y = f(x) + D$ affects the output values of the function. For $D > 0$, the graph vertically shifts up. For $D < 0$, the graph vertically shifts down. The amount of shift is given by $|D|$.

For example, the function $y = x + 3$ translates the graph of $y = x$ vertically up 3 units.

$$y = x \qquad\qquad\qquad\qquad y = x + 3$$

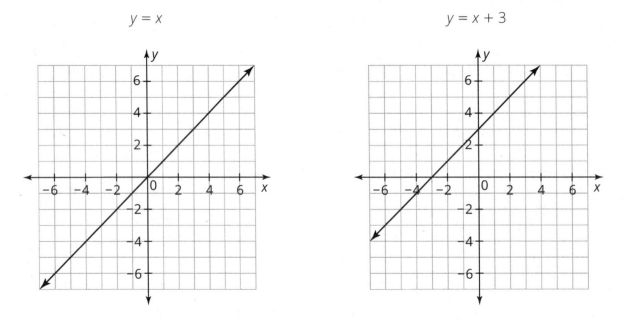

You can algebraically prove that a line and its translation are parallel to each other.

Line AB was translated a units up to create line $A'B'$.

The coordinates of point A' are $(x_1, y_1 + a)$ and the coordinates of point B' are $(x_2, y_2 + a)$.

slope of line $AB = \dfrac{(y_2 - y_1)}{(x_2 - x_1)}$

slope of line $A'B' = \dfrac{[(y_2 + a) - (y_1 + a)]}{(x_2 - x_1)} = \dfrac{(y_2 - y_1)}{(x_2 - x_1)}$

Since the slope of line AB is equal to the slope of line $A'B'$, the lines are parallel.

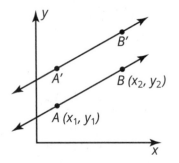

For the basic function $f(x) = x$, the transformed function $y = A \cdot f(x)$ affects the output values of the function. For $|A| > 1$, the graph vertically stretches by a factor of A units. For $0 < |A| < 1$, the graph vertically compresses by a factor of A units. For $A < 0$, the graph reflects across the x-axis.

For example, the function $y = 2x$ dilates the graph of $y = x$ by a factor of 2.

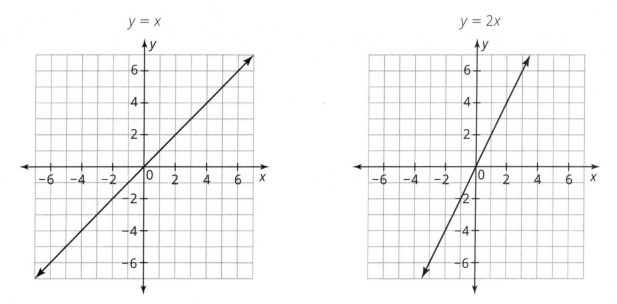

When a function is both translated and vertically dilated, the resulting function can be written in the form $A \cdot f(x) + D$, where D represents the vertical translation of $f(x)$ and A represents the vertical dilation of $f(x)$.

For example, the graph of $y = 2x + 3$ represents both a vertical translation of 3 units and vertical dilation by a factor of 2.

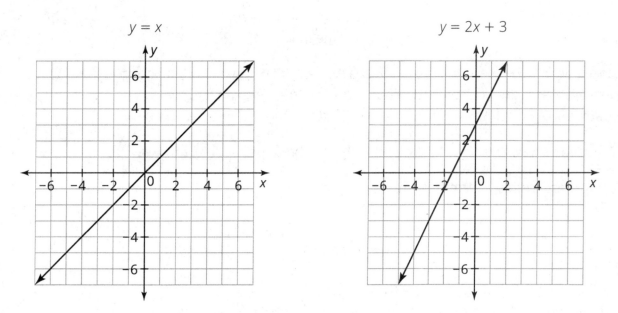

Perpendicular lines or line segments form a right angle at the point of intersection. You can think of perpendicular lines as a line and its rotation 90° about a point, which is also the point of intersection.

The product of the slopes of perpendicular lines is −1.

For example, consider the theorem.

Theorem: If two lines are perpendicular, their slopes are negative reciprocals.

Use the graph and the proof shown to analyze the validity of the theorem.

Given: $p \perp q$

Let m_1 = slope of line p and let m_2 = slope of line q.

Point R lies on line p.

Prove: $m_1 = -\dfrac{1}{m_2}$

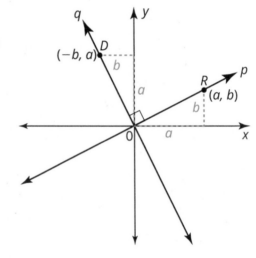

Rotate point R 90° counterclockwise using point O as the center of rotation. Since p and q are perpendicular, the image (point D) will lie on line q under this 90° rotation.

Since this rotation maps the positive x-axis to the positive y-axis, and the positive y-axis to the negative x-axis, then the coordinates of R (a, b) are transformed into the coordinates of D ($-b$, a). Graphically, you can see the movement of lengths a and b under the rotation.

The graph shows the slope of line p, $m_1 = \dfrac{b}{a}$, and the slope of line q, $m_2 = \dfrac{a}{-b}$.

Using these slopes, we can demonstrate that $m_1 = -\dfrac{1}{m_2}$.

$$\dfrac{b}{a} = -\dfrac{1}{\dfrac{a}{-b}}$$
$$= -1 \cdot \dfrac{-b}{a}$$
$$= \dfrac{b}{a}$$

The slope of line q is the negative reciprocal of the slope of line p.

The slope of any horizontal line is 0 since no matter the change for x, there is 0 change for y.

$$\frac{0}{x_2 - x_1} = 0$$

The slope of any vertical line is undefined since no matter the change for y, there is 0 change for x.

$\frac{y_2 - y_1}{0}$ is undefined since a value cannot be divided by zero.

All horizontal lines are parallel to each other since their slopes are equal and all vertical lines are parallel since their slopes are equal. A horizontal and a vertical line are always perpendicular to each other.

For example, to write an equation for a line that passes through the point $(-4, -2)$ and is perpendicular to the line $y = 3$, first determine that the line given by $y = 3$ is a horizontal line. Therefore, a line that is perpendicular to $y = 3$ is a vertical line. A vertical line that passes through the point $(-4, -2)$ has the equation $x = -4$.

You can use what you know about the slopes of perpendicular lines and slope-intercept form to write the equation of a perpendicular line.

For example, consider the line $y = 4x - 1$. Write the equation of the line that passes through the point $(-4, 2)$ and is perpendicular to $y = 4x - 1$.

The slope of $y = 4x - 1$ is 4. The slope of the line perpendicular to $y = 4x - 1$ must have a slope of $-\frac{1}{4}$, since $4 \cdot -\frac{1}{4} = -1$.

Using the given point and slope-intercept form, you can set up an equation to solve for b, the y-intercept.

$$2 = -\frac{1}{4}(-4) + b$$
$$2 = 1 + b$$
$$b = 1$$

Therefore, the equation of the line that passes through the point $(-4, 2)$ and is perpendicular to $y = 4x - 1$ is $y = -\frac{1}{4}x + 1$.

Functions can be represented using tables, equations, graphs, and with verbal descriptions. Features of linear functions such as *y*-intercepts, slopes, and independent and dependent quantities can be determined from different representations of functions.

A table can help you calculate solutions given a few specific input values. A graph can help you determine exact solutions if the graph of the function crosses the grid lines exactly. A function can be solved for any value, so any and all solutions can be determined. Technology can allow for more accuracy when using a graph to determine a solution.

For example, suppose Tyler had $100 in his car fund. He earns $7.50 per hour at his after-school job. He works 3 hours each day, including weekends. Tyler puts all of his earned money in his car fund. How many days will it take him to have enough money to buy a car that costs $3790?

A table can be used to estimate that it will take between 100 and 175 days to buy the car. A graph can be used to estimate that it will take about 160 days to buy the car. A function will give an exact solution. It will take exactly 164 days to buy a car that costs $3790.

d	100 + 22.50*d*
0	100
10	325
20	550
50	1225
100	2350
175	4037.5

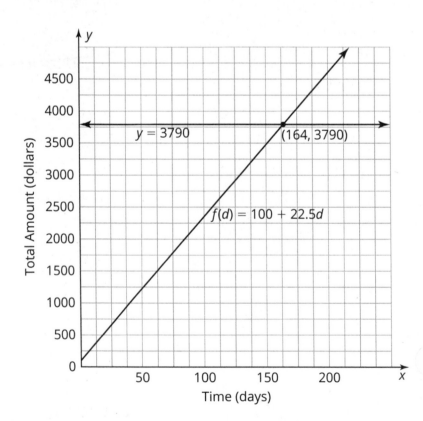

$f(d) = 100 + 22.50d$

$3790 = 100 + 22.50d$

$3690 = 22.50d$

$\dfrac{3690}{22.50} = \dfrac{22.50d}{22.50}$

$164 = d$

Solving Linear Equations and Inequalities

A region can be described as above, below, to the left, or to the right of a line.

Module 2: Exploring Constant Change

TOPIC 2: SOLVING LINEAR EQUATIONS AND INEQUALITIES

In this topic, students analyze linear functions and the key characteristics that define linear functions. They solve equations in one variable, examining the structure of each equation to predict whether the equation has one solution, no solutions, or infinite solutions. Students use the Properties of Equality and basic number properties to construct a viable argument to justify a solution method. They generalize their knowledge of solving equations in one variable to solve literal equations for given variables. Students then graph linear inequalities and explore solving an inequality with a negative slope, which affects the sign of the inequality. Finally, students solve compound inequalities and represent the solutions of a conjunction and a disjunction on a number line.

Where have we been?

Throughout middle school, students gained proficiency in solving increasingly complex linear equations, and students solved two-step inequalities and graphed the solutions on a number line. Coming into this course, students have solved two-step equations with variables on both sides. They understand the underpinnings of solving equations by maintaining equality. From this intuitive understanding, students use properties to justify each step in the equation-solving process.

Where are we going?

Students will use their knowledge of equations and inequalities to solve linear absolute value equations. By recognizing the connections between algebraic and graphical solutions to an equation or inequality, students are preparing to solve linear absolute value equations and inequalities, exponential equations, and quadratic equations and inequalities.

Compound Inequalities

The compound inequality shown involves *and*, and is a conjunction: $x \leq 1$ and $x > -3$.

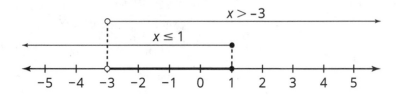

The solution is the region that satisfies both inequalities: $-3 < x \leq 1$. Graphically, the solution is the overlapping, or the intersection, of the separate inequalities.

$E = mc^2$

Quite possibly the most famous equation ever is Albert Einstein's equation from his theory of general relativity which shows the relationship of energy to mass. The energy of an object at rest is equal to its mass (m) times the speed of light (c) squared.

But this is only for objects at rest. The full equation, for moving objects with momentum (p) is $E^2 = (mc^2)^2 + (pc)^2$.

You may recognize the form of this equation, which is identical to another famous equation: $a^2 + b^2 = c^2$.

Talking Points

Inequalities can be an important topic to know about for college admissions tests.

Here is a sample question:

Solve for x in the inequality $\frac{x}{2} - 3 < 2y$.

To solve for x, isolate the variable x.

$$\frac{x}{2} - 3 < 2y$$

$$\frac{x}{2} - 3 + 3 < 2y + 3$$

$$\frac{x}{2} < 2y + 3$$

$$2\left(\frac{x}{2}\right) < 2(2y + 3)$$

$$x < 4y + 6$$

Key Terms

infinite solutions

A linear equation with infinite solutions means that any value for the variable makes the equation true.

literal equation

Literal equations are equations in which the variables represent specific measures.

solve an inequality

To solve an inequality means to determine the values of the variable that make the inequality true.

disjunction

A compound inequality in the form $x < a$ or $x > b$, where a and b are any real numbers, is a disjunction.

Strike a Balance

Solving Linear Equations

Warm Up

Solve each equation for *x*.

1. $\frac{1}{3}x = 8$

2. $5 + x = 12.7$

3. $2x - 9 = 6$

4. $12 + 2x = 3x - 1$

Learning Goals

- Write equivalent equations using Properties of Equality.
- Use Properties of Equality to solve linear equations and justify a solution method.
- Determine whether an equation has one solution, no solution, or infinite solutions.
- Solve linear equations with variables on both sides.

Key Terms

- solution
- no solution
- infinite solutions

You know that equations are one way to represent a linear function, and you have used equations to evaluate linear functions for a given input value. How can you use equations to solve for unknown input values of a function?

Equation Creation

An equation is a mathematical sentence that uses an equals sign to show that two expressions are equivalent. When one of those expressions contains a variable, you can solve the equation.

Consider the equation $x = 2$. You can substitute the value 2 for x to create the true statement $2 = 2$. Because this is the only value that makes the statement true, 2 is the only solution to the equation $x = 2$.

By performing the same operation on each side of an equation, you can create more complex equations that have the same solution.

A **solution** to an equation is a value for the variable that makes the equation a true statement.

1. **Consider the equation $x = 2$.**

   a. **Choose any constant. Add that constant to each side of the equation and simplify.**

   b. **Choose any constant other than 0. Multiply each side of the equation you created in part (a) by that constant and simplify.**

   c. **Choose any number other than 0 to represent a in the expression ax. Subtract the term ax from each side of the equation you created in part (b) and simplify.**

   d. **Choose any constant other than 0. Divide each side of the equation you created in part (c) by that constant and simplify.**

Think about:

What strategies can you use to verify a solution?

2. **Have a partner solve the equation you created in Question 1 to verify that $x = 2$ is the solution.**

© Carnegie Learning, Inc.

Using Properties to Justify Solutions

Recall that the Properties of Equality are rules that allow you to maintain balance and rewrite equations to isolate the variable.

Properties of Equality	For all numbers a, b, and c
Addition Property of Equality	If $a = b$, then $a + c = b + c$.
Subtraction Property of Equality	If $a = b$, then $a - c = b - c$.
Multiplication Property of Equality	If $a = b$, then $ac = bc$.
Division Property of Equality	If $a = b$ and $c \neq 0$, then $\frac{a}{c} = \frac{b}{c}$.

Sara and Ethan both created new equations starting from the solution statement $x = 2$.

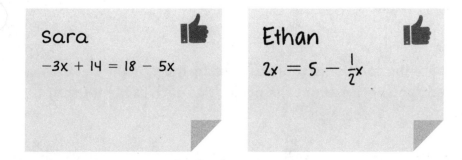

Sara 👍

$-3x + 14 = 18 - 5x$

Ethan 👍

$2x = 5 - \frac{1}{2}x$

1. **Verify that both equations are equivalent to $x = 2$ using the given strategy.**

   a. **substitution**

   b. **Properties of Equality**

There are also basic number properties that you are already familiar with that can be used to justify your steps when solving equations.

Number Properties	For all numbers a, b, and c
Commutative Property	$a + b = b + a$ $ab = ba$
Associative Property	$a + (b + c) = (a + b) + c$ $a(bc) = (ab)c$
Distributive Property	$a(b + c) = ab + ac$

2. **Solve each equation and check your solution. Write the properties that justify each step of your solving strategy.**

   a. $24x + 7 = -4x$ b. $3(2x + 1) = 4x + 6$

   c. $\frac{1}{2}x - 6 = 2 + (2x + 1)$

3. **Compare the solution strategies used by Kaleigh and Destiny. What do you notice about the properties each student used?**

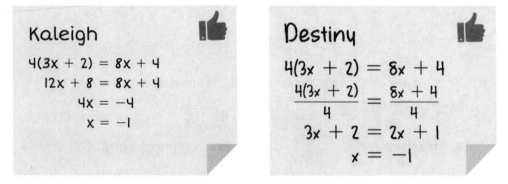

Kaleigh 👍
$4(3x + 2) = 8x + 4$
$12x + 8 = 8x + 4$
$4x = -4$
$x = -1$

Destiny 👍
$4(3x + 2) = 8x + 4$
$\frac{4(3x + 2)}{4} = \frac{8x + 4}{4}$
$3x + 2 = 2x + 1$
$x = -1$

In the Getting Started, you built equations from $x = 2$. In this activity, you will build equations from two mathematical sentences and compare your results.

1. **Consider the mathematical sentence 2 = 2.**
   Is there any variable or constant that you could add, subtract, multiply, or divide to both sides using the Properties of Equality to make this true sentence false? Choose variables and constants to create new mathematical sentences to justify your conclusion.

2. **Consider the mathematical sentence 2 = 3.**
   Is there any variable or constant that you could add, subtract, multiply, or divide to both sides using the Properties of Equality to make this false sentence true? Choose variables and constants to create new mathematical sentences to justify your conclusion.

A linear equation can have *one solution*, *no solution*, or *infinite solutions*. The equations you solved in the previous activity are examples of linear equations with one solution. A linear equation with **no solution** means that there is no value for the variable that makes the equation true. A linear equation with **infinite solutions** means that any value for the variable makes the equation true.

3. Consider the equations you created in this activity.

   a. Explain whether the equation(s) you created in Question 1 have one solution, no solution, or infinite solutions.

   b. Explain whether the equation(s) you created in Question 2 have one solution, no solution, or infinite solutions.

4. Consider the equation $2x = 3x$. Does this equation have one solution, no solution, or infinite solutions? Explain your reasoning.

ACTIVITY 1.3 Tic-Tac-Bingo

In this activity, you are going to play a game called Tic-Tac-Bingo. The object of the game is to match two expressions to create an equation with specific solution types. Use the Tic-Tac-Bingo sheet located at the end of the lesson.

Prepare the board.

The board has 9 spaces. Three spaces are already designated. Fill each remaining space with one of the solution types listed. Each option must be used at least once.

> **Solution Types**
> • positive rational solution
> • negative rational solution
> • non-zero integer solution

Play the game.

Your teacher will assign you an expression. When you and a classmate have created an equation with one of the solution types, write your equation in the corresponding box.

Try to be the first person to fill three spaces in a row. Then, try to be the first person to completely fill your board with equations.

1. **Reflect on the equations you created.**

   a. **How can you look at an equation and determine that it has no solution?**

   b. **How can you look at an equation and determine that it has infinite solutions?**

TALK the TALK

One Step at a Time

1. Write the property that justifies each step to solve the given equation.

$$-\frac{1}{3}(6x - 21) = -5(x + 1)$$

$$-2x + 7 = -5x - 5 \qquad \rule{4cm}{0.4pt}$$

$$-2x + 5x + 7 = -5x + 5x - 5 \qquad \rule{4cm}{0.4pt}$$

$$3x + 7 - 7 = -5 - 7 \qquad \rule{4cm}{0.4pt}$$

$$\frac{3x}{3} = \frac{-12}{3} \qquad \rule{4cm}{0.4pt}$$

$$x = -4$$

2. Solve the equation using the justification given for each step.

$$5x + 7 = \frac{(-15x - 1)}{3} + \frac{4}{3}$$

\rule{5cm}{0.4pt}   Multiplication Property of Equality

\rule{5cm}{0.4pt}   Distributive Property

\rule{5cm}{0.4pt}   Associative Property

\rule{5cm}{0.4pt}   Subtraction Property of Equality

\rule{5cm}{0.4pt}   Addition Property of Equality

\rule{5cm}{0.4pt}   Division Property of Equality

$$x = -\frac{3}{5}$$

Tic-Tac-Bingo Board

	Solution is neither positive or negative	
Equation: Solution:	Equation: Solution:	Equation: Solution:
No solution Equation: Solution:	**FREE SPACE**	Equation: Solution:
Equation: Solution:	Equation: Solution:	**Infinite solutions** Equation: Solution:

Assignment

Write

Explain how you know when an equation has no solution and when it has infinite solutions.

Remember

To solve an equation, use the Properties of Equality to isolate the variable. A linear equation can have one solution, no solution, or infinite solutions.

Practice

1. Solve each equation. Write the properties that justify each step in the solution method.

   a. $3x - 8 = -7x + 18$

   b. $-2(4 - x) = 12x - 3$

   c. $\frac{1}{2}(-10x + 4) = -4(-3 + 2x) + 8$

   d. $\frac{(-2x - 4)}{5} + \frac{8}{5} = 3(x - 1)$

   e. $\frac{4}{3}x - 2\left(9 - \frac{1}{3}x\right) = -\frac{7}{3}x + 9$

2. Determine whether each equation has one solution, no solution, or infinite solutions. Explain your reasoning.

   a. $-2(x + 5) = -6x + 4(x - 2)$

   b. $4(0.2x - 1.2) = -0.5x + 3.4$

   c. $\frac{\left(\frac{1}{2}x - 7\right)}{2} = -3x + 4$

   d. $2(x - 4) + x = 3(x - 2) - 2$

   e. $3 - \frac{2}{5}x - \frac{12}{5} = \frac{10 - 2x}{5}$

   f. $6(x - 1) + 21 = 6x + 15$

Stretch

Consider the equation $2x - 5(x - 1) = 50$.

   a. Solve the equation for x.

   b. Chen was asked to solve the inequality: $2x - 5(x - 1) < 50$. She gave an answer of $x < -15$. Substitute in any value for x less than -15 to determine if Chen is correct. If not, determine the correct solution.

Review

1. Determine whether the table of values represents a linear function. If it does represent a linear function, write the function. If it does not represent a linear function, explain why.

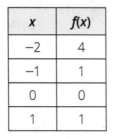

x	f(x)
−2	4
−1	1
0	0
1	1

2. Nelson grows tomatoes and sells them at a nearby farmer's roadside stand. He sells them for $2.50 each. The farmer charges him $15 a day to use the stand. Write a linear function in factored form and general form that represents the amount of money, M, Nelson will make from selling x tomatoes.

3. Clean Green Landscapers uses a graph to show what they charge, and Sunshine Landscaper lists what they charge in a table.

Clean Green Landscapers

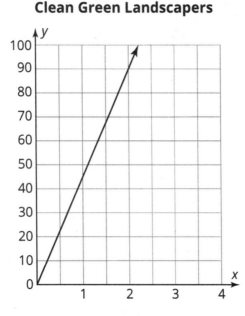

Sunshine Landscaper

0.5	$25
1	$50
1.5	$75
2	$100
2.5	$125

a. Each representation shows a functional relationship between quantities. Label the quantities and their units in the table and on the graph.

b. Let C(x) represent the function for Clean Green Landscapers, and let S(x) represent the function for Sunshine Landscapers. Which function has a steeper slope? Explain how you know.

4. Evaluate the function $f(x) = 0.4x^2 − 3x − 8$ for the value $x = −2$.

5. The cost to install x number of central air conditioning units for a company is given by the function $C(x) = \frac{4000x + 1300}{3}$. Use the function to determine the cost to install 45 air conditioners.

It's Literally About Literal Equations

Literal Equations

Warm Up

The formula for the circumference of a circle is $C = 2\pi r$. Determine the radius for each circle with the given circumference. Use 3.14 for π and round to the nearest tenth of a unit, if necessary.

1. $C = 62.8$ in.

2. $C = 10$ cm

3. $C = 15.7$ ft

4. $C = 48$ mm

Learning Goals

- Rewrite linear equations in different forms.
- Analyze the structure of different forms of linear equations.
- Recognize and use literal equations.
- Rearrange literal equations to highlight quantities of interest.

Key Term

- literal equation

You have used different properties to solve linear equations to determine which value makes the equation true. How can you use those same properties to solve for one specific variable in an equation that has multiple variables?

Perimeter Perspectives

Cody and Jessica have rectangular backyards that each share a side with a neighborhood park. The sides shared with the park are adjacent to each other as shown.

Cody and Jessica are each responsible for constructing their own fence to separate their yard from the park. The city gives them the measure of the perimeter of the park in feet. So that each knows how much fencing to buy, Cody needs to determine the width of the park, and Jessica needs to determine the length of the park.

1. **How can you write an equation for the perimeter of the park from each person's perspective to help them determine the information they need?**

Remember:

The formula for the perimeter of a rectangle is $P = 2l + 2w$.

2. **Show that the two equations are equivalent.**

The slope, x-intercept, and y-intercept are each important characteristics of linear functions. The structure of equations can reveal these characteristics of a function.

1. Consider the equation $y = -\frac{2}{3}x + 4$. Determine each characteristic and then explain your work.

   a. slope

   b. *y*-intercept

   c. *x*-intercept

   d. How did you determine each characteristic?

2. Consider the equation $y = 4(x - 2)$. Determine each characteristic and then explain your work.

   a. slope

   b. *y*-intercept

   c. *x*-intercept

   d. How did you determine each characteristic?

3. Consider the equation $3x - 2y = 8$. Determine each characteristic and then explain your work.

   a. slope

   b. *y*-intercept

   c. *x*-intercept

   d. How did you determine each characteristic?

There are three useful forms of linear equations.

General Form	**Factored Form**	**Standard Form**
$y = ax + b$	$y = a(x - c)$	$Ax + By = C$

In general and factored form, the values of a, b, and c can be any real numbers. In standard form, however, there are constraints on the variables: A must be a positive integer, and A and B cannot both be 0.

4. **Identify the form for each equation in Questions 1 through 3.**

Consider how the structure of the standard form of a linear function reveals its key characteristics.

5. **For the equation $Ax + By = C$, determine the slope, x-intercept, and y-intercept.**

6. **Which form of a linear equation is more efficient for determining each characteristic?**

   a. **slope**

   b. **x-intercept**

   c. **y-intercept**

7. **If you want to graph an equation using your calculator, which form is more efficient? Explain your reasoning.**

Rewriting Literal Equations

Literal equations are equations in which the variables represent specific measures. You most often see literal equations when you study formulas. These literal equations can be manipulated in order to allow you to solve for one specific variable.

You have used a common literal equation, the formula for converting degrees Fahrenheit to degrees Celsius.

$$C = \frac{5}{9}(F - 32)$$

Josh is talking on the phone to his friend Greg who lives in Europe. Greg is used to describing temperatures in °C, while Josh is used to describing temperatures in °F. Greg can use the formula above to quickly convert the temperatures Josh describes to °C.

1. **How can you rewrite the formula so that Josh can quickly convert the temperatures that Greg describes to °F? Justify your solution method.**

2. **Josh tells Greg that the temperature where he lives is currently 77°F. Greg tells Josh that the temperature where he lives is currently 30°C. Josh says it is warmer where he lives and Greg says it is warmer where he lives. Who is correct? Explain your reasoning.**

3. Maya, Sherry, and Brian each convert the given formula to degrees Fahrenheit.

Maya 👍

$$C = \frac{5}{9}(F - 32)$$

$$C = \frac{5}{9}F - \frac{160}{9}$$

$$9(C) = 9\left(\frac{5}{9}F - \frac{160}{9}\right)$$

$$9C = 5F - 160$$

$$9C + 160 = 5F$$

$$\frac{9C}{5} + \frac{160}{5} = \frac{5F}{5}$$

$$\frac{9}{5}C + 32 = F$$

a. Explain Maya's reasoning.

Sherry 👎

$$C = \frac{5}{9}(F - 32)$$

$$C = \frac{5}{9}F - 32$$

$$9(C) = 9\left(\frac{5}{9}F - 32\right)$$

$$9C = 5F - 288$$

$$9C + 288 = 5F$$

$$\frac{9C}{5} + \frac{288}{5} = \frac{5F}{5}$$

$$\frac{9}{5}C + 57.6 = F$$

Brian 👎

$$C = \frac{5}{9}(F - 32)$$

$$C = \frac{5}{9}F - \frac{160}{9}$$

$$9(C) = 9\left(\frac{5}{9}F - \frac{160}{9}\right)$$

$$9C = 45F - 1440$$

$$9C + 1440 = 45F$$

$$\frac{9C}{45} + \frac{1440}{45} = \frac{45F}{45}$$

$$\frac{1}{5}C + 32 = F$$

b. Explain the error in Sherry's work.

c. Explain the error in Brian's work.

4. **Carlos and Mikala do not like working with fractions. Each rewrites the equation so that it does not have fractions. Their work is shown.**

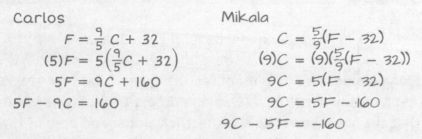

Carlos

$$F = \frac{9}{5}C + 32$$
$$(5)F = 5\left(\frac{9}{5}C + 32\right)$$
$$5F = 9C + 160$$
$$5F - 9C = 160$$

Mikala

$$C = \frac{5}{9}(F - 32)$$
$$(9)C = (9)\left(\frac{5}{9}(F - 32)\right)$$
$$9C = 5(F - 32)$$
$$9C = 5F - 160$$
$$9C - 5F = -160$$

Carlos and Mikala got two different equations. Who is correct? Explain your reasoning.

5. **In the original equations, the coefficients $\frac{9}{5}$ and $\frac{5}{9}$ as well as the constant 32 had meaning based on temperature. What do the coefficients, 9 and 5, and the constant, 160, represent in Carlos's and Mikala's equations?**

6. **How is the literal equation $y = a(bx + c)$ similar to the equation for converting °F to °C? How would you solve this equation for the variable x?**

Solving Literal Equations for Specific Variables

Convert each literal equation to solve for the given variable.

1. **Think Inside the Box is manufacturing new boxes for You Pack 'Em, We Ship 'Em (YPEWSE). YPEWSE told Think Inside the Box that the boxes must have a specific volume and area of the base. However, YPEWSE did not specify a height for the boxes.**

   a. **Write a literal equation to calculate the volume of a box. Then convert the volume formula to solve for height.**

   b. **YPEWSE specified the volume of the box must be 450 cubic inches and the area of the base must be 75 square inches. Use your formula to determine the height of the new boxes.**

Remember:

Volume is measured in cubic units since it calculated using three dimensions. Height measures only one dimension.

The formula for the volume of a cone is
$$V = (\pi)r^2\left(\frac{h}{3}\right)$$
where r is the radius and h is the height.

2. **The volume of an ice cream cone is the measure of how much ice cream fits inside the cone. An ice cream cone company wants to make an ice cream cone with a greater height that still holds the same amount of ice cream.**

   a. **Write an equation to calculate the volume of a cone. Then convert the equation to solve for the height.**

   b. **Explain how your equation determines a linear measurement when the original equation determined a cubic measurement.**

3. The formula for the area of a trapezoid is $A = \frac{1}{2}h(b_1 + b_2)$, where h is its height and b_1 and b_2 are the lengths of each base.

   a. Convert the area formula to solve for the height.

   b. Use your formula to determine the height of a trapezoid with an area of 24 cubic centimeters and base lengths of 9 cm and 7 cm.

4. For the given literal equation $Z = \frac{A}{B} + \frac{C}{D}$, solve for each variable given. Justify your solution method.

   a. A

   b. D

TALK the TALK

This Ought to Be Duck Soup

1. The formula for the volume of a cylinder is $V = 2\pi rh$ where *V* is the volume, *r* is the length of the radius of the base, and *h* is the height. Convert the formula to solve for the height.

2. The volume of a can of soup is 37.68 cubic inches and the length of the radius of the base of the can is 1.5 inches. Use the formula to determine the height of the can of soup. Use 3.14 for π.

3. The formula for the surface area of a cylinder is $SA = 2\pi r^2 + 2\pi rh$ where *SA* is the surface area, *r* is the length of the radius of the base, and *h* is the height. Convert the formula to solve for the height.

4. The surface area of a can of soup is 51.81 square inches and the length of the radius of the base is 1.5 inches. Use your formula to determine the height of the can of soup. Use 3.14 for π.

Assignment

Write

Define the term *literal equation* in your own words.

Remember

Literal equations can be rewritten using properties of equality to allow you to solve for one specific variable.

Practice

1. In the USA, the shoe sizes for men are approximated by the equation $3f - s = 24$, where f represents the length of the foot in inches and s represents the shoe size.
   a. The average man's foot is 11.5 inches long. What is the average man's shoe size?
   b. Use the function to determine the x- and y-intercept. State the meaning of each in terms of this problem situation.
   c. Which form can most easily be used to determine the slope of this equation? Determine the slope of this equation and describe what it means in terms of the problem situation.

2. The boxes that shoes come in are often used in other capacities once the shopper has bought the shoes. Sometimes the boxes are used to hold other items, so it is helpful to know the volume of the box.
   a. Write the equation to solve for the volume of the shoe box.
   b. If the area of the base of the box is 112 square inches and the height is 3.5 inches, what is the volume of the box?
   c. Rewrite the equation to solve for width. Show your work.
   d. A box has a volume of 456 cubic inches, with a length of 1 foot and a height of 4 inches. Determine the width of the box.

3. Solve each equation for the specified variable.
   a. $V = \frac{1}{3}Bh$ for B
   b. $I = prt$ for r
   c. $\frac{x+y}{3} = 6$ for y
   d. $A + B + C = 180$ for C

Stretch

A simple pendulum is made of a long string and a small metal sphere. The period of oscillation can be found by the formula $T = 2\pi \sqrt{\left(\frac{L}{g}\right)}$, where g is the acceleration due to gravity, and L is the length of the string. Solve the formula for g, the acceleration due to gravity.

Review

1. The Peters Creek restaurant has an all-you-can eat shrimp deal. Currently, the cost of the deal is 50 cents per shrimp, with free soft drinks. The cost for the shrimp deal is modeled by the function $c(x) = 0.50x$, where x represents the number of shrimp eaten. A new manager decides to change the cost of the deal to 25 cents per shrimp, but a $5.00 charge for soft drinks. Let $p(x)$ be the function that represents the new cost for the all-you-can-eat shrimp deal.

   a. Sketch the graph of $c(x)$ and $p(x)$ on the same coordinate plane.

   b. Complete the table of corresponding points on $p(x)$.

   c. Write an equation for $p(x)$ in terms of $c(x)$. Describe the transformation performed on $c(x)$ to produce $p(x)$.

   d. Write the equation for the function $p(x)$ in general form.

x	p(x)
0	
10	
40	
60	
70	
90	

2. Solve the equation. Write the properties that justify each step.
$$-\frac{2}{3}x(-9x + 24) = 2x - 4$$

3. Determine if the equation has one solution, no solution, or infinite solutions.
$$3\left(2 + \frac{2}{3}x\right) = 5 + 2(x + 1)$$

4. The table shows the relationship between y and x. Write an equation that represents the relationship between the variables.

x	y
−3	2
−1	6
1	10
3	14
6	20

5. A clothing store decides to give out bonus points that can be used for future purchases. If a customer applies for a bonus card they are automatically given 50 bonus points. After that, they get 25 bonus points for every $1.00 that they spend. Write an equation that shows the number of bonus points, b, that a customer will earn for x dollars that they spend.

Not All Statements Are Made Equal

Modeling Linear Inequalities

3

Warm Up

Solve each statement for *x*.

1. $x + 1 = 6$

2. $x - 2 > 5$

3. $\frac{x}{3} \leq -1$

4. $-x > 4$

Learning Goals

- Write and solve inequalities.
- Analyze a graph on a coordinate plane to solve problems involving inequalities.
- Interpret how a negative rate affects how to solve an inequality.

Key Term

- solve an inequality

You have used horizontal lines on a graph and Properties of Equality with equations to solve problems that can be modeled with linear equations. Can you use these same methods to solve problems involving linear inequalities?

Fundraising Function

Alan's camping troop is selling popcorn to earn money for an upcoming camping trip. Each camper starts with a credit of $25 toward his sales, and each box of popcorn sells for $3.75.

1. Write a function, $f(b)$, to show Alan's total sales as a function of the number of boxes of popcorn he sells, b.

Ask yourself:

How will you represent $25 credit in your function?

2. Analyze the function you wrote.

   a. Identify the independent and dependent quantities and their units.

   b. What is the slope of the function? What does it represent in this problem situation?

   c. What is the y-intercept? What does it represent in this problem situation?

The graph shown represents the function you wrote in the previous activity, $f(b) = 3.75b + 25$.

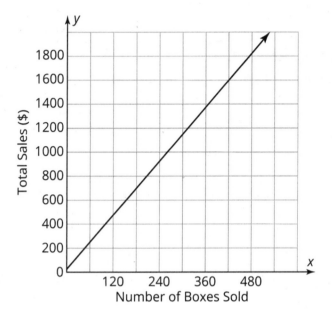

1. **Suppose Alan has a sales goal of $1600.**

   a. **Draw a horizontal line from the *y*-axis until it intersects with the graphed function to determine the point on the graph that represents $1600 in total sales.**

   b. **How many boxes would Alan have to sell to make $1600 in total sales? Explain your reasoning.**

   c. **Use the number line to represent the number of boxes sold if the total sales is equal to $1600.**

Think about:

Will the points you graph on the number line be open or closed?

© Carnegie Learning, Inc.

2. Analyze the region of the graph that lies below the horizontal line you drew, up to and including the point intersected by the line.

a. What does this region of the graph represent?

b. Write an inequality to represent this region.

c. Use the number line to represent the number of boxes that are solutions to the inequality you wrote.

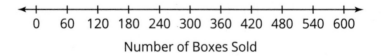

Number of Boxes Sold

d. Do all the solutions make sense in context of the problem? Explain your reasoning.

3. Analyze the region of the graph that lies above the horizontal line you drew, not including the point intersected by the line.

a. What does this region of the graph represent?

b. Write an inequality to represent this region.

c. Use the number line to represent the number of boxes that are solutions to the inequality you wrote.

```
←+——+——+——+——+——+——+——+——+——+——+——+→
  0   60  120 180 240 300 360 420 480 540 600
```
Number of Boxes Sold

d. Do all the solutions make sense in context of the problem? Explain your reasoning.

4. Explain the difference between the open and closed circles on your number lines.

Ask
yourself:

How does determining the intersection point help you determine your answers?

5. Use the graph to answer each question. Write an equation or inequality statement for each.

   a. How many boxes would Alan have to sell to earn at least $925?

   b. How many boxes would Alan have to sell to earn less than $2050?

   c. How many boxes would Alan have to sell to earn exactly $700?

To **solve an inequality** means to determine the values of the variable that make the inequality true.

Another way to determine the solution set of any inequality is to solve it algebraically. The objective when solving an inequality is similar to the objective when solving an equation: You want to isolate the variable on one side of the inequality symbol.

To make the first deposit on the trip, Alan's total sales, $f(b)$, need to be at least $1100.

> ### Worked Example
>
> You can set up an inequality and solve it to determine the number of boxes Alan needs to sell.
>
> $$f(b) \geq 1100$$
> $$3.75b + 25 \geq 1100$$
>
> Solve the inequality in the same way you would solve an equation.
>
> $$3.75b + 25 \geq 1100$$
> $$3.75b + 25 - 25 \geq 1100 - 25$$
> $$3.75b \geq 1075$$
> $$\frac{3.75b}{3.75} \geq \frac{1075}{3.75}$$
> $$b \geq 286.66 \ldots$$

Think about:

How accurate does your answer need to be?

1. **How many boxes of popcorn does Alex need to sell to make the first deposit? Explain your reasoning.**

2. **Write and solve an inequality for each. Show your work.**

   a. **What is the greatest number of boxes Alan could sell and still not have made $600 in sales?**

   b. **At least how many boxes would Alan have to sell to make $1500 in sales?**

3. **The worked example showed how to solve an inequality of the form, $y = ax + b$. How does your method change if the inequality is in a different form?**

Sea level has an elevation of 0 feet.

Alan's camping troop hikes down from their campsite at an elevation of 4800 feet to the base of the mountain, which is at sea level. They hike down at a rate of 20 feet per minute.

1. **Write a function, $h(m)$, to show the troop's elevation as a function of time in minutes. Label the function on the coordinate plane.**

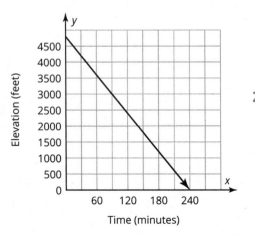

2. **Identify the independent and dependent quantities and their units.**

3. **Analyze the function. Identify each characteristic and explain what it means in terms of this problem situation.**

   a. **slope**

   b. **y-intercept**

   c. **x-intercept**

   d. **domain of the function**

4. Use the graph to determine how many minutes passed if the troop is below 3200 feet. Draw an oval on the graph to represent this part of the function and write the corresponding inequality statement.

5. Write and solve an inequality to verify the solution set you interpreted from the graph.

6. Compare and contrast the solution sets you wrote using the graph and the function. What do you notice?

7. Analyze the relationship between the inequality statements representing $h(m)$ and m.

   a. Complete the table by writing the corresponding inequality statement that represents the number of minutes for each height.

$h(m)$	m
$h(m) > 3200$	
$h(m) \geq 3200$	
$h(m) = 3200$	
$h(m) < 3200$	
$h(m) \leq 3200$	

   b. Compare each row in the table shown. What do you notice about the inequality signs?

   c. Explain your answer from part (b). Use what you know about solving inequalities when you have to multiply or divide by a negative number.

The inequalities that you have solved in this lesson so far have all been two-step inequalities. Let's consider inequalities in different forms.

Allison and John each solved the inequality $5x + 2 \geq 3x - 10$.

Allison 👍

$$5x + 2 \geq 3x - 10$$

$$5x - 3x + 2 \geq 3x - 3x - 10$$

$$2x + 2 \geq -10$$

$$2x + 2 - 2 \geq -10 - 2$$

$$2x \geq -12$$

$$\frac{2x}{2} \geq \frac{-12}{2}$$

$$x \geq -6$$

John 👍

$$5x + 2 \geq 3x - 10$$

$$5x - 5x + 2 \geq 3x - 5x - 10$$

$$2 \geq -2x - 10$$

$$2 + 10 \geq -2x - 10 + 10$$

$$12 \geq -2x$$

$$\frac{12}{-2} \leq \frac{-2x}{-2}$$

$$-6 \leq x$$

1. Describe the process each student used to solve the inequality.

   a. Allison

   b. John

2. How does the process of solving an inequality with variables on both sides compare to the process of solving an equation with variables on both sides?

Curran and Ajani each solved the inequality $-4(x - 6) < 22$.

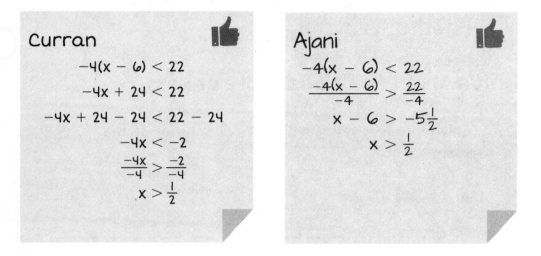

Curran

$$-4(x - 6) < 22$$
$$-4x + 24 < 22$$
$$-4x + 24 - 24 < 22 - 24$$
$$-4x < -2$$
$$\frac{-4x}{-4} > \frac{-2}{-4}$$
$$x > \frac{1}{2}$$

Ajani

$$-4(x - 6) < 22$$
$$\frac{-4(x - 6)}{-4} > \frac{22}{-4}$$
$$x - 6 > -5\frac{1}{2}$$
$$x > \frac{1}{2}$$

3. **Describe the process each student used to solve the inequality.**

   a. **Curran**

   b. **Ajani**

4. **How does the process of solving an inequality using the Distributive Property compare to the process of solving an equation using the Distributive Property?**

TALK the TALK

It's About Solutions, More or Less

1. Solve each inequality and graph the solution on the number line.

    a. $-\frac{2}{3}x \geq 7$

    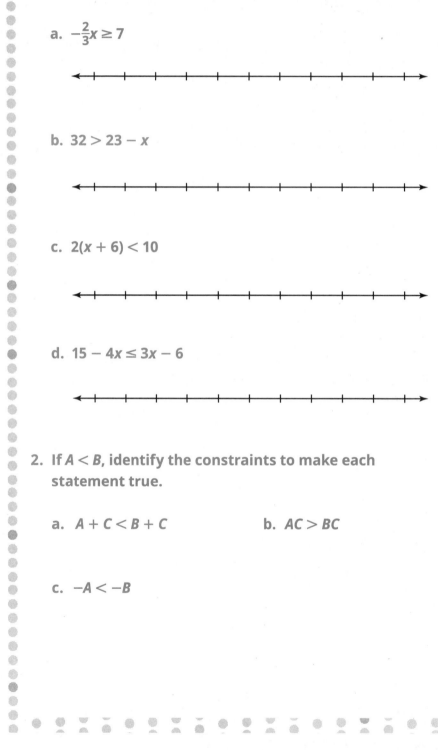

    b. $32 > 23 - x$

    c. $2(x + 6) < 10$

    d. $15 - 4x \leq 3x - 6$

2. If $A < B$, identify the constraints to make each statement true.

    a. $A + C < B + C$ b. $AC > BC$

    c. $-A < -B$

Assignment

Write

Describe how to solve an inequality in your own words.

Remember

The methods for solving linear inequalities are similar to the methods for solving linear equations. Be sure to reverse the direction of the inequality symbol when multiplying or dividing both sides by a negative number.

Practice

1. Chang-Ho is going on a trip to visit some friends from summer camp. He will use $40 for food and entertainment. He will also need money to cover the cost of gas. The price of gas at the time of his trip is $3.25 per gallon.
   a. Write a function to represent the total cost of the trip as a function of the number of gallons used.
   b. Identify the independent and dependent quantities and their units.
   c. Identify the rate of change and the y-intercept. Explain their meanings in terms of the problem situation.
   d. Graph the function representing this situation on a coordinate plane.
   e. Use the graph to determine how many gallons of gas Chang-Ho can buy if he has $170 saved for the trip. Draw an oval on the graph to represent the solution. Then write your answer in words and as an inequality.
   f. Verify the solution set you interpreted from the graph.
   g. Chang-Ho's mom gives him some money for his trip. He now has a total of $220 saved for the trip. What is the greatest number of gallons of gas he can buy before he runs out of money? Show your work and graph your solution on a number line.
   h. If Chang-Ho spent more than $92 on his trip, how much gas could he have bought? Show your work and graph your solution on a number line.
2. Chang-Ho is on his way to visit his friends at camp. Halfway to his destination, he realizes there is a slow leak in one of the tires. He checks the pressure and it is at 26 psi. It appears to be losing 0.1 psi per minute.
   a. Write a function to represent the tire's pressure as a function of time in minutes.
   b. Chang-Ho knows that if the pressure in a tire goes below 22 psi it may cause a tire blowout. What is the greatest amount of time that he can drive before the tire pressure hits 22 psi? Show your work and graph the solution.
3. Solve each inequality for the unknown value.
   a. $13 + 4x > 9$
   b. $3(4 - 5x) > 8x - 149$
   c. $99 - 5d \geq 4d$
   d. $3k - 9 \leq -6k - 225$

Stretch

The Crunch Yum Company orders its nut mixes every month from a distributor. The distributor charges $4.50 per pound of nut mix. There is a handling fee of $8.50 for every order. There is free shipping on any order between $100 and $400. Write a compound inequality to represent the number of pounds of nuts the company can order and get free shipping. Solve the inequality and graph the solution on one number line.

Review

1. Calculate the average rate of change for the linear function using the rate of change formula. Show your work.

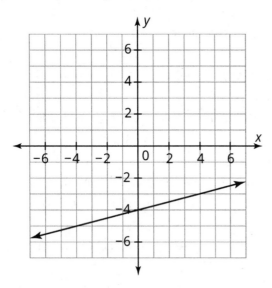

2. Determine whether the table of values represents a linear function. If so, write the function.

x	y
−2	$4\frac{1}{2}$
0	$3\frac{1}{2}$
3	2
6	$\frac{1}{2}$

3. The formula for the area of a trapezoid is $A = \frac{1}{2}h\,(b_1 + b_2)$, where h is its height and b_1 and b_2 are the lengths of each base.
   a. Determine the area of a trapezoid if its height is 10 cm and the lengths of its bases are 22 cm and 18 cm.
   b. Rewrite the equation to solve for b_1.
   c. Determine the length of the other base of a trapezoid if one base measures 10 m, the height is 20 m, and the area of the trapezoid is 600 square meters.

4. The formula for the area of a triangle is $A = \frac{1}{2}bh$. Convert the equation to solve for b.

Don't Confound Your Compounds

Solving and Graphing Compound Inequalities

Warm Up

Graph each inequality on the number line shown.

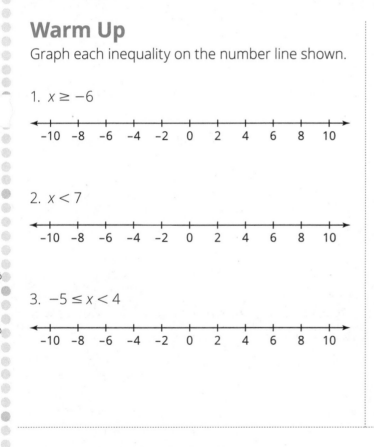

1. $x \geq -6$

2. $x < 7$

3. $-5 \leq x < 4$

Learning Goals

- Write simple and compound inequalities.
- Graph compound inequalities.
- Solve compound inequalities.

Key Terms

- compound inequality
- solution of a compound inequality
- conjunction
- disjunction

You have graphed and solved linear inequalities in two or more steps. How can you determine the solution to a pair of inequalities joined by the words *and* or *or*?

Ask
yourself:

What numbers do you expect to see along the number line?

Human Number Line

In this activity you will form a human number line with the other students in your class.

On the index card provided to you, write down the number of the day on which you were born. Use the numbers on your cards to line up from least to greatest.

Follow your teacher's directions to complete the activity. Then, reflect on what you noticed.

1. **What patterns did you observe on the number line in response to the different directions?**

2. **Why do you think every student raised their card if they were born after the 10th or before the 20th?**

3. **Why do you think no student raised their card if they were born before the 10th and after the 20th?**

Writing Compound Inequalities

GoodSportsBuys.com is an online store that offers discounts on sports equipment to high school athletes. When customers buy items from the site, they must pay the cost of the items as well as a shipping fee. At GoodSportsBuys.com, a shipping fee is added to each order based on the total cost of the items purchased. This table provides the shipping fee categories for GoodSportsBuys.com.

Total Cost of Items	Shipping Fee
$0.01 up to and including $20	$6.50
More than $20 up to and including $50	$9.00
Between $50 and $75	$11.00
From $75 up to, but not including, $100	$12.25
$100 or more	$13.10

You can use inequalities to represent the various shipping fee categories at GoodSportsBuys.com. If you let x represent the total cost of items purchased, you can write an inequality to represent each shipping fee category.

1. **Complete each inequality using an inequality symbol.**

   a. **$6.50 shipping fees:** x ___ **$0.01 and** x ___ **$20**

   b. **$9.00 shipping fees:** x ___ **$20   and** x ___ **$50**

   c. **$11.00 shipping fees:** x ___ **$50   and** x ___ **$75**

   d. **$12.25 shipping fees:** x ___ **$75   and** x ___ **$100**

   e. **$13.10 shipping fees:** x ___ **$100**

2. **Identify the inequalities in Question 1 that are compound inequalities.**

> A **compound inequality** is an inequality that is formed by the union *or*, or the intersection *and*, of two simple inequalities.

Let's consider two examples of compound inequalities.

Worked Example

$$x > 2 \text{ and } x \le 7$$

This inequality is read as "all numbers greater than 2 *and* less than or equal to 7."

This inequality can also be written in the compact form of
$$2 < x \le 7.$$

Worked Example

$$x \le -4 \text{ or } x > 2$$

This inequality is read as "all numbers less than or equal to −4 *or* greater than 2."

Only compound inequalities containing *and* can be written in compact form.

3. **Write the compound inequalities from Question 1 in compact form.**

   a. **$6.50 shipping fees:** _____

   b. **$9.00 shipping fees:** _____

   c. **$11.00 shipping fees:** _____

   d. **$12.25 shipping fees:** _____

Problems with More than One Solution

1. Water becomes non-liquid when it is 32°F or below, or when it is at least 212°F.

   a. Represent this information on the number line.

   b. Write a compound inequality to represent the same information. Define your variable.

   c. Is your inequality always true, sometimes true, or never true? Explain your reasoning.

2. Luke and Logan play for the same baseball team. They practice at the Lions Park baseball field. Luke lives 3 miles from the field, and Logan lives 2 miles from the field.

   a. What is the shortest distance, *d*, that could separate their homes? The longest distance, *d*?

   b. Write a compound inequality to represent all the possible distances that could separate their homes.

   c. Represent the solution on the number line.

   d. Luke bikes to Logan's house. He has been biking for 0.5 mile. What is the greatest number of miles he may have left to bike to reach Logan's house?

Ask
yourself:

Would a diagram be helpful?

Think
about:

How accurate does your answer need to be?

3. Jodi bought a new car with a 14-gallon gas tank. Around town she is able to drive 336 miles on one tank of gas. On her first trip traveling on highways, she drives 448 miles on one tank of gas.

a. Write a compound inequality in compact form that represents how many miles Jodi can drive on a tank of gas. Let m represent the number of miles per gallon of gas.

Ask

yourself:

How can you solve the compound inequality without rewriting it as two simple inequalities?

b. Rewrite the compound inequality as two simple inequalities separated by either *and* or *or*.

c. Solve each simple inequality. Then write the solution in compact form.

d. Explain your solution in terms of the problem situation.

e. Represent the solution on the number line. Describe the shaded region in terms of the problem situation.

Remember, a compound inequality is an inequality that is formed by the union *or*, or the intersection *and*, of two simple inequalities.

The **solution of a compound inequality** in the form $a < x < b$, where a and b are any real numbers, is the part or parts of the solutions that satisfy both of the inequalities. This type of compound inequality is called a **conjunction**. The solution of a compound inequality in the form $x < a$ or $x > b$, where a and b are any real numbers, is the part or parts of the solution that satisfy either inequality. This type of compound inequality is called a **disjunction**.

1. **Classify each solution to all the questions in the previous activity as either a conjunction or disjunction.**

Let's consider two examples for representing the solution of a compound inequality on a number line.

> ### Worked Example
>
> The compound inequality shown involves *and* and is a conjunction.
> $$x \le 1 \text{ and } x > -3$$
> Represent each part above the number line.
>
>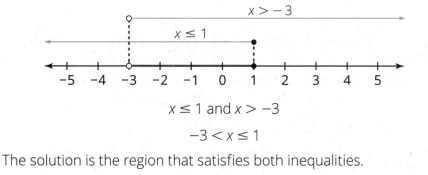
>
> $$x \le 1 \text{ and } x > -3$$
> $$-3 < x \le 1$$
>
> The solution is the region that satisfies both inequalities. Graphically, the solution is the overlapping, or the intersection, of the separate inequalities.

Worked Example

The compound inequality shown involves *or* and is a disjunction.

$$x < -2 \text{ or } x > 1$$

Represent each part above the number line.

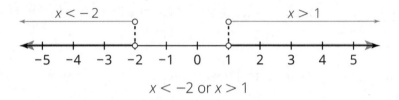

$$x < -2 \text{ or } x > 1$$

The solution is the region that satisfies either inequality. Graphically, the solution is the union, or all the regions, of the separate inequalities.

2. Consider the two worked examples in a different way.

   a. If the compound inequality in the first worked example, $x \le 1$ and $x > -3$, was changed to the disjunction, $x \le 1$ or $x > -3$, how would the solution set change? Explain your reasoning.

   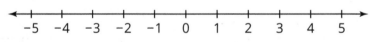

   b. If the compound inequality in the second worked example, $x < -2$ or $x > 1$, was changed to the conjunction, $x < -2$ and $x > 1$, how would the solution set change? Explain your reasoning.

   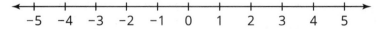

3. Represent the solution to each compound inequality on the number line shown. Then, write the final solution that represents the graph.

   a. $x < 2$ or $x > 3$

b. $-1 \geq x \geq -1$

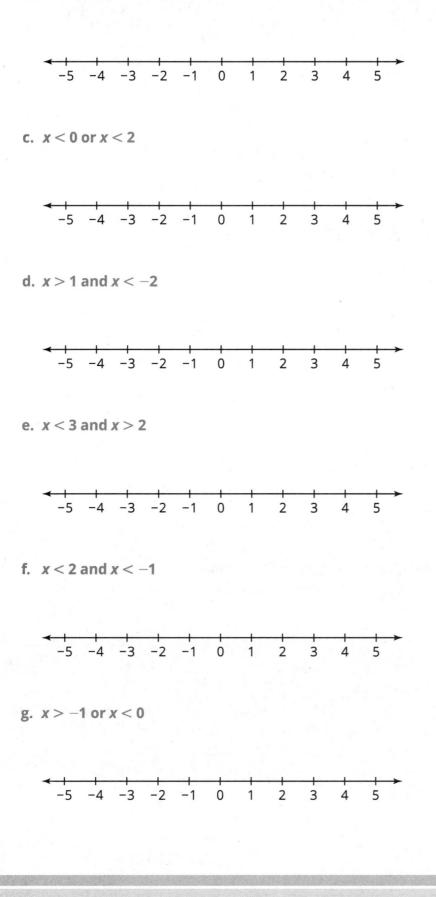

Think
about:

Pay attention to whether the inequality uses *and* or *or*.

c. $x < 0$ or $x < 2$

d. $x > 1$ and $x < -2$

e. $x < 3$ and $x > 2$

f. $x < 2$ and $x < -1$

g. $x > -1$ or $x < 0$

ACTIVITY
4.4

Solving Inequalities in
Compact Form

To solve a conjunction written in compact form, isolate the variable between the two inequality signs, and then graph the resulting statement. To solve a disjunction, simply solve each inequality separately, keeping the word *or* between them, and then graph the resulting statements.

Worked Example

Consider the compound inequality $-3 \leq 2x + 7 < 11$. You can solve this equation in compact form by isolating the variable.

$$-3 \leq 2x + 7 < 11$$
$$-3 - 7 \leq 2x + 7 - 7 < 11 - 7$$
$$-10 \leq 2x < 4$$
$$-\frac{10}{2} \leq \frac{2x}{2} < \frac{4}{2}$$
$$-5 \leq x < 2$$

```
←+——+——+——◆——+——+——+——+——+——+——◇——+——+——+→
 -8  -7  -6  -5  -4  -3  -2  -1   0   1   2   3   4   5
```

---

1. **How is solving a compound inequality in compact form similar to solving a simple inequality? How is it different?**

2. **Solve and graph each compound inequality showing the steps you performed. Then, write the final solution that represents the graph.**

a. $6 < x - 6 \leq 9$

b. $-2 < -x < 6$

c. $-4 \leq -3x + 1 \leq 12$

d. $2x + 7 < 10$ or $-2x + 7 > 10$

e. $\frac{1}{2}x + 3 > 4$ or $-x < 3$

f. $1 + 6x > 11$ or $x - 4 < -5$

TALK the TALK

Make a Match

Match each graph with the correct inequality.

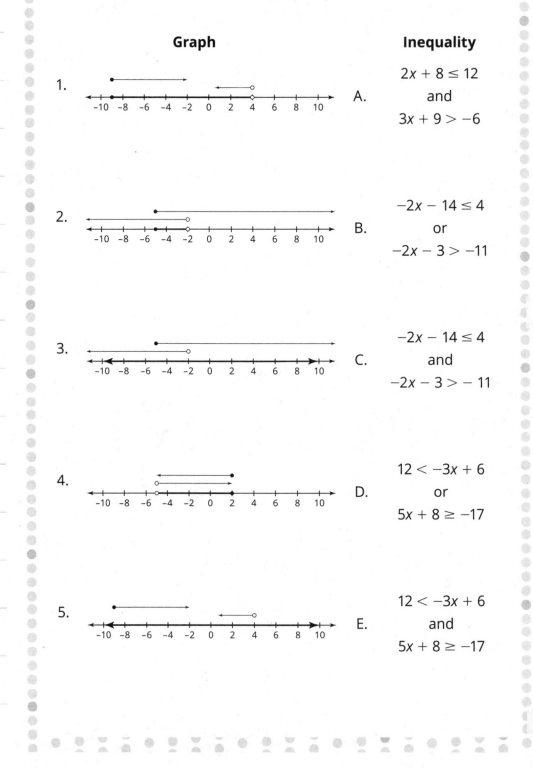

Graph	Inequality

1.

A. $2x + 8 \leq 12$
and
$3x + 9 > -6$

2.

B. $-2x - 14 \leq 4$
or
$-2x - 3 > -11$

3.

C. $-2x - 14 \leq 4$
and
$-2x - 3 > -11$

4.

D. $12 < -3x + 6$
or
$5x + 8 \geq -17$

5.

E. $12 < -3x + 6$
and
$5x + 8 \geq -17$

Assignment

Write

Match each definition to its corresponding term.

1. compound inequality

2. conjunction

3. disjunction

a. a solution of a compound inequality in the form $a < x < b$, where a and b are any real numbers

b. an inequality that is formed by the union *or*, or the intersection *and*, of two simple inequalities

c. a solution of a compound inequality in the form $x < a$ or $x > b$, where a and b are any real numbers

Remember

The solution of a compound inequality in the form $a < x < b$, where a and b are any real numbers, is the part or parts of the solutions that satisfy both of the inequalities. The solution of a compound inequality in the form $x < a$ or $x > b$, where a and b are any real numbers, is the part or parts of the solution that satisfy either inequality.

Practice

1. Taneisha's family has signed up for a new cell phone plan. Taneisha now has a limit on the number of texts she can send or receive each month. She can text no more than 300 times per month.
   a. Write a compound inequality to represent the number of texts, n, that Taneisha can send in a month.
   b. Write the compound inequality in compact form.
   c. Graph the inequality. Describe your number line representation.
2. John owns a 50-acre apple orchard. Among his many concerns during the growing season is the amount of rainfall. Unfavorable conditions such as drought and flooding will affect tree production. John does not want rainfall amounts to be less than 10 inches or more than 50 inches.
   a. Represent the undesirable rainfall amounts on a number line.
   b. Write a compound inequality to represent the same information. Define your variable.
3. At John's apple orchard, the profit he will make depends on the number of bushels he grows and sells. He makes $25 per bushel but must subtract $300,000 for costs associated with growing the trees in order to calculate his profit.
   a. Write an expression to represent the profit John will make. Let b represent the number of bushels he will produce and sell.

b. John must make at least $80,000 to pay the bills, but he does not want to make more than $250,000 because it will put him in a higher tax bracket. Write a compound inequality that represents the amount of profit John can make.

c. Solve the compound inequality. Show your work.

d. Graph the solution to the compound inequality. Describe the solution region in terms of the problem situation.

4. Solve each compound inequality.

   a. $-6x + 1 > -5$ and $3x + 4 \geq 1$

   b. $1 \leq 3j + 4 < 13$

   c. $2k - 4 \geq 2$ or $-4k + 6 > 3$

   d. $-10 < 4t - 2 \leq 10$

Stretch

A company produces T-shirts. There is a fixed monthly cost of $500 to produce the T-shirts and a cost of $4.50 per T-shirt for production. The company plans on selling the T-shirts for $11.50 each.

Write an expression to determine the cost to produce x t-shirts in a month. The company would like the profit next month to be at least $2,000 but no more than $10,000 for tax purposes. Write and solve a compound inequality that represents the amount of profit the company can make. Describe the solution region in terms of the problem situation.

Review

1. Consider the explicit formula $a_n = \frac{3}{2} + \frac{1}{2}(n - 1)$.

   a. Write the formula in function notation.

   b. Graph the function on a coordinate plane. Label the first 3 values of the sequence on the graph.

2. Joan received $100 in gift cards for an online music store. Each time she buys a new song it costs $1.29. She has already bought 10 songs. Write an inequality that models this situation. Then determine the number of songs she can buy and not run out of gift card money.

3. Evaluate each function for the given value of x.

   a. $f(x) = 3x + 2(8 - x)$ for $x = -2$

   b. $f(x) = -\frac{2}{9}x - 4\left(\frac{1}{8}x + 3\right)$ for $x = 3$

Solving Linear Equations and Inequalities Summary

KEY TERMS

- solution
- no solution
- infinite solutions
- literal equation
- solve an inequality

- compound inequality
- solution of a compound inequality
- conjunction
- disjunction

LESSON 1 Strike a Balance

A **solution** to an equation is any variable value that makes the equation true. Solving equations requires the use of number properties and properties of equality. The Properties of Equality state that if an operation is performed on both sides of the equation, to all terms of the equation, the equation maintains its equality. When the Properties of Equality are applied to an equation, the transformed equation will have the same solution as the original equation.

A linear equation in the form $y = ax + b$ can have one solution, **infinite solutions**, or **no solution**.

Linear equations with infinite solutions are created by equating two equivalent expressions.

$$2x + 6 = 2(x + 3)$$
$$= (2 \cdot x) + (2 \cdot 3)$$
$$= 2x + 6$$

Linear equations with no solution are created by equating expressions of the form $ax + b$ with the same value for a and different values for b.

$$4x + 2 = 4x + 5$$
$$4x - 4x + 2 = 4x - 4x + 5$$
$$2 \neq 5$$

Linear equations with the solution $x = 0$ are created by equating expressions of the form $ax + b$ with different values for a and the same value for b.

$$2x + 3 = 5x + 3$$
$$2x - 2x + 3 = 5x - 2x + 3$$
$$3 = 3x + 3$$
$$3 - 3 = 3x + 3 - 3$$
$$0 = 3x$$
$$0 = x$$

It's Literally About Literal Equations

There are three useful forms of linear equations.

General Form

$$y = ax + b$$

Factored Form

$$y = a(x - c)$$

Standard Form

$$Ax + By = C$$

In general and factored form, the values of a, b, and c can be any real numbers. In standard form, however, there are constraints on the variables: A must be a positive integer, and A and B cannot both be 0.

It is often necessary to change between forms, as the structure of each form reveals different key characteristics of the equation, such as the slope and x- and y-intercepts. Remember, to convert to general form from standard form, solve for y. To convert to standard form from general form, isolate both variables on the same side of the equation and the constant on the other side of the equation.

Literal equations are equations in which the variables represent specific measures. Literal equations are most often seen when studying formulas. These literal equations can be manipulated in order to solve for one specific variable.

For example, a common literal equation is the formula for converting degrees Fahrenheit to degrees Celsius, $C = \frac{5}{9}(F - 32)$. You can use the Properties of Equality to rewrite the equation to convert degrees Celsius to degrees Fahrenheit, $F = \frac{9}{5}C + 32$.

© Carnegie Learning, Inc.

Not All Statements are Made Equal

To **solve an inequality**, first write a function to represent the problem situation. Then write the function as an inequality based on the independent quantity. To determine the solution, identify the values of the variable that make the inequality true. The objective when solving an inequality is similar to the objective when solving an equation: isolate the variable on one side of the inequality symbol. Finally, interpret the meaning of the solution.

For example, consider the situation in which Cameron has $25 in his gift fund that he is going to use to buy graduation gifts. Graduation is 9 weeks away. If he would like to have at least $70 to buy gifts, how much should he save each week?

The function is $f(x) = 25 + 9x$, so the inequality is $25 + 9x \geq 70$.

$$25 + 9x \geq 70$$
$$9x \geq 45$$
$$\frac{9x}{9} \geq \frac{45}{9}$$
$$x \geq 5$$

Cameron needs to save at least $5 each week to meet his goal.

When you divide each side of an inequality by a negative number, the inequality sign reverses. For example, consider the inequality $250 - 9.25x < 398$.

$$250 - 9.25x < 398$$
$$-9.25x < 148$$
$$-\frac{9.25x}{9.25} > \frac{148}{-9.25}$$
$$x > -16$$

Don't Confound Your Compounds

A **compound inequality** is an inequality that is formed by the union, "or," or the intersection, "and," of two simple inequalities. Compound inequalities containing "and" can be written in compact form.

For example, consider the situation in which you pay a discounted rate if you are 12 years old or less or 65 years old or more. The solution is the union of two simple inequalities.

$$x < 12 \text{ or } x > 65$$

The intersection of two simple inequalities is used for the situation in which you pay the full rate if you are more than 12 years old and less than 65 years old.

$$x < 12 \text{ and } x > 65; \ 12 < x < 65$$

The **solution of a compound inequality** in the form $a < x < b$, where a and b are any real numbers, is the part or parts of the solutions that satisfy both of the inequalities. This type of compound inequality is called a **conjunction**. The solution of a compound inequality in the form $x < a$ or $x > b$ where a and b are any real numbers, is the part or parts of the solution that satisfy either inequality. This type of compound inequality is called a **disjunction**.

Graphically, the solution to a disjunction is all of the regions that satisfy the separate inequalities.

$x < 4 \text{ or } x > 8$

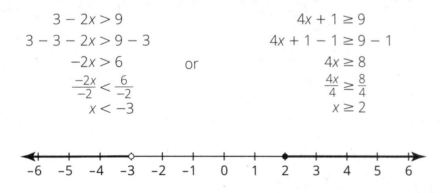

Graphically, the solution to a conjunction is the intersection of the separate inequalities.

$4 < x < 8$

To solve a compound inequality written in compact form, isolate the variable between the two inequality signs, and then graph the resulting statement.

$-3 \leq 4x + 5 < 21$
$-3 - 5 \leq 4x + 5 - 5 < 21 - 5$
$-8 \leq 4x < 16$
$\dfrac{-8}{4} \leq \dfrac{4x}{4} < \dfrac{16}{4}$
$-2 \leq x < 4$

To solve an inequality involving "or," solve each inequality separately, keeping the word "or" between them, and then graph the resulting statements.

$3 - 2x > 9$ $4x + 1 \geq 9$
$3 - 3 - 2x > 9 - 3$ $4x + 1 - 1 \geq 9 - 1$
$-2x > 6$ or $4x \geq 8$
$\dfrac{-2x}{-2} < \dfrac{6}{-2}$ $\dfrac{4x}{4} \geq \dfrac{8}{4}$
$x < -3$ $x \geq 2$

Systems of Equations and Inequalities

Multiple lines (a system of equations) can define all sorts of regions (systems of inequalities). Imagine graphing this tile pattern!

Module 2: Exploring Constant Change

TOPIC 3: SYSTEMS OF EQUATIONS AND INEQUALITIES

In this topic, students begin by writing systems of linear equations and solving them graphically and algebraically using substitution. They then move on to solve systems of linear equations using the linear combinations method. Students consider linear inequalities in two variables and learn that their solutions are represented as half-planes on a coordinate plane. They then graph two linear inequalities on the same plane and identify the solution set as the intersection of the corresponding half-planes. Finally, students synthesize their understanding of systems by encountering problems that can be solved by using either a system of equations or a system of inequalities.

Where have we been?

Coming into this topic, students know that every point on the graph of an equation represents a value that makes the equation true. They have learned that the point of intersection of two graphs provides x- and y-values that make both equations true. Students have written systems of linear equations and have solved them either graphically or algebraically using substitution.

Where are we going?

Knowing how to solve systems of linear equations prepares students to solve systems that include nonlinear equations. In later courses, students may encounter more advanced methods, such as matrices or Cramer's Rule, to solve systems of equations with more than two variables and more than two equations.

Linear Combinations

The linear combinations method is a process used to solve a system of equations by adding two equations together, resulting in an equation with one variable.

For example, to solve the system of equations shown, both equations can be rewritten as equivalent equations with coefficients that are additive inverses. Then, the two equations can be added together to eliminate one of the variables. After solving for the remaining variable, substitution can be used to determine the value of the other variable.

$$\begin{cases} 4x + 2y = 3 \\ 5x + 3y = 4 \end{cases}$$

$$-5(4x + 2y) = -5(3)$$
$$4(5x + 3y) = 4(4)$$

$$-20x - 10y = -15$$
$$\underline{20x + 12y = 16}$$
$$2y = 1$$
$$y = \frac{1}{2}$$

$$4x + 2\left(\frac{1}{2}\right) = 3$$
$$4x + 1 = 3$$
$$4x = 2$$
$$x = \frac{1}{2}$$

$$\left(\frac{1}{2}, \frac{1}{2}\right)$$

Optimizing

A coffee company produces just two flavors of coffee: cinnamon creme and regular dark roast. The company expects a demand of at least 100 bags of cinnamon creme and 80 bags of dark roast each day. Yet, no more than 200 bags of cinnamon creme and 170 bags of dark roast can be made every day. To satisfy a shipping contract, a total of at least 200 bags of coffee must be shipped each day.

If each bag of cinnamon creme sold results in a $2 loss, but each bag of dark roast sold produces a $5 profit, how many bags of each should be made every day to maximize profits?

Companies solve problems like this every day, and they do so using systems of equations and inequalities.

Talking Points

Systems of equations is an important topic to know about for college admissions tests.

Here is a sample question:

If (x, y) is a solution to the system of equations, what is the value of $x - y$?

$$2x - 3y = -14$$
$$3x - 2y = -6$$

Multiplying the first equation by 3 and the second equation by −2 gives

$$6x - 9y = -42$$
$$-6x + 4y = 12$$

Then, adding the equations gives

$$-5y = -30$$
$$y = 6$$

The value of y can be substituted in one of the equations to get the value of x.
The solution is (4, 6), so $x - y = -2$.

Key Terms

consistent system
Systems that have one or many solutions are called consistent systems.

inconsistent system
Systems with no solution are called inconsistent systems.

half-plane
The graph of a linear inequality in two variables is a half-plane, or half of a coordinate plane.

boundary line
A boundary line, determined by an inequality, divides the plane into two half-planes and the inequality symbol indicates which half-plane contains all the solutions.

Double the Fun

Introduction to Systems of Equations

Warm Up

Determine an ordered pair that represents a solution to each equation.

1. $4x + 7y = 24$

2. $5x - 2y = -6$

3. $\frac{1}{2}x + \frac{3}{4}y = 10$

Learning Goals

- Write equations in standard form.
- Determine the intercepts of an equation in standard form.
- Use intercepts to graph an equation.
- Write a system of equations to represent a problem context.
- Solve systems of linear equations exactly and approximately.
- Interpret the solution to a system of equations in terms of a problem situation.
- Use slope and y-intercept to determine whether the system of two linear equations has one solution, no solution, or infinite solutions.

Key Terms

- system of linear equations
- consistent systems
- inconsistent systems

You have examined different linear functions and solved for unknown values. How can you solve problems that require two linear functions? How many solutions exist when you consider two functions at the same time?

Ticket Tabulation

The Marshall High School Athletic Association sells tickets for the weekly football games. Students pay $5 and adults pay $10 for a ticket. The athletic association needs to raise $3000 selling tickets to send the team to an out-of-town tournament.

1. **Write an equation to represent this situation.**

2. **What combination of student and adult ticket sales would achieve the athletic association's goal?**

3. **Compare your combination of ticket sales with your classmates'. Did you all get the same answer? Explain why or why not.**

Consider the goal of the athletic association described in the previous activity. Let *s* represent the number of student tickets sold, and let *a*, represent the number of adult tickets sold. Written in standard form, the equation that represents the situation is $5s + 10a = 3000$.

One efficient way to graph a linear function in standard form is to use *x*- and *y*-intercepts. You can calculate the *x*-intercept by substituting $y = 0$ and solving for *x*. You can calculate the *y*-intercept by substituting $x = 0$ and solving for *y*.

1. **Use the *x*-intercept and *y*-intercept to graph the equation.**

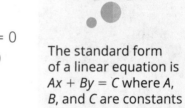

Remember:

The standard form of a linear equation is $Ax + By = C$ where *A*, *B*, and *C* are constants and *A* and *B* are not both zero.

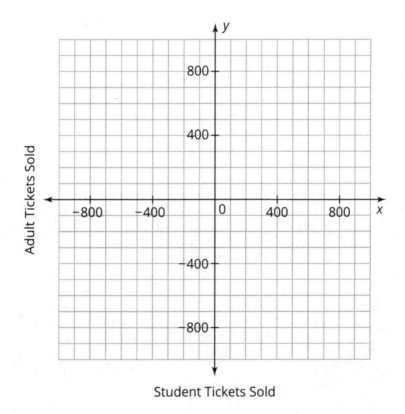

Student Tickets Sold

Ask yourself:

Which quantity is represented on each axis?

2. **Determine the domain and range of each.**

   a. **the mathematical function**

   b. **the function modeling the real-world situation**

3. Explain what each intercept means in terms of the problem situation.

4. Identify the slope of the function. Interpret its meaning in terms of the problem situation.

Ask yourself:

What does each point on the graph of an equation represent?

5. How can you use the graph to determine a combination of ticket sales to meet the goal of $3000?

6. Felino graphed the equation $5s + 10a = 3000$ in a different way. Explain why Felino's graph is correct.

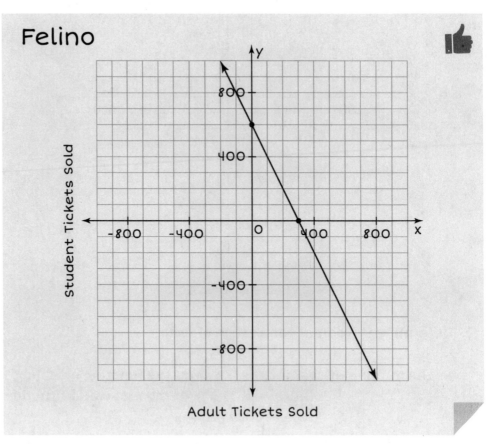

7. Use Felino's graph to describe the domain and range of each.

   a. the mathematical function   b. the function modeling the
                                                real-world situation

8. Explain what each intercept means in terms of the
problem situation.

9. Identify the slope of the function. Interpret its meaning in
terms of the problem situation.

10. Compare the domain and range of the two functions that
model the real-world situation. What do you notice?

11. Compare the x-intercepts and the y-intercepts of the two
graphs. What do you notice?

12. Is there a way to determine the total amount of money
collected from either graph? Explain why or why not.

ACTIVITY 1.2

Determining the Solution to a System of Linear Equations

The athletic director of the Marshall High School Athletic Association says that 450 total tickets were sold to the home game.

1. **Write an equation that represents this situation. Let *s* represent the number of student tickets sold, and let *a* represent the number of adult tickets sold.**

The coordinate planes shown already contain the function that models the earnings from ticket sales.

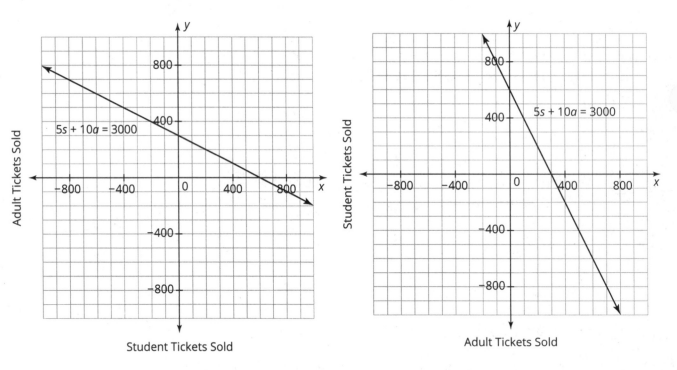

2. **Use *x*- and *y*-intercepts to graph the function modeling the total number of tickets sold on each coordinate plane.**

3. If the athletic association reached its goal of $3000 in ticket sales, how many of each type of ticket was sold? Is there more than one solution?

Remember:

According to the situation, 450 tickets were sold to the game.

4. Use technology to locate the exact point of intersection. Explain the process you used.

5. Justify algebraically that your solution is correct.

The two graphed equations share a relationship between quantities. Each equation describes a relationship between the number of adult tickets sold and the number of student tickets sold. In one, the relationship is defined by the cost of each ticket and the total amount collected. In the second, the relationship is defined by the total number of tickets sold. The two equations together form a *system of linear equations*. When two or more linear equations define a relationship between quantities, they form a **system of linear equations**.

© Carnegie Learning, Inc.

Marcus and Phillip are in the Robotics Club. They are both saving money to buy materials to build a new robot.

Marcus opens a new bank account. He deposits $25 that he won at a robotics competition. He also plans on depositing $10 a week that he earns from tutoring. Phillip decides he wants to save money as well. He already has $40 saved from mowing lawns over the summer. He plans to also save $10 a week from his allowance.

1. **Write equations to represent the amount of money Marcus saves and the amount of money Phillip saves.**

2. **Use your equations to predict when Marcus and Phillip will have the same amount of money saved.**

You can prove your prediction by solving and graphing a system of linear equations.

3. **Analyze the equations in your system.**

   a. **How do the slopes compare? Describe what this means in terms of this problem situation.**

   b. **How do the *y*-intercepts compare? Describe what this means in terms of this problem situation.**

© Carnegie Learning, Inc.

4. Determine the solution of the system of linear equations algebraically and graphically.

   a. Use the substitution method to determine the intersection point.

   b. Does your solution make sense? Describe what this means in terms of the problem situation.

   c. Predict what the graph of this system will look like. Explain your reasoning.

   d. Graph both equations on the coordinate plane.

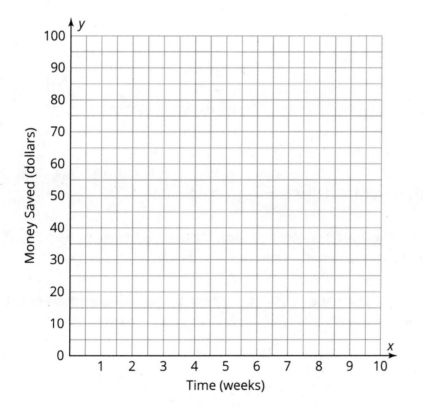

5. Analyze the graph you created.

   a. Describe the relationship between the graphs.

   b. Does this linear system have a solution?
      Explain your reasoning.

6. Was your prediction in Question 2 correct? Explain how you algebraically and graphically proved your prediction.

Tonya is also in the Robotics Club and has heard about Marcus's and Phillip's savings plans. She wants to be able to buy her new materials before Phillip, so she opens her own bank account. She is able to deposit $40 in her account that she has saved from her job as a waitress. Each week she also deposits $4 from her tips.

7. Use equations and graphs to determine when Tonya and Phillip have saved the same amount of money.

   a. Write a linear system to represent the total amount of money Tonya and Phillip have saved after a certain amount of time.

Remember:

Don't forget to define your variables!

© Carnegie Learning, Inc.

b. Graph the linear system on the coordinate plane.

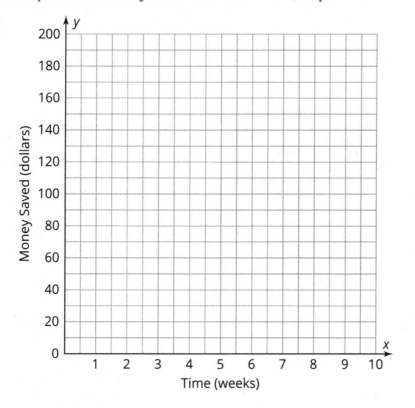

c. Do the graphs intersect? If so, describe the meaning in terms of this problem situation.

Phillip and Tonya went on a shopping spree this weekend and spent all their savings except for $40 each. Phillip is still saving $10 a week from his allowance. Tonya now deposits her tips twice a week. On Tuesdays she deposits $4 and on Saturdays she deposits $6.

8. Phillip claims he is still saving more each week than Tonya.

a. Do you think Phillip's claim is true? Explain your reasoning.

b. How can you prove your prediction?

9. Prove your prediction algebraically and graphically.

   a. Write a new linear system to represent the total amount of money each friend has after a certain amount of time.

   b. Graph the linear system on the coordinate plane.

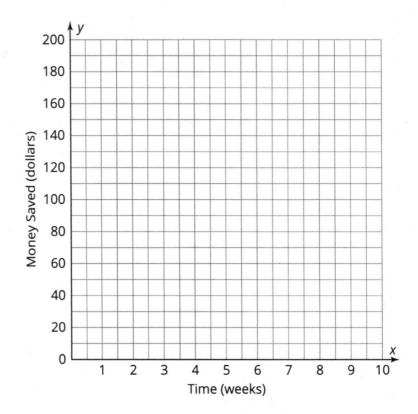

10. **Analyze the graph.**

   a. **Describe the relationship between the graphs. What does this mean in terms of this problem situation?**

   b. **Algebraically prove the relationship you stated in part (a).**

   c. **How does this solution prove the relationship? Explain your reasoning.**

11. **Was Phillip's claim that he is still saving more than Tonya a true statement? Explain why or why not.**

TALK the TALK

Beating the System

1. How does solving a linear system in two variables compare to solving an equation in one variable?

A system of equations may have one unique solution, no solution, or infinite solutions. Systems that have one or many solutions are called **consistent systems.** Systems with no solution are called **inconsistent systems.**

2. Complete the table.

System of Two Linear Equations	Consistent Systems		Inconsistent Systems
Description of y-Intercepts	y-intercepts can be the same or different	y-intercepts are the same	y-intercepts are different
Number of Solutions			
Description of Graph			

3. Explain why the *x*- and *y*-coordinates of the points where the graphs of a system intersect are solutions.

Assignment

Write

Define each term in your own words.

1. consistent systems
2. inconsistent systems

Remember

When two or more equations define a relationship between quantities, they form a system of linear equations. The point of intersection of a graphed system of linear equations is the solution to both equations. A system of linear equations can have one solution, no solution, or infinite solutions.

Practice

1. Mr. Johanssen gives his class 50-question multiple choice tests. Each correct answer is worth 2 points, while a half point is deducted for each incorrect answer. If the student does not answer a question, that question does not get any points.

   a. A student needs to earn 80 points on the test in order to keep an A grade for the semester. Write an equation in standard form that represents the situation. Identify 3 combinations of correct and incorrect answers that satisfy the equation.

   b. Determine the x- and y-intercepts of the equation and use them to graph the equation. Explain what each intercept means in terms of the problem situation.

2. Wesley owns a dairy farm. In the morning, it takes him 0.3 hour to set up for milking the cows. Once he has set up, it takes Wesley 0.2 hour to milk each cow by hand. He is contemplating purchasing a milking machine in hopes that it will speed up the milking process. The milking machine he is considering will take 0.4 hour to set up each morning and takes 0.05 hour to milk each cow.

   a. Write a system of linear equations that represents the total amount of time Wesley will spend milking the cows using the two different methods.

   b. Graph both equations on a coordinate plane.

   c. Estimate the point of intersection. Explain how you determined your answer.

   d. What does the point of intersection represent in this problem situation?

   e. Verify your answer to part (c) by solving the system algebraically.

   f. Does the solution make sense in terms of this problem situation? Explain your reasoning.

   g. Is this system of equations consistent or inconsistent? Explain your reasoning.

3. Identify whether each system is consistent or inconsistent. Explain your reasoning.

   a. $\begin{cases} -3x + 4y = 3 \\ -12x + 16y = 8 \end{cases}$
   b. $\begin{cases} 7x + 3y = 0 \\ 14x + 6y = 0 \end{cases}$
   c. $\begin{cases} 6x + y = 1 \\ -6x - 4y = -4 \end{cases}$

Stretch

Solve the system of equations shown. Explain your reasoning.

$$\begin{cases} 3x + 5y = 18 \\ \qquad\quad y = |x - 4| \end{cases}$$

Review

1. Solve and graph each compound inequality.

   a. $10 < x - 10 \leq 25$ 　　　　　　b. $2x - 11 \leq -5$ or $\frac{1}{3}x + 5 \geq 2$

2. Solve the equation and check your solution.

$$\tfrac{3}{4}x - 11 = 4 + \left(-\tfrac{3}{4}x + 3\right)$$

3. Consider the equation $\frac{2}{5}x - 2y = 14$. Write the equation in general form and identify the slope and y-intercept.

4. Determine the linear regression equation for each data set. Which regression equation is the better fit? Explain your reasoning.

Set A	
x	y
1	12
2	11
5	30
7	39
10	50

Set B	
x	y
12	3
10	9
8	11
5	14
0	0

The Elimination Round

Using Linear Combinations to Solve a System of Linear Equations

Warm Up

Determine the additive inverse for each expression.

1. 4

2. x

3. $20x$

4. $-9x$

5. $78.5x$

Learning Goals

- Write a system of equations to represent a problem context.
- Solve a system of equations algebraically using linear combinations.
- Interpret the solution to a system of equations in terms of a problem situation.

Key Term

- linear combinations method

You have solved a system of linear equations graphically and algebraically, using the substitution method. What are other algebraic strategies for solving systems of equations?

Comic-Con(line)

There are a total of 324 people who joined the Comic Gurus group on a social media site. Female group members outnumber males by 34.

1. **Use reasoning to determine the number of males and females who joined the Comic Gurus.**

2. **How can you check that your solution is correct?**

Consider the scenario from the Getting Started. Let's explore an algebraic strategy to determine a solution.

1. **Write the system that represents the problem situation. Use *x* to represent the female members of the group, and use *y* to represent the male members of the group. Write the equations in standard form.**

Chloe and Mara used different strategies to solve the system of equations in a similar way. Analyze each student's reasoning.

Chloe
I can use the substitution method to solve this system.

$$x + y = 324$$
$$x - y = 34 \rightarrow x = y + 34 \qquad x = 145 + 34$$
$$\qquad\qquad x = 179$$
$$(y + 34) + y = 324$$
$$2y + 34 = 324$$
$$2y = 290$$
$$y = 145$$

Remember:

As long as you maintain equality you can rewrite equations any way you want.

Mara
You can eliminate one of the quantities by adding the two equations together.

$$\begin{array}{r} x + y = 324 \\ + \; x - y = \;\; 34 \\ \hline 2x = 358 \\ x = 179 \end{array} \qquad \begin{array}{l} 179 + y = 324 \\ y = 145 \end{array}$$

2. **Explain why each student is correct in their reasoning.**

3. **Examine the structure of the system. What characteristic of the system made Mara's strategy efficient?**

4. **Identify the solution to the linear system as an ordered pair. Then interpret the solution in terms of this problem situation.**

© Carnegie Learning, Inc.

The algebraic method used by Mara to solve the linear system is called the linear combinations method. The **linear combinations method** is a process used to solve a system of equations by adding two equations together, resulting in an equation with one variable. You can then determine the value of that variable and use it to determine the value of the other variable.

5. **Solve each system of equations using the linear combinations method.**

a. $\begin{cases} -4x + y = 10 \\ -2x - y = -1 \end{cases}$

b. $\begin{cases} -\frac{1}{2}x + 5y = -6 \\ \frac{1}{2}x + y = -6 \end{cases}$

© Carnegie Learning, Inc.

Using Additive Inverses to Combine Linear Systems

In the system of equations from the previous activity, one of the variables in both equations has coefficients that are additive inverses. What if a system doesn't have variables that are additive inverses? Let's use the strategy of linear combinations to solve other systems.

Worked Example

Consider this system of equations: $\begin{cases} 7x + 2y = 24 \\ 4x + y = 15 \end{cases}$.

$7x + 2y = 24$
$-2(4x + y) = -2(15)$ Multiply the second equation by a constant that results in coefficients that are additive inverses for one of the variables.

$7x + 2y = 24$
$+ \ -8x - 2y = -30$ Now that the y-values are additive inverses, you can solve this linear system for x.
———————————
$-x = -6$
$x = 6$

$7(6) + 2y = 24$ Substitute the value for x into one of the
$42 + 2y = 24$ equations to determine the value for y.
$2y = -18$
$y = -9$

The solution to the system of linear equations is $(6, -9)$.

Remember:

Two numbers with a sum of zero are called additive inverses.

1. **In the worked example, only one equation needs to be rewritten to solve using the linear combinations method. Why?**

Ask
yourself:

How can you solve the system of equations by transforming the first equation instead of the second?

Now, let's consider a system where both equations need to be rewritten.

Worked Example

$$\begin{cases} 4x + 2y = 3 \\ 5x + 3y = 4 \end{cases}$$

$3(4x + 2y) = 3(3)$ Multiply each equation by a constant that
$-2(5x + 3y) = -2(4)$ results in coefficients that are additive
                        inverses for one of the variables

$12x + 6y = 9$
$-10x - 6y = -8$

Ask yourself:

If you multiply both sides of an equation by the same number, is the equation still true?

2. Determine the solution for the linear system shown in the second worked example.

3. How could you have solved this system by creating *x*-values that are additive inverses?

4. Describe the first step needed to solve each system using the linear combinations method. Identify the variable that will be solved for when you add the equations.

a. $\begin{cases} 5x + 2y = 10 \\ 3x + 2y = 6 \end{cases}$

b. $\begin{cases} x + 3y = 15 \\ 5x + 2y = 7 \end{cases}$

c. $\begin{cases} 4x + 3y = 12 \\ 3x + 2y = 4 \end{cases}$

5. **Analyze each system. How would you rewrite the system to solve for one variable? Explain your reasoning.**

a. $\begin{cases} \frac{1}{2}x - 5y = -45 \\ -\frac{1}{2}x + 10y = -20 \end{cases}$

b. $\begin{cases} 4x + 3y = 24 \\ 3x + y = -2 \end{cases}$

c. $\begin{cases} 3x + 5y = 17 \\ 2x + 3y = 11 \end{cases}$

d. $\begin{cases} 6x + 3y = 5 \\ 2x + y = 1 \end{cases}$

e. $\begin{cases} x + 2y = -6 \\ 2x + 4y = -12 \end{cases}$

Let It Snow Resort offers two winter specials: the Get-Away Special and the Extended Stay Special. The Get-Away Special offers two nights of lodging and four meals for $270. The Extended Stay Special offers three nights of lodging and eight meals for $435. Determine what Let It Snow charges per night of lodging and per meal.

1. **Write the system of linear questions that represents the problem situation. Let *n* represent the cost for one night of lodging at the resort and *m* represent the cost for each meal. Write the equations in standard form.**

2. **How are these equations the same? How are these equations different?**

3. **Solve the system comparing the two winter specials.**

4. Interpret the solution of the linear system in the problem situation.

5. Check your solution algebraically.

6. Is the Extended Stay Special the better deal? Explain why or why not.

The School Spirit Club is making beaded friendship bracelets with the school colors to sell in the school store. The bracelets are black and orange and come in two lengths: 5 inches and 7 inches. The club has enough beads to make a total of 84 bracelets. So far, they have made 49 bracelets, which represents $\frac{1}{2}$ the number of 5-inch bracelets plus $\frac{3}{4}$ the number of 7-inch bracelets they plan to make and sell. Determine how many 5-inch and 7-inch bracelets the club plans to make.

1. **Let *x* represent the number of 5-inch bracelets, and let *y* represent the number of 7-inch bracelets. Write a system of equations in standard form to represent this problem situation.**

2. **Karyn says that the first step to solve this system is to multiply the second equation by the least common denominator (LCD) of the fractions. Jacob says that the first step is to multiply the first equation by $-\frac{1}{2}$. Who is correct? Explain your reasoning.**

3. Rewrite the equation containing fractions as an equivalent equation without fractions.

4. Determine the solution to the system of equations by using linear combinations and check your answer.

5. Interpret the solution of the linear system in terms of this problem situation.

TALK the TALK

There's a Method in My Madness

You have used three different methods for solving systems of equations: graphing, substitution, and linear combinations.

1. **Describe how to use each method and the characteristics of the system that makes this method most appropriate.**

    a. **Graphing Method:**

    b. **Substitution Method:**

    c. **Linear Combinations Method:**

Assignment

Write

Explain how you would combine the two equations to solve for x and y. Use the following terms in your explanation: *linear combination* and *additive inverses*.

$$3x + 2y = -25$$
$$x - 4y = 5$$

Remember

You can use the linear combinations method to solve a system of equations by adding two equations together, resulting in an equation with one variable. You can then determine the value of that variable and use it to determine the value of the other variable.

Practice

1. The two high schools, Jefferson Hills East and Jefferson Hills West, are taking field trips to the state capital. A total of 408 students from Jefferson Hills East will be going in 3 vans and 6 buses. A total of 516 students from Jefferson Hills West will be going in 6 vans and 7 buses. Each van has the same number of passengers and each bus has the same number of passengers.

   a. Write a system of equations that represents this problem situation. Let x represent the number of students in each van, and let y represent the number of students in each bus.

   b. How are the equations in the system the same? How are they different?

   c. Describe the first step needed to solve the system using the linear combinations method. Identify the variable that will be eliminated as well as the variable that will be solved for when you add the equations.

   d. Solve the system of equations using the linear combinations method. Show your work.

   e. Interpret the solution of the linear system in terms of the problem situation.

   f. Check your solution algebraically.

2. Solve each system of linear equations.

   a. $\begin{cases} 3x + y = 9 \\ 7x + y = 32 \end{cases}$
   b. $\begin{cases} 5x - 8y = 25 \\ -x + 4y = -8 \end{cases}$
   c. $\begin{cases} \frac{2}{3}x + \frac{1}{4}y = 18 \\ \frac{1}{6}x - \frac{3}{8}y = -6 \end{cases}$
   d. $\begin{cases} 5x + 4y = -14 \\ 3x + 6y = 6 \end{cases}$

Stretch

Use linear combinations to solve the given system of three equations in three variables. Show your work.

$$\begin{cases} 3x + y + 3z = -2 \\ 6x + 2y + 9z = 5 \\ -2x - y - z = 3 \end{cases}$$

Review

1. The drama department sold a total of 360 tickets to their Friday and Saturday night shows. They sold three times as many tickets for Saturday's show than for Friday's show.

   a. Write a system of equations to represent this scenario.

   b. Graph the system of equations on a coordinate plane.

   c. How many tickets were sold for Friday? Saturday? Is there more than one solution?

   d. Justify algebraically that your solution is correct.

2. Analyze the data in the table.

   a. Write the equation of the regression line for the data.

   b. Predict the population after 20 years. Round your answer to the nearest whole number.

Number of years	Population
1	240
2	360
3	280
5	500
6	625
7	830
8	720
9	813
10	900

© Carnegie Learning, Inc.

Throwing Shade

3

Graphing Inequalities in Two Variables

Warm Up

Determine if each point is a solution to $y > x$, $y < x$, or $y = x$.

1. $(8, -2)$

2. $(0, 7)$

3. $(-1, -1)$

4. $(-4, -3)$

5. $(9, 9)$

6. $(-3, -10)$

Learning Goals

- Write an inequality in two variables.
- Graph an inequality in two variables on a coordinate plane.
- Determine whether a solid or dashed boundary line is used to graph an inequality on a coordinate plane.
- Interpret the solutions of inequalities mathematically and in the context of real-world problems.

Key Terms

- half-plane
- boundary line

You have graphed linear inequalities in one variable. What does the graph of a linear inequality in two variables look like? How does it compare to the graph of a linear equation?

Making a Statement

Consider each solution statement.

$$x = 2$$

$$x < 2 \qquad\qquad x \leq 2$$

$$x > 2 \qquad\qquad x \geq 2$$

1. Compare the solution statements. What does each one mean?

2. Choose a solution statement and write a scenario to represent it. Then, modify the scenario so the resulting interpretation is one of the other four solution statements.

1. Coach Purvis is analyzing the scoring patterns of players on his basketball team. Bena is averaging 20 points per game from scoring on two-point and three-point shots.

   a. If she scores 6 two-point shots and 2 three-point shots, will Bena meet her points-per-game average?

   b. If she scores 7 two-point shots and 2 three-point shots, will Bena meet her points-per-game average?

   c. If she scores 7 two-point shots and 4 three-point shots, will Bena meet her points-per-game average?

2. Write an equation to represent the number of two-point shots and the number of three-point shots that total 20 points.

3. Graph the equation you wrote on the coordinate plane.

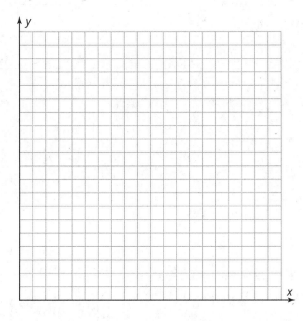

Ask yourself:

How should you label the graph?

© Carnegie Learning, Inc.

4. **Coach Purvis believes that Danvers High School can win the district playoffs if Bena scores at least 20 points per game.**

   a. **How can you rewrite the equation you wrote in Question 2 to represent that Bena must score at least 20 points per game?**

   b. **Write an inequality in two variables that represents this problem situation.**

5. **Complete the table of values. Then, add the ordered pairs in the table to the graph in Question 3. If the number of total points scored does not meet or exceed Bena's points-per-game average, use an "x" to plot the point. If the number of total points scored meets or exceeds Bena's points-per-game average, use a dot to plot the point.**

Number of Two-Point Shots Scored	Number of Three-Point Shots Scored	Number of Total Points Scored
4	1	
6	1	
7	1	
8	2	
6	4	
9	5	

6. **What do you notice about your graph?**

7. What can you interpret about the solutions of the inequality from the graph?

8. Choose a different ordered pair located above the line and a different ordered pair that is located below the graph. How do these points confirm your interpretation of the situation? Explain your reasoning.

9. Shade the side of the graph that contains the combinations of shots that are greater than or equal to Bena's points-per-game average.

10. How do the solutions of the linear equation $2x + 3y = 20$ differ from the solutions of the linear inequality $2x + 3y \geq 20$?

11. Does the ordered pair (6.5, 5.5) make sense as a solution in the context of this problem situation? Explain why or why not.

Like linear equations, linear inequalities take different forms. Each of the linear inequalities in two variables shown represent a different relationship between the variables.

$$ax + by < c \qquad ax + by > c$$
$$ax + by \leq c \qquad ax + by \geq c$$

The graph of a linear inequality in two variables is a **half-plane**, or half of a coordinate plane. A **boundary line**, determined by the inequality, divides the plane into two half-planes and the inequality symbol indicates which half-plane contains all the solutions. These solutions are represented by shading the appropriate half-plane.

Consider the linear inequality $y > 4x - 6$. The boundary line that divides the plane is determined by the equation $y = 4x - 6$.

If the inequality symbol is ≤ or ≥, the boundary line is a solid line because all points on the line are part of the solution set. If the symbol is < or >, the boundary line is a dashed line because no point on that line is a solution.

1. **Should the boundary line in this graph be a solid line or a dashed line? Explain your reasoning.**

2. **Graph the inequality on the coordinate plane shown.**

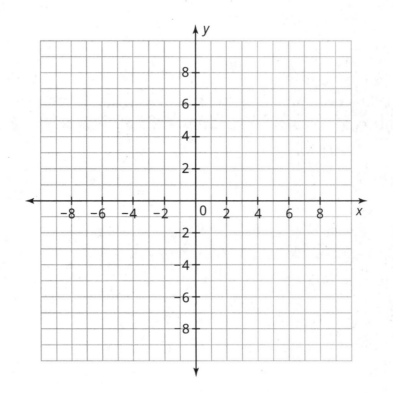

After you graph the inequality with either a solid or a dashed boundary line, you need to decide which half-plane to shade. To make your decision, consider the point (0, 0). If (0, 0) is a solution, then the half-plane that contains (0, 0) contains the solutions and should be shaded. If (0, 0) is *not* a solution, then the half-plane that does not contain (0, 0) contains the solutions and should be shaded.

3. **Decide which half-plane to shade.**

   a. **Is (0, 0) a solution? Explain your reasoning.**

Think

about:

It's a good idea to check points in both half-planes to verify your solution.

   b. **Shade the correct half-plane on the coordinate plane.**

4. **Match each graph to one of the inequalities given. In part (d), graph the inequality that was not graphed in parts (a) through (c).**

$$y \geq \tfrac{1}{2}x - 3 \qquad y \leq \tfrac{1}{2}x - 3$$

$$y > \tfrac{1}{2}x - 3 \qquad y < \tfrac{1}{2}x - 3$$

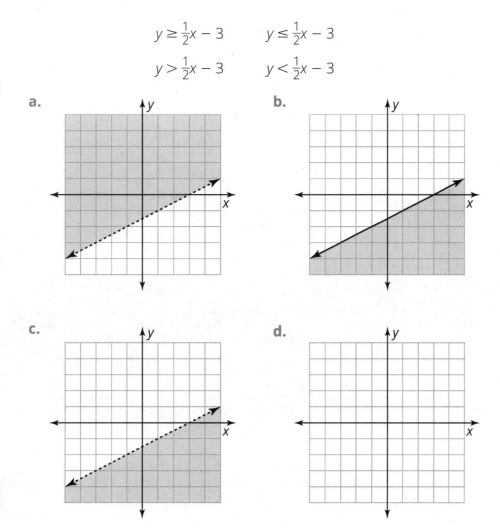

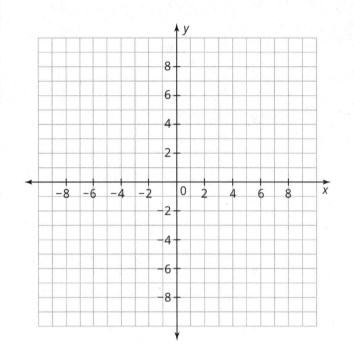

5. **Graph each linear inequality.**

a. $y > x + 3$

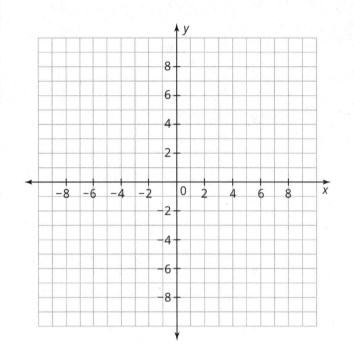

Consider the inequality symbol and which half-plane will be shaded before you test any points.

b. $y \leq -\frac{1}{3}x + 4$

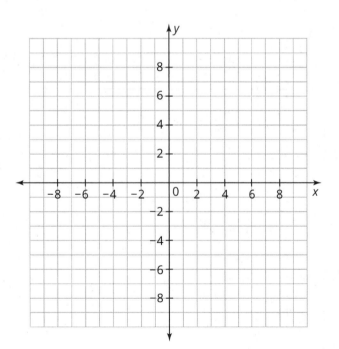

c. $2x - y < 4$

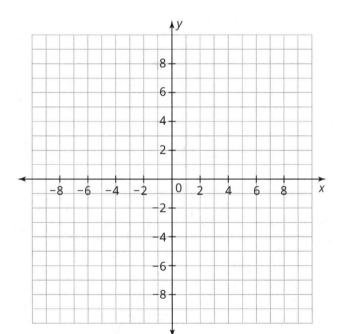

© Carnegie Learning, Inc.

Previously you have written a linear equation given various representations, including two points, one point and the slope, a table of values, or a graph. You can use a similar approach when writing a linear inequality.

Worked Example

Write a linear equality for the graph.

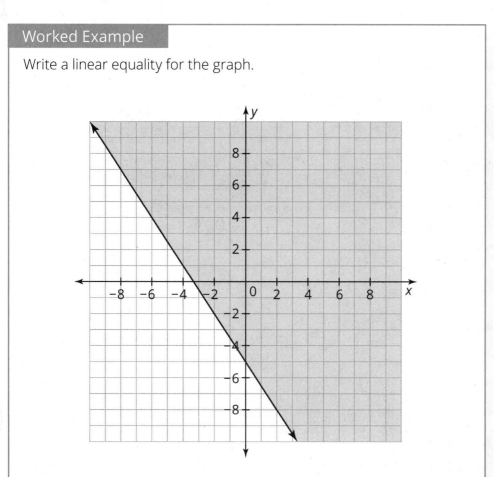

You can use what you have previously learned about the graphs of linear equations to determine that the boundary line is represented by the equation $y = -\frac{3}{2}x - 5$. Now you must decide which inequality symbol should replace the equals sign in the equation.

Since the graph shows a solid boundary line and the half-plane above the line is shaded, use the symbol $\geq$.

$$y \geq -\frac{3}{2}x - 5$$

Test a point in the solution set to check the linear inequality.

Test the point (0, 0):

$$0 \overset{?}{\geq} -\frac{3}{2}(0) - 5$$

$$0 \geq -5 \checkmark$$

Remember:

The point (0, 0) can be used as a test point unless the boundary line passes through (0, 0).

6. Write a linear inequality for each graph.

a.

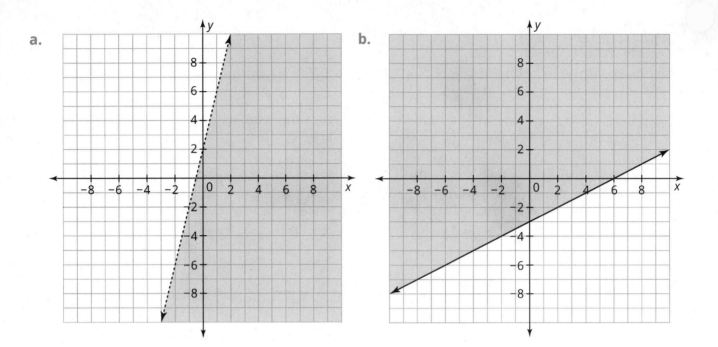

b.

c.

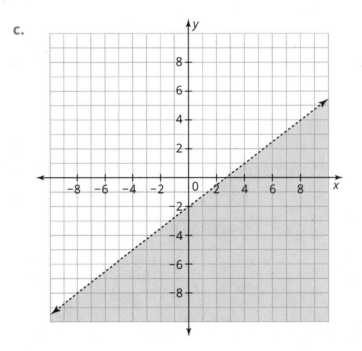

Interpreting the Graph of a Linear Inequality

César has relatives living in both the United States and Mexico. He is given a prepaid phone card worth $50 for his birthday. The table of values shows combinations of minutes for calls within the United States, x, and calls to Mexico, y, that expend his $50 prepaid phone card.

Length of Calls within United States (minutes)	Length of Calls to Mexico (minutes)
0	100
50	80
140	44
200	20
240	4

1. **Write an inequality modeling the number of minutes César can use for calls within the United States and for calls to Mexico.**

2. **Graph your inequality on the given coordinate grid. Be sure to label your axes.**

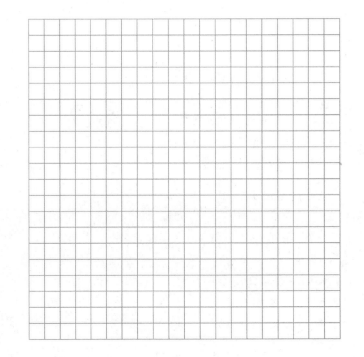

3. If César speaks with his aunt in Guadalajara, Mexico, for 70 minutes using his phone card, how long can he speak with his cousin in New York using the same card?

4. Can César call his uncle in San Antonio for 100 minutes and also call his grandmother in Juárez, Mexico, for 80 minutes using his phone card? Explain your reasoning.

5. Can César call his brother in Mexico City, Mexico, for 55 minutes and also call his sister in Denver, for 90 minutes using his phone card? Explain your reasoning.

6. Interpret the meaning of each.

   a. points on the line

   b. points above the line

   c. points below the line

TALK the TALK

There's a Fine Line

Consider the graph of the linear equation $x + y = 12$.

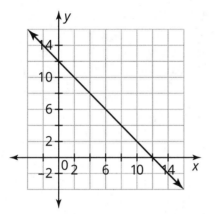

Use the graph to answer each question.

1. **Describe how to graph $x + y < 12$ and choose a point to test this region.**

2. **Describe how to graph $x + y \leq 12$ and choose a point to test this region.**

3. **Describe how to graph $x + y > 12$ and choose a point to test this region.**

4. Complete the table.

Equation or Inequality	Description of the Solution Set
$x + y = 0$	
$x + y \geq 0$	
$x + y \leq 0$	
$x + y > 0$	
$x + y < 0$	

Assignment

Write

Describe a half-plane in your own words.

Remember

The graph of a linear inequality in two variables is the half-plane that contains all the solutions. If the inequality symbol is ≥ or ≤, the graph shows a solid boundary line because the line is part of the solution set. If the symbol is > or <, the boundary line is a dashed line because no point on the line is a solution.

Practice

1. Jeremy is working two jobs to save money for his college education. He makes $8 per hour working for his uncle at Pizza Pie bussing tables and $10 per hour tutoring peers after school in math. His goal is to make $160 per week.
   a. If Jeremy works 8 hours at Pizza Pie and tutors 11 hours during the week, does he reach his goal?
   b. Write an expression to represent the total amount of money Jeremy makes in a week from working both jobs. Let x represent the number of hours he works at Pizza Pie and y represent the number of hours he tutors.
   c. After researching the costs of colleges, Jeremy decides he needs to make more than $160 each week. Write an inequality in two variables to represent the amount of money Jeremy needs to make.
   d. Graph the inequality from part (c).
   e. Is the point (0, 0) in the shaded region of the graph? Explain why or why not.
   f. According to the graph, if Jeremy works 5 hours at Pizza Pie and tutors for 10 hours, will he make more than $160? Explain why or why not.
   g. Due to days off from school, Jeremy will only be tutoring for 6 hours this week. Use the graph to determine the least amount of full hours he must work at Pizza Pie to still reach his goal. Then show that your result satisfies the inequality.

2. Graph each inequality on a coordinate plane.
   a. $x + 3y > 9$
   b. $2x - 6y \leq 15$
   c. $2x + y < 6$
   d. $3x - y \geq 1$

Stretch

Use what you know about absolute value functions to graph the inequality $y > 2|x - 3| - 5$.

Review

1. Solve each compound inequality. Graph the final solution on a number line.

   a. $-4 \leq 3x + 2 \leq 14$

   b. $\frac{1}{3}x + 3 \geq 4$ or $-x < 2$

2. Solve each system using the Linear Combinations Method.

   a. $\begin{cases} 8x - 6y = -20 \\ -16x + 7y = 30 \end{cases}$

   b. $\begin{cases} x + 3 = -7y + 3 \\ 2x - 8y = 22 \end{cases}$

3. Write the equation of the line that has the given slope and passes through the point given.

   a. $m = \frac{2}{3}$; $(2, -4)$

   b. $m = -4$; $(0.5, 7)$

© Carnegie Learning, Inc.

Working with Constraints

Systems of Linear Inequalities

Warm Up

Determine an ordered pair (x, y) that satisfies each inequality.

1. $x + y < 18$

2. $x - y > -7$

3. $2x + 3y \leq -5$

4. $-5x - 2y \geq 10$

Learning Goals

- Represent constraints in a problem situation with systems of inequalities.
- Write and graph systems of linear inequalities.
- Graph the solutions to a system of linear inequalities in two variables as the intersection of the corresponding half-planes.
- Verify solutions to systems of linear inequalities algebraically.

Key Terms

- constraints
- solution of a system of linear inequalities

You have graphed a linear inequality in two variables and interpreted the solutions. What does the graph of a system of linear inequalities look like, and how can you describe the solution set?

A River Runs Through It

Chase is an experienced whitewater rafter who guides groups of adults and children out on the water for amazing adventures. The raft he uses can hold 800 pounds of weight. Any weight greater than 800 pounds can cause the raft to sink, hit more rocks, and/or maneuver more slowly.

Chase estimates the weight of each adult as approximately 200 pounds and the weight of each child as approximately 100 pounds. Chase charges adults $75 and children $50 to ride down the river with him. His goal is to earn at least $150 each rafting trip.

Think about:

Does Chase count himself when determining the weight and the cost?

1. **Write an inequality to represent the most weight Chase can carry in terms of rafters. Define your variables.**

2. **Write an inequality to represent the minimum amount of money Chase wants to collect for each rafting trip.**

3. **Write a system of linear inequalities to represent the maximum weight of the raft and the minimum amount of money Chase wants to earn per trip.**

Determining Solutions to Systems of Linear Inequalities

In a system of linear inequalities, the inequalities are known as **constraints** because the values of the expressions are "constrained" to lie within a certain region on the graph.

1. **Let's consider two trips that Chase guides. Determine whether each combination of rafters is a solution of the system of linear inequalities. Then describe the meaning of the solution in terms of this problem situation.**

   a. **First Trip: Chase guides 2 adults and 2 children.**

   b. **Second Trip: Chase guides 5 adults.**

2. **Graph the system of linear inequalities.**

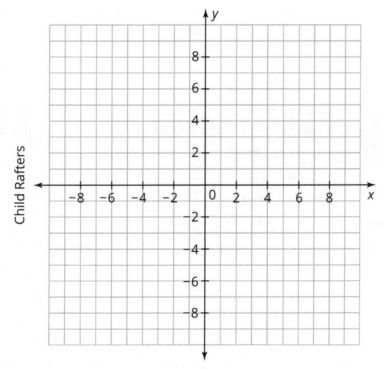

Shade the half-plane of each inequality differently. You can use colored pencils or simply vertical and horizontal lines.

Child Rafters

Adult Rafters

The **solution of a system of linear inequalities** is the intersection of the solutions to each inequality. Every point in the intersection region satisfies all inequalities in the system.

3. **Analyze your graph.**

   a. **Describe the possible number of solutions for a system of linear inequalities.**

   b. **Is the intersection point a solution to this system of inequalities? Why or why not?**

   c. **Identify three different solutions of the system of linear inequalities you graphed. What do the solutions represent in terms of the problem situation?**

   d. **Determine one combination of adults and children that is not a solution for this system of linear inequalities. Explain your reasoning.**

Analyzing Graphs of Systems of Linear Inequalities

Determine the solution set of the given system of linear inequalities.

$$\begin{cases} x + y > 1 \\ -x + y \le 3 \end{cases}$$

1. Graph the system of linear inequalities.

Think

.•● about:

Notice the inequality symbols. How does this affect your graph?

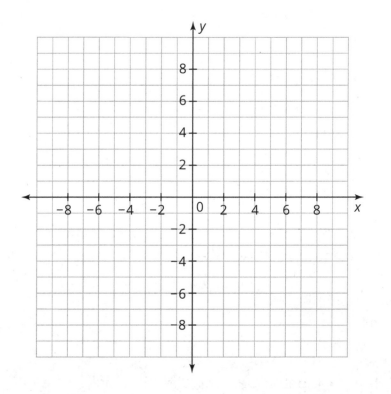

2. **Choose a point in each shaded region of the graph. Determine whether each point is a solution of the system. Then describe how the shaded region represents the solution.**

Point	$x + y > 1$	$-x + y \leq 3$	Description of location
$(-8, 2)$	$-8 + 2 > 1$ $-6 > 1$ X	$-(-8) + 2 \leq 3$ $10 \leq 3$ X	The point is not a solution to either inequality and it is located in the region that is not shaded by either inequality.

3. **Alan makes the statement about the intersection point of a system of inequalities. Explain why Alan's statement is incorrect.**

Alan
The intersection point is always a solution to a system of inequalities because that is where the two lines meet.

4. **Solve each system of linear inequalities by graphing the solution set. Then identify two points that are solutions of the system.**

a. $\begin{cases} y > 5x + 3 \\ y < 5x - 3 \end{cases}$

b. $\begin{cases} x \geq -5 \\ x \geq 1 \end{cases}$

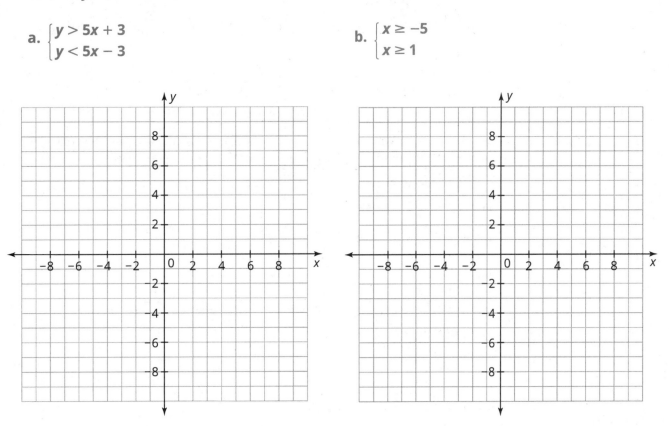

Applying Systems of Linear Inequalities

Jackson and a group of friends decide to use the fitness room after school. A sign on the wall provides the information shown.

Exercise	Calories Burned per Minute
Treadmill—light effort	7.6
Treadmill—vigorous effort	12.4
Stair Stepper—light effort	6.9
Stair Stepper—vigorous effort	10.4
Stationary Bike—light effort	5.5
Stationary Bike—vigorous effort	11.1

Jackson decides to use the stair stepper. He has at most 45 minutes to exercise and he wants to burn at least 400 calories.

1. **Write a system of linear inequalities to represent Jackson's workout. Define your variables.**

2. **Graph the system of inequalities from Question 1 on the coordinate plane. Be sure to label your axes.**

Use technology to graph your inequalities and check your answer.

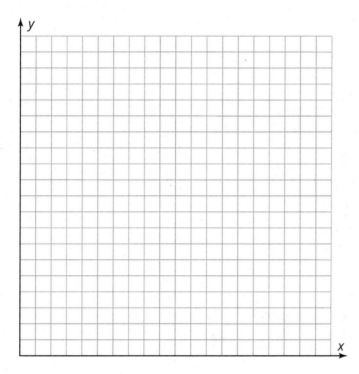

3. **Analyze your graph.**

   a. **Identify two different solutions of the system of inequalities.**

   b. **Interpret your solutions in terms of Jackson's workout.**

   c. **Algebraically prove that your solutions satisfy the system of linear inequalities.**

Consider the four systems shown.

System A	System B	System C	System D

$$\begin{cases} y < \frac{3}{5}x + 3 \\ y > -\frac{3}{5}x + 3 \end{cases} \quad \begin{cases} y > \frac{3}{5}x + 3 \\ y > -\frac{3}{5}x + 3 \end{cases} \quad \begin{cases} y > \frac{3}{5}x + 3 \\ y < -\frac{3}{5}x + 3 \end{cases} \quad \begin{cases} y < \frac{3}{5}x + 3 \\ y < -\frac{3}{5}x + 3 \end{cases}$$

1. **Analyze Adele's statement and explain why it is incorrect.**

> **Adele**
> Since the equations in each system are the same, the graphs and solutions should all be identical.

2. **Match a graph and possible solution to each given system of linear inequalities. Complete the blank graph and partial solution set to make 4 complete sets.**

Graph A

Graph B

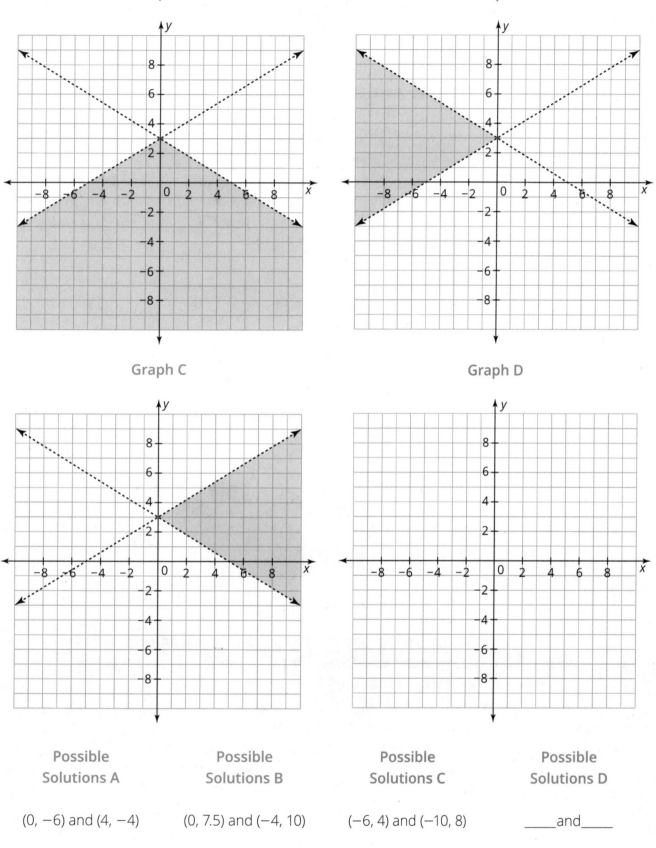

Graph C

Graph D

Possible Solutions A	Possible Solutions B	Possible Solutions C	Possible Solutions D
(0, −6) and (4, −4)	(0, 7.5) and (−4, 10)	(−6, 4) and (−10, 8)	____ and ____

NOTES

TALK the TALK

Get to Know the Region

The solution set to a system of inequalities can be any of four regions on the coordinate plane.

1. Consider each system of linear inequalities and decide which region represents the solution set. Explain your reasoning.
   - A region above both lines.
   - A region below both lines.
   - A region between the lines.
   - No solution.

   a. $y < 8 + 2x$
      $3 + 2x > y$

   b. $5 + x < y$
      $y > 7 + x$

   c. $y > 12 - 3x$
      $10 - 3x > y$

   d. $6 - x < y$
      $y < 9 - x$

2. How is the solution to a system of linear inequalities the same as or different from the solution to a system of linear equations?

Assignment

Write

Describe how you know which region, if any, represents the solution to a system of linear inequalities.

Remember

The solution of a system of linear inequalities is the intersection of the solutions to each inequality. Every point in the intersection region satisfies all inequalities in the system.

Practice

1. Samuel is remodeling his basement. One part of the planning involves the flooring. He knows that he would like both carpet and hardwood, but isn't sure how much of each he will use. The most amount of flooring area he can cover is 2000 square feet. The carpet is $4.50 per square foot and the hardwood is $8.25 per square foot. Both prices include labor costs. Samuel has budgeted $10,000 for the flooring.

   a. Write a system of inequalities to represent the maximum amount of flooring needed and the maximum amount of money Samuel wants to spend.

   b. One idea Samuel has is to make two rooms—one having 400 square feet of carpeting and the other having 1200 square feet of hardwood. Determine whether this amount of carpeting and hardwood are solutions to the system of inequalities. Explain your reasoning in terms of the problem situation.

   c. Graph this system of inequalities.

   d. Determine the intersection point of the two lines. Is this a solution to this system of inequalities in terms of the problem situation?

   e. Identify two different solutions to the system of inequalities. Explain what the solutions represent in terms of the problem situation.

   f. Determine one combination of amounts of carpet and hardwood that is not a solution for the system of inequalities. Explain your reasoning.

2. Solve each system of linear inequalities.

   a. $\begin{cases} -x + 3y \leq -6 \\ -5x + 3y \geq 6 \end{cases}$

   b. $\begin{cases} -x + 2y < 6 \\ 3x + 2y \leq 2 \end{cases}$

   c. $\begin{cases} -x + 3y \leq 18 \\ x \leq 3 \end{cases}$

Stretch

1. Is it possible to create a system of inequalities that has no solutions? If so, create one and explain how the graph would show no solutions. If not, explain why.

2. Is it possible to create a system of two inequalities that has only one solution? If so, create one. If not, explain why.

3. Is it possible to create a system of three inequalities that has only one solution? If so, sketch a graph to show the solution. If not, explain why.

Review

1. Determine whether each equation has one solution, no solution, or infinite solutions.

   a. $24x - 22 = -3(1 - 8x)$

   b. $-3(4a + 3) + 2(12a + 2) = 43$

   c. $4(x + 1) = 6x + 4 - 2x$

2. Graph $3x + y \leq 7$ on a coordinate plane.

3. Write a linear inequality for the graph.

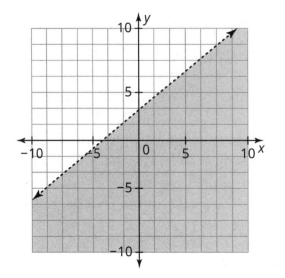

4. A new workout gym opens up down the street from your house. Below are their total membership numbers for the first months of business.

Month	January	February	March	April	May
Number of Members	120	190	290	370	450

   a. Write the equation of the regression line for the data.

   b. Use the equation to predict the gym's total membership at the end of the year.

5

Working the System

Solving Systems of Equations and Inequalities

Warm Up

Determine whether the point (1, 7) is a solution to each system.

1. $\begin{cases} 4x - y = -3 \\ -2x + y = 5 \end{cases}$

2. $\begin{cases} x + y > 4 \\ 4x - y < -4 \end{cases}$

3. $\begin{cases} y = -3.5x - 2 \\ y = 4.5x - 10 \end{cases}$

4. $\begin{cases} -2x + y < 8 \\ x - y > -8 \end{cases}$

Learning Goals

- Use various methods of solving systems of linear equations to determine the better buy or the better job offer.
- Solve systems of linear inequalities with more than two inequalities.
- Graph the solutions to a system of linear inequalities in two variables as the intersection of the corresponding half-planes.

You have solved systems of linear equations by graphing, by using substitution, and by using linear combinations. You have also graphed systems of linear inequalities to determine possible solutions. How can you use these various methods to reason about real-world problems?

Systems for Summer Savings

A neighborhood pool club offers two membership plans. Plan A includes a seasonal sign-up fee of $100 and charges $2 each time you use the pool. Plan B has no sign-up fee but charges $6 each time you use the pool. Susan chooses Plan A. She has a budget of $200 to spend on pool fees during the months of July and August.

Susan wants to be sure she uses the pool enough times so that the plan she chooses works out to be the better deal between the two plans, but she does not want to go over her budget.

1. **Use a system of linear equations and a system of linear inequalities to make a recommendation to Susan as to how often she should use the pool in July and August.**

The Bici Bicycle Company is planning to make a low price ultra-light bicycle. There are two different plans being considered for building this bicycle. The first plan includes a cost of $125,000 to design and build a prototype bicycle. The combined materials and labor costs for each bike made under the first plan will be $225. The second plan includes a cost of $100,000 to design and build the prototype. The combined materials and labor costs for each bike made under the second plan will be $275.

1. **You recently got a job at Bici Bicycle Company as a financial analyst. Analyze the costs for each proposed bicycle prototype and determine which plan Bici should follow. Provide evidence for your proposal.**

Demetrius is in search of a new cell phone plan. He is considering two different cell phone services from two different providers.

Bouncing Cell Service offers a monthly fee of $99.99 and 2000 Mb of data per month. Once a user exceeds the free monthly data allowance, each additional Mb of data used is $0.05. Rolling Cell Service offers a monthly fee of $79.99 and 1500 Mb of data per month. Once a user exceeds the free monthly data allowance, each additional Mb of data used is $0.08. Demetrius is unsure which plan to choose. He wasn't very careful with his last contract and paid a lot of extra money in charges for data.

1. **Write an email to advise Demetrius which plan to choose. Provide evidence in your response.**

Solving a System of Linear Inequalities with Four Constraints

Miguel's eye doctor informed him that he needs glasses. Luckily, the local vision store is having a sale on all eyeglass frames. The advertisement in the window is as shown.

Previously, you solved a system containing two linear inequalities. However, systems can consist of more than two linear inequalities.

> **Save 60% to 75% On All Frames**
> **Regularly Priced at**
> **$120–$360**

1. **Use the advertisement to write two inequalities that represent the regular price of eyeglass frames. Let _r_ represent the regular price of the frames.**

2. **Use the same advertisement to write two inequalities that represent the reduced price of the eyeglass frames. Let _s_ represent the sales price of the frames in terms of _r_.**

> **Remember:**
>
> When an item is 20% off the regular price, you can think of that item costing 80% of the regular price.

3. **Heather wrote this system of linear inequalities for the problem situation. Explain why it is incorrect.**

Heather
$$\begin{cases} r \geq 120 \\ r \leq 360 \\ s \leq 0.6r \\ s \geq 0.75r \end{cases}$$

4. Graph each inequality on the grid.

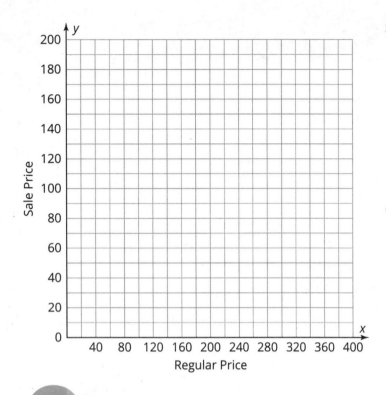

5. Shade the portion of the graph that satisfies the system of linear inequalities. What shape does the solution region resemble?

6. About how much would Miguel expect to spend if he purchases eyeglasses that are regularly priced at $320?

7. Miguel is definitely going to purchase a pair of eyeglasses that are on sale. What is the least amount of money Miguel can expect to spend? What is the greatest amount he can expect to spend?

8. Miguel decides on a pair of eyeglasses that are regularly priced at $240.

   a. Can Miguel expect to save more or less than $140 off the purchase price of this pair of eyeglasses? Use your graph to determine an approximate answer.

   b. Use algebra to determine the greatest amount of money Miguel can save by purchasing eyeglasses that are regularly priced at $240.

The graph shows you the sale price of the eyeglasses, but how can you determine how much he will save?

© Carnegie Learning, Inc.

Jose interviewed for two different sales positions at competing companies. Reliable Robotics has offered Jose a salary of $31,200 per year, plus a 9% commission on his total sales. Robot Renegades will offer him $26,000 per year, plus a 15% commission on his total sales.

Jose isn't sure which offer to accept. He's great at making a sale, but he's just not sure which job will be better in terms of his pay. He is confident that he can make at least $2000 worth of sales each week.

1. **Write an email to Jose with your recommendation of which job offers better compensation. Provide evidence in your response.**

TALK the TALK

Which Cab Is More Fab?

The Red Cab Company charges $3.50 upon entry and an additional $1.25 per mile driven. The Yellow Cab Company charges $5 upon entry and an additional $1.15 per mile driven.

1. **Emma needs to take a cab to the airport. Which company should she use if she wants to minimize the cost? Use any method to solve.**

Assignment

Write

You have used three methods to solve systems: graphing, substitution, and linear combinations. Describe the characteristics you would look for when determining which method to use.

Remember

The solution set to a system of inequalities with more than two constraints can be described as the region where all the graphs overlap.

Practice

1. Antonio wants to subscribe to a service that will allow him to rent DVDs and stream movies online. Movie Madness offers a subscription for $14.25 a month. With this subscription, Antonio can check out as many DVDs as he wants each month and must pay $1.40 for each movie he streams online. The Show Must Go On! offers a subscription for $8.50 a month. With this subscription, Antonio can checkout as many DVDs as he wants each month and must pay $3.25 for each movie he streams online.

   a. Write a system of linear equations to represent this problem situation.

   b. Analyze the two subscription plans and determine which one is the better deal. Use any or all of the methods you have learned to determine your answer.

   c. Write a short paragraph recommending which subscription Antonio should choose.

   d. Which method do you think provides the quickest way to analyze a system of equations to determine which one is the better deal? Explain your reasoning.

2. The Brunstown Ballet Company needs to rent a venue for their production of the Nutcracker. There are a number of arenas they are considering. The arenas have seating capacities that range from 800 to 1876 seats. The management of the company knows the ticket sales may not be good this year but their goal is to sell between 65% and 90% of the available seats. Whichever arena they choose, one hundred seats must be set aside for the company's donors.

   a. Write a system of inequalities that represents the problem situation. Define your variables.

   b. Graph each inequality on a coordinate plane.

   c. One of the arenas they are considering has 1200 available seats. Determine the minimum and maximum number of seats they would need to sell in order for management to reach their goal.

   d. If the company sold 900 seats, what is the range of seating capacities for the arenas they may have rented?

   e. If they rented an arena that had a 1300-seat capacity and sold 800 tickets, would management reach their goal? Explain your reasoning.

Stretch

Isla sells baked good from her home kitchen. She offers decorated cookies for $15 per dozen and cupcakes for $13 per dozen. It takes her an hour to decorate a dozen cookies, but only 20 minutes to decorate a dozen cupcakes. She would like to make at least $300 per week and not put in more than 20 hours of work per week.

1. Create a system of linear inequalities that fits the situation and graph them.
2. Isla just discovered that she is running out of cake mix for the cupcakes and royal icing for the cookies. She can make a maximum of 40 dozen cupcakes and 12 dozen cookies. What are the new inequalities you need to add to your problem? Add them to your graph.
3. What is the maximum amount of baked goods that she could make? How much will she earn? How long will it take her?
4. What is the least amount of time she could work and still earn $300? What baked goods would she make?

Review

1. Consider the equation $6x - 2y = -12$.
   a. What is the slope of the equation?
   b. What are the intercepts of the equation?
2. The equation to calculate the area of a trapezoid is $A = \frac{1}{2}(a+b)h$. Rewrite the equation to solve for a.
3. Graph each system of inequalities. Then identify two points that are solutions of the system.

   a. $\begin{cases} y \geq 5x - 3 \\ y < -3x + 5 \end{cases}$

   b. $\begin{cases} y \geq x + 4 \\ x - y \geq 2 \end{cases}$

4. What is the equation for the line that has a slope of 0 and passes through the point (3, 7)?
5. What is the equation for the line that has a slope of $\frac{1}{5}$ and passes through the point $\left(-\frac{2}{3}, \frac{1}{2}\right)$?

Take It to the Max...or Min

Linear Programming

6

Warm Up

Evaluate each function.

1. $f(x) = 3x + 8$ for $x = -2$

2. $f(a) = -\frac{1}{2}a + 5$ for $a = 12$

3. $f(p) = 4p - 10$ for $p = 1.5$

4. $f(w) = 36 - 2.5w$ for $w = -8$

Learning Goals

- Write systems of inequalities with more than two inequalities.
- Determine constraints from a problem situation.
- Graph systems of linear inequalities and determine the solution set.
- Identify the maximum and minimum values of a linear expression.

Key Term

- linear programming

You have graphed a system of linear inequalities with more than two constraints and determined the region of the solution set. How can you use the boundaries of this graphed region to determine maximum profit or minimum cost in a real-world problem?

A New Notation

Tara has four math tests to take this semester. It takes Tara 2 minutes to complete a multiple-choice question, m, and it takes her 5 minutes to complete a short-answer question, s.

You can write an equation for this function using function notation with two variables.

$$f(m, s) = 2m + 5s$$

Given a value for each variable in the function, you can determine the output.

1. Use the function $f(m, s)$ to determine how long it takes Tara to complete each test.

   a. Test 1
      $f(15, 5)$

   b. Test 2
      $f(10, 8)$

   c. Test 3
      $f(25, 0)$

   d. Test 4
      $f(0, 13)$

Introduction to Linear Programming

A company, TVs4U, makes and sells two different television models: the HD Big View and the MegaTeleBox.

- The HD Big View takes 2 person-hours to make, and the MegaTeleBox takes 3 person-hours to make.
- TVs4U has 24 employees, each working 8 hours a day, which is equivalent to 192 person-hours per day.
- TVs4U's total manufacturing capacity is 72 televisions per day.
- TVs4U cannot make a negative number of televisions.

1. **Define variables to represent the number of each model television produced.**

Linear programming is a branch of mathematics that determines the maximum and minimum value of linear expressions on a region produced by a system of linear inequalities.

2. **Identify the constraints as a system of linear inequalities.**

Ask yourself:

How do you represent the fact that TVs4U cannot make a negative number of televisions?

3. **Graph the system of inequalities on the coordinate plane. Shade the region that represents the solution set.**

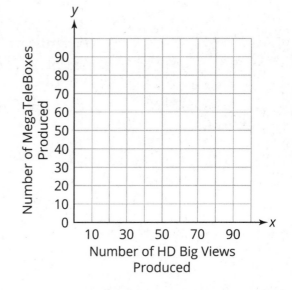

Number of MegaTeleBoxes Produced (y-axis: 0, 10, 20, 30, 40, 50, 60, 70, 80, 90)

Number of HD Big Views Produced (x-axis: 10, 30, 50, 70, 90)

Many companies and businesses are interested in determining when they are maximizing or minimizing their profit or costs. The maximum and minimum values of a system of inequalities occur at a vertex of the shaded region that represents the solution set of the system.

4. Label the vertices of the shaded region that represents the solution set of the system.

To determine the maximum and minimum values, you must substitute the coordinates of each vertex of the solution set into a given function.

Worked Example

Let's say TVs4U profits $175 for each HD Big View it sells and profits $205 for each MegaTeleBox it sells. They want to determine how many of each television they should make and sell to maximize their profits.

Write the function for the given problem situation.

$$P(b, m) = 175b + 205m$$

Insert the coordinates of each intersection point of the system.

$P(0, 0) = 175(0) + 205(0) = 0$
$P(0, 64) = 175(0) + 205(64) = 13{,}120$
$P(24, 48) = 175(24) + 205(48) = 14{,}040$
$P(72, 0) = 175(72) + 205(0) = 12{,}600$

The maximum profit is represented by the number of televisions made and sold that results in the greatest value.

---

5. How many of each television should TVs4U produce to earn the maximum profit? Explain your reasoning.

6. TVs4U is trying to determine the price of each model of television. For each set of profits, determine how many of each model should be made to maximize the profit. Then determine the maximum profit. Assume all televisions that are made are sold.

   a. The profit on the HD Big View is $250 and the profit on the MegaTeleBox is $300.

   b. The profit on the HD Big View is $250 and the profit on the MegaTeleBox is $375.

7. TVs4U's boss, Mr. Corazon, sends out a memo with his ideas on maximizing the company's profit. Examine Mr. Corazon's idea and explain why it is incorrect.

Mr. Corazon

Obviously, we will make the most money by only making and selling the television model that gives us the most profit. Therefore, we should focus on producing and selling 72 MegaTeleBoxes each day for a profit of $375 a piece.

ACTIVITY 6.2 Maximizing Profit

The cell phone company, Speed of Sound (SOS), produces two types of cell phones. The SOS Smartcall has advanced download speeds and capability which the SOS Basic does not. The assembly lines can produce at most a total of 180 cell phones each day and the company always has at least 40 of each type of cell phone produced and ready for shipping. One SOS Smartcall requires 3 person-hours and $75 worth of materials to produce. One SOS Basic requires 4 person-hours and $60 worth of materials to produce. The company has 640 person-hours of labor available daily. The company has budgeted $12,900 for the cost of materials each day.

1. **Define your variables and identify the constraints as a system of linear inequalities.**

2. **Graph the solution set for the system of linear inequalities on the coordinate plane shown. Label all intersection points of the boundary lines.**

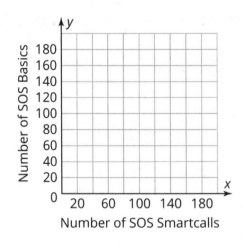

3. The profit from the Smartcall is $30 and the profit from the Basic is $35.

   a. Write a function to represent the total profit.

   b. Paige states that this problem is unrealistic because no one would ever sell a really good cell phone for only $30. Is Paige's statement correct? Why or why not?

4. How many of each type of cell phone should the company produce and sell to maximize its profit? Determine the maximum profit.

5. A competitor has reduced the price of its advanced capability cell phone. In order to compete, SOS will have to decrease its profit on the Smartcall to $25. How will this affect the number and type of cell phones SOS needs to produce and sell in order to maximize its profit?

TALK the TALK

Minimizing Cost

A building developer is planning a new housing development. He plans to build two types of houses: townhouses and single-family homes. The plot of land has room for the developer to build 100 houses. It takes the workers 2 months to build a townhouse and 3 months to build a single-family home. The developer wants this development complete in 20 years.

It costs the developer $300,000 to build each townhouse and $450,000 to build each single-family home. The developer wants to save as much money as possible while building the houses.

1. **How many of each type of house should he build if he wants to minimize his costs while still completing the development? Explain your reasoning.**

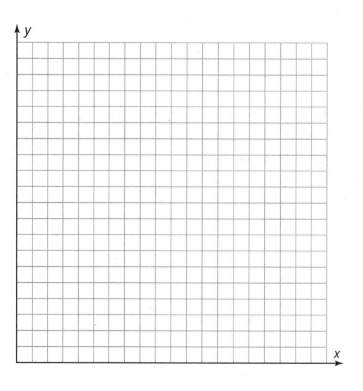

Remember:

When comparing or calculating, you must use the same units of measure.

Assignment

Write

Describe linear programming in your own words.

Remember

The vertices of the solution region determined by a system of linear inequalities can be used to determine maximum and minimum values of linear expressions.

Practice

The Smartway Rental Car Company has $180,000 to invest in the purchase of at most 16 cars of two different types, compact and full-size.

	Purchase Price	Rental Fee	Maintenance Cost
Compact Car	$9000	$30	$8
Full-Size Car	$15,000	$48	$10

1. Due to demand, Smartway needs to purchase at least 5 compact cars.
   a. Identify the constraints as a system of linear inequalities. Define your variables.
   b. Graph the solution set for the system of linear inequalities. Label all points of the intersection of the boundary lines.
   c. Smartway Rental Car's income comes from renting out their cars. How many of each type of car should they purchase if they want to maximize their income? What is the maximum income?
   d. In order to keep up with their competitors, Smartway must purchase at least 3 full-size cars and at least 5 compact cars.
   Identify the constraints as a system of linear inequalities. Define your variables.
   e. Graph the solution set for this system of linear inequalities.
   f. Smartway Rental is still unable to keep up with their competitors so they are going to try and cut their maintenance fees to save money. How many of each type of car should they purchase to minimize their maintenance fees?

Stretch

Some nutritional information for granola and yogurt is given in the table.

	Protein (g)	Fiber (g)	Potassium (mg)	Calories
Granola (2 Tbsp)	1.5	2	0	70
Yogurt (3 oz)	3	1.5	260	75

Reagan wants at least 10 grams of protein, 9 grams of fiber, 300 milligrams of potassium, and 250 calories from her breakfast.

1. Create a system of inequalities.

2. Graph your system.

3. Determine the intersection points of your boundary lines.

4. What is the cheapest Reagan can eat breakfast that meets her requirements if granola is $0.34 per serving and yogurt is $0.50 per serving? (Use only full serving sizes, always round the serving up.)

Review

1. Solve each linear inequality.

   a. $-2(x + 1) + 4 < 8$ b. $20 - 2x > -2(x + 2) + 4x$

2. Declan is moving and needs to rent a truck for a day. Company A charges $70 a day and $0.99 per mile. Company B charges $100 a day and $0.75 per mile after the first 20 miles.

   a. Create a system of equations to model the situation.

   b. For what amount of miles does Company A make more sense? Company B?

3. Tessa has three daughters. Her 8-year-old weighs 60 pounds, her 6-year-old weighs 45 pounds, and her 2-year-old weighs 25 pounds.

   a. Write the equation of the regression line for the data.

   b. Use the equation to predict how much Tessa's 4-year-old niece weighs.

© Carnegie Learning, Inc.

Systems of Equations and Inequalities Summary

KEY TERMS

- system of linear equations
- consistent systems
- inconsistent systems
- linear combinations method
- half plane

- boundary line
- constraints
- solution of a system of linear inequalities
- linear programming

LESSON 1 Double the Fun

When two or more linear equations define a relationship between quantities, they form a **system of linear equations**. The solution of a linear system is an ordered pair (x, y) that is a solution to both equations in the system. One way to predict the solution to a system of equations is to graph both equations and identify the point at which the two graphs intersect.

For example, suppose George sells 550 tickets for a spaghetti dinner to raise $3000 for charity. Adult tickets cost $6, and child tickets cost $4.50. To determine how many adult tickets and child tickets were sold, let a represent the number of adult tickets purchased, and let c represent the number of child tickets purchased.

$$\begin{cases} a + c = 550 \\ 6a + 4.5c = 3000 \end{cases}$$

You can use x- and y-intercepts to graph each of the two equations to determine how many of each type of tickets were sold.

The intersection point appears to be (350, 200). There were 350 adult tickets and 200 child tickets sold.

A system of equations may have one unique solution, no solution, or infinite solutions. Systems that have one or many solutions are called **consistent systems**. Systems with no solution are called **inconsistent systems**.

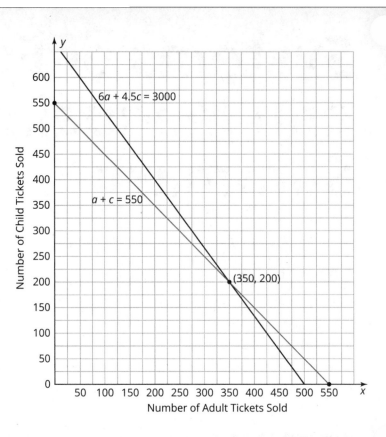

The Elimination Round

The **linear combinations method** is a process used to solve a system of equations by adding two equations so they result in an equation with one variable. Once the value of this variable is determined, it can be used to calculate the value of the other variable. In many cases, one or both of the equations may need to be multiplied by a constant so that the coefficients of the term containing either x or y are opposites. Then when the equations are added, the result is an equation in one variable.

For example, consider the system of linear equations shown.

$$\begin{cases} 7x + 2y = 24 \\ 4x + y = 15 \end{cases}$$

$$\begin{aligned} 7x + 2y &= 24 \\ -2(4x + y) &= -2(15) \end{aligned}$$

Multiply the bottom equation by a constant that results in opposite coefficients for one of the variables.

$$7x + 2y = 24$$
$$+ \ -8x - 2y = -30$$

$$-x = -6$$
$$x = 6$$

Now that the *y*-values are opposite, you can solve this linear system.

$$7(6) + 2y = 24$$
$$42 + 2y = 24$$
$$-2y = -18$$
$$y = -9$$

Substitute the value for *x* into one of the equations to calculate the value for *y*.

The solution to the system of linear equation is (6, −9).

LESSON 3 — Throwing Shade

The graph of a linear inequality in two variables is a **half-plane**, or half of a coordinate plane. A **boundary line**, determined by the inequality, divides the plane into two half-planes. The inequality symbol identifies which half-plane contains the solutions. If the symbol is ≤ or ≥, the boundary line is part of the solution and is solid. If the symbol is < or >, the boundary line is not part of the solution and is represented with a dashed line. Use (0, 0) as a test point to determine which half of the plane is the solution of the inequality and should, therefore, be shaded.

For example, the graph shows the solution to the inequality $y < 5x - 2$. Since the inequality symbol in the solution is <, the shaded half-plane does not include points on the line. Since (0, 0) is not a solution, then the region to the right of the dashed line is the solution set.

$$y < 5x - 2$$
$$0 < 5(0) - 2$$
$$0 < -2x$$

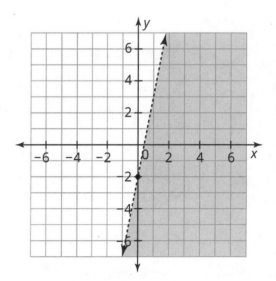

Working with Constraints

In a system of linear inequalities, the inequalities are known as **constraints** because the values of the expressions are "constrained" to lie within a certain region.

The **solution of a system of linear inequalities** is the intersection of the solutions of each inequality. Every point in the intersection region satisfies the system. To determine the solution set of the system, graph each inequality on the same coordinate plane. The region that overlaps is the solution to the system.

For example, the overlapping region of the graphs of the inequalities $2x + y \leq 7$ and $x > 3$ is the solution to the system.

$$\begin{cases} 2x + y \leq 7 \\ \quad\ x > 3 \end{cases}$$

Two points that are solution of the system are $(4, -5)$ and $(5, -8)$

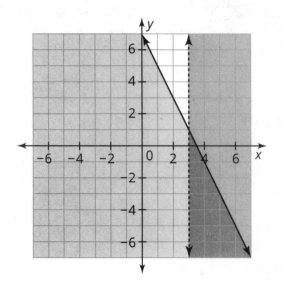

Substitution, linear combinations, and graphing are three methods for determining the solution of a linear system of equations. Use substitution when a variable in one equation can easily be isolated or when the equations are in general form. Use the linear combinations method when the coefficients of like terms are opposites or can be easily made into opposites by multiplication. Use the graphing method when the numbers are convenient to graph or if an exact solution is not needed.

To solve a system of linear inequalities with more than two inequalities, graph each linear inequality and shade the correct region that contains the solution sets that satisfy all the inequalities in the system. Also, determine all the points of intersection for the boundary lines that make the vertices of the solution region. Use a closed point if the point is part of the solution region, and use an open dot if the point is not part of the solution region but is a point of intersection.

The graphs show the solution to a system of four inequalities.

$$\begin{cases} x \geq -4 \\ y > -2 \\ y \leq 6 \\ y > 4x + 3 \end{cases}$$

A solution of the system of inequalities is $(-2, 2)$.

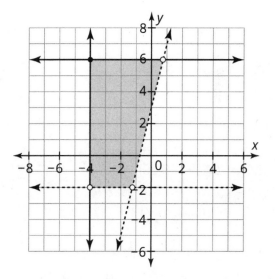

Take It to the Max...or Min

Linear programming is a branch of mathematics that determines the maximum and minimum value of linear expressions on a region produced by a system of linear inequalities. Use the given information to define your variables and identify the constraints as a system of linear inequalities. Graph the solution set for the system of linear inequalities and shade the region that contains the solution set. Label all points of intersection of the boundary lines. The maximum and minimum values of a system of inequalities occur at a vertex of the region defined by the system. To determine the maximum and minimum, substitute each point into a given function.

For example, consider the situation in which Tony mows lawns and trims shrubbery to make extra money. It takes him 30 minutes to mow an average lawn and 60 minutes to trim shrubbery. Tony can spend no more than 20 hours a week on his landscaping business because of school. He can afford to buy enough gas for the lawnmower to mow no more than 14 lawns a week. After the cost of gas, Tony makes a profit of $20 for each lawn mowed and $15 for each lawn in which he trims the shrubbery. Let x represent the number of lawns Tony mows per week, and let y represent the number of yards in which Tony trims shrubbery.

$$\begin{cases} 0.5x + y \le 20 \\ x \le 14 \\ x \ge 0 \\ x \ge 0 \end{cases}$$

$P(x, y) = 20x + 15y$
$P(0, 0) = 20(0) + 15(0) = 0$
$P(0, 20) = 20(0) + 15(20) = 300$
$P(14, 0) = 20(14) + 15(0) = 280$
$P(14, 13) = 20(14) + 15(13) = 475$

To maximize his profit, Tony should mow 14 lawns and trim shrubbery in 13 yards each week. His maximum profit would be $475.

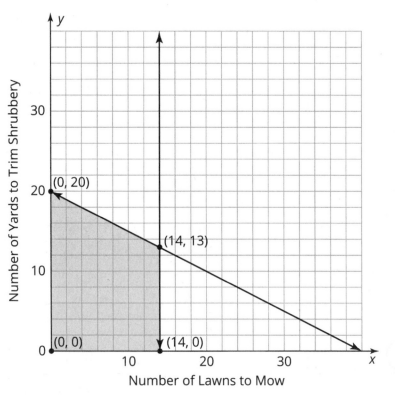

© Carnegie Learning, Inc.

Shapes on a Coordinate Plane

Familiar geometric shapes like triangles, squares, and rectangles can be specified in terms of coordinates.

Module 2: Exploring Constant Change

TOPIC 2: SHAPES ON A COORDINATE PLANE

In this topic, students investigate strategies for determining the perimeters and areas of rectangles, triangles, parallelograms, and composite plane figures on the coordinate plane. Students also explore the effects of proportional and non-proportional changes to the dimensions of a plane figure on its perimeter and area. Students apply the Distance Formula and slope formula to calculate the area and perimeter of composite figures in real-world scenarios. Students extend this knowledge to include scenarios comparing speed and time

Where have we been?

Students have been calculating the area and perimeter of triangles, quadrilaterals, and other figures given side lengths in many of their previous years of school. This topic adds another step to the process by providing only vertices of the figure and requiring students to calculate side lengths before applying area or perimeter formulas. It builds upon students' understanding of the area formulas for squares, rectangles, and triangles; the Pythagorean Theorem; the slope criteria for parallel and perpendicular lines; and methods of solving a system of linear equations.

Where are we going?

Proving relationships and performing geometric measurements algebraically integrates geometry and algebra. As with much of high school geometry, students formalize concepts that they investigated informally in elementary and middle school. And by connecting algebraic reasoning with geometric properties, students can better make sense of formal Euclidean proofs for these properties.

Distance Formula

The Distance Formula is derived from the formula for the Pythagorean Theorem: $a^2 + b^2 = c^2$. If c is the side length we want to know, and a and b are the leg lengths, then c is equal to $\sqrt{a^2 + b^2}$. Substituting in the horizontal and vertical parts of the right triangle, $x_2 - x_1$ and $y_2 - y_1$, gives us $\sqrt{(x_2 - x_1)^2 + (y_2 - y_1)^2}$.

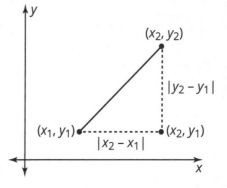

The Bermuda Triangle

One of the most famous stretches of ocean in the Atlantic is an area that stretches between the United States, Puerto Rico, and Bermuda known as the Bermuda Triangle.

A heavily traveled area by planes and ships, it has become famous because of the many stories about ships and planes lost or destroyed as they moved through the Triangle.

For years, the Bermuda Triangle was suspected of having mysterious, supernatural powers that fatally affected all who traveled through it. Others believe natural phenomena, such as human error and dangerous weather, are to blame for the incidents. In 2016, a group of scientists announced that hexagon-shaped clouds in the area, which create 170 mph "air bombs" are responsible for most, if not all, of the lost craft in the Triangle.

Talking Points

Coordinate geometry can be an important topic to know about for college admissions tests. Here is an example of a sample question:

In the *xy*-plane, a triangle has vertices at (5, 0), ($\sqrt{2}$, 0), and (2, $\sqrt{10}$). What is the approximate area of the triangle?

You can think of the base as the horizontal line segment. Its length is $5 - \sqrt{2}$, and the height is $\sqrt{10}$. So, the area is

$$\frac{1}{2}\left(\sqrt{10}\right)\left(5 - \sqrt{2}\right) \approx 5.67$$

So, the area of the triangle is approximately 5.67 square units.

Key Terms

Distance Formula

The Distance Formula states that if (x_1, y_1) and (x_2, y_2) are two points on the coordinate plane, then the distance d between (x_1, y_1) and (x_2, y_2) is given by

$$d = \sqrt{(x_2 - x_1) + (y_2 - y_1)}.$$

composite figure

A composite figure is a figure that is formed by combining different shapes.

The Shape of Things

Classifying Shapes on the Coordinate Plane

Warm Up

Determine the length of each hypotenuse. Round your answer to the nearest tenth, if necessary.

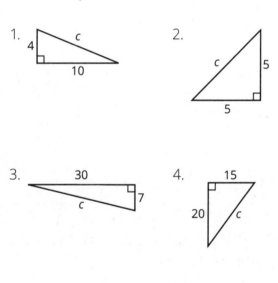

1.

2.

3.

4.

Learning Goals

- Use the Pythagorean Theorem to derive the Distance Formula.
- Apply the Distance Formula on the coordinate plane.
- Classify a triangle given the locations of its vertices on a coordinate plane.
- Determine the coordinates of a fourth vertex, given the coordinates of three vertices of a quadrilateral and a description of the quadrilateral.
- Classify a quadrilateral given the locations of its vertices on a coordinate plane.

Key Terms

- Distance Formula
- midpoint
- Midpoint Formula

You have classified triangles and quadrilaterals by the lengths of their sides and the measures of their angles. How can you classify polygons that lie on a coordinate plane?

In Top Shape

Polygons such as triangles and quadrilaterals can be classified by different properties—by the lengths of their sides, the relationship between their sides, and the measures of their angles.

Properties

- two pairs of opposite sides that are parallel
- all angles congruent
- at least one pair of perpendicular sides
- a pair of consecutive congruent sides
- no two sides with the same measure

1. **Cut out the shape names located at the end of the lesson. Sort the shapes based on the property assigned to you. Record the property and the names of the shapes that are characterized by the property.**

2. **Select a different property from the given list. Sort the shapes based on a combination of the two properties. Record the properties and the names of the shapes that are characterized by them.**

Remember:

A trapezoid has *at least* one pair of parallel sides.

3. **Compare your sorts with your classmates' sorts. Analyze how different combinations of properties characterized different shapes.**

4. Determine whether each statement is always, sometimes, or never true. Explain your reasoning.

   a. A rectangle is a parallelogram.

   b. A rhombus is a square.

   c. A scalene triangle is a right triangle.

   d. A parallelogram is a trapezoid.

   e. A right triangle is an equilateral triangle.

Calculating Distance on the Coordinate Plane

Let's analyze quadrilaterals that lie on a coordinate plane and classify them by their properties.

Consider quadrilateral *ABCD* shown.

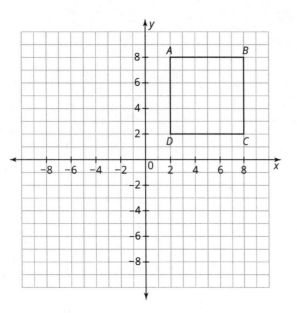

1. **Classify the quadrilateral. Justify your reasoning.**

Now consider quadrilateral *EFGH* shown.

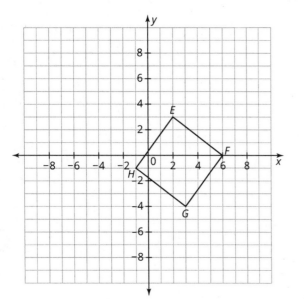

2. **Determine whether quadrilateral *EFGH* can be classified as a parallelogram. Justify your reasoning.**

3. **Determine whether quadrilateral *EFGH* can be classified as a rectangle. Justify your reasoning.**

4. What information do you need to classify quadrilateral *EFGH* as a square?

5. On quadrilateral *EFGH*, draw a right triangle *EFR* such that $\overline{EF}$ is the hypotenuse. Use the Pythagorean Theorem to determine the length of $\overline{EF}$.

You used the Pythagorean Theorem to calculate the distance between two points on the coordinate plane. Your method can be written as the *Distance Formula*. The **Distance Formula** states that if (x_1, y_1) and (x_2, y_2) are two points on the coordinate plane, then the distance d between (x_1, y_1) and (x_2, y_2) is calculated using the formula given.

$$d = \sqrt{(x_2 - x_1)^2 + (y_2 - y_1)^2}$$

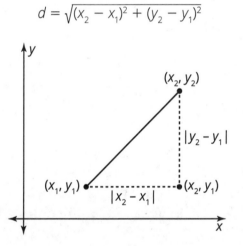

The absolute value symbols are used because the difference represents a distance.

6. When you use the Distance Formula, does it matter which point you identify as (x_1, y_1) and which point you identify as (x_2, y_2)? Explain your reasoning.

7. Can quadrilateral *EFGH* be classified as a square? Justify your reasoning.

8. Use the Distance Formula to calculate the distance between each pair of points. Round your answer to the nearest tenth, if necessary. Show all your work.

   a. (1, 2) and (3, 7)

   b. (−6, 4) and (2, −8)

   c. (−5, 2) and (−6, 10)

9. Calculate the distance between the points (−1, −2) and (−3, −7). Notice the similarity between this problem and Question 8, part (a).

   Carlos says that the solution must be the negative of the solution of part (a). Mandy disagrees and says that the solution will be the same as the solution of part (a). Who is correct? Explain your reasoning and state the correct solution.

Classifying Triangles on the Coordinate Plane

Let's analyze triangles that lie on a coordinate plane and classify them by their properties.

Consider △ABC.

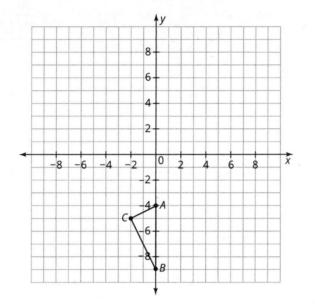

1. **Classify △ABC.**

   a. **Consider the sides of △ABC to describe it as scalene, isosceles, or equilateral. Explain your reasoning.**

Ask
yourself:

How can you determine the lengths of the sides of this triangle?

   b. **Consider the slope of each side to determine whether △ABC is a right triangle. Justify your conclusion.**

c. Zach used the Pythagorean Theorem to determine whether △*ABC* was a right triangle.

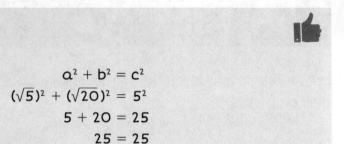

Zach

$$a^2 + b^2 = c^2$$
$$(\sqrt{5})^2 + (\sqrt{20})^2 = 5^2$$
$$5 + 20 = 25$$
$$25 = 25$$

Describe why Zach's reasoning is correct.

You can use the relationship among the sides of a triangle to determine whether the triangle is acute or obtuse. Given a, b, and c are the sides of a triangle with c as the longest side, when $c^2 < a^2 + b^2$, the triangle is acute, and when $c^2 > a^2 + b^2$, the triangle is obtuse.

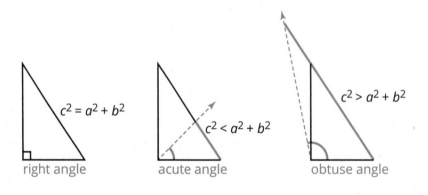

2. **Determine whether each set of side lengths creates an acute, right, or obtuse triangle.**

a. **42 cm, 36 cm, 15 cm**

b. **18.5 m, 11 m, 15 m**

c. **4 ft, $\sqrt{65}$ ft, 7 ft**

3. Graph △*JKL* using points *J* (−2, 4), *K* (8, 4), and *L* (6, −2).

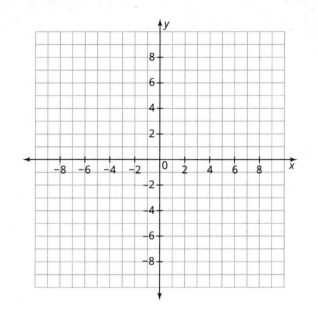

Are you using a
straightedge to draw
the triangle?

4. Classify △*JKL*.

   a. Consider the sides of △*JKL*. Describe the triangle as scalene,
      isosceles, or equilateral. Explain your reasoning.

   b. Consider the angles of △*JKL*. Describe the triangle as acute,
      obtuse, or right. Explain your reasoning.

ACTIVITY

1.3

Determining an Unknown Point of a Quadrilateral

You have classified quadrilaterals by their sides and angles. You can use this information to compose quadrilaterals on a coordinate plane.

Analyze the given points *A*, *B*, and *C*. Suppose you want to plot point *D* such that quadrilateral *ABCD* is a square.

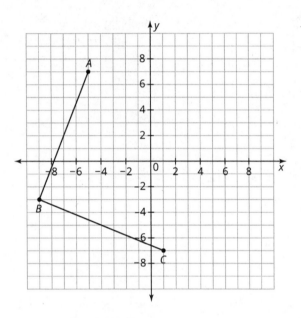

1. **Consider the properties of a square.**

   a. **How does knowing that a square has two pairs of parallel sides help to determine the unknown location?**

   b. **How does knowing that a square has four right angles help to determine the unknown location?**

2. **Determine the location of point *D*. Plot and label point *D* on the coordinate plane.**

3. Use the same locations for points *A*, *B*, and *C* to identify the location of a new point *E*, such that quadrilateral *ABCE* is a trapezoid with only one pair of parallel sides.

   a. Identify information that is helpful to locate point *E*. Explain your reasoning.

   b. Describe the possible locations of point *E* such that quadrilateral *ABCE* is a trapezoid with only one pair of parallel sides.

Classifying a Quadrilateral on the Coordinate Plane

In this activity, you will classify quadrilaterals by examining the lengths and relationships of their sides.

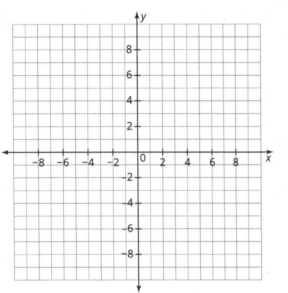

1. Graph quadrilateral *ABCD* using points *A* (−5, 6), *B* (−8, 2), *C* (−5, −2), and *D* (−2, 2).

2. Consider the sides of quadrilateral *ABCD*.

   a. Determine each side length of quadrilateral *ABCD*. Can you classify quadrilateral *ABCD* from its side lengths? If so, identify the type of figure. If not, explain why not.

Think about:

What is the difference between a square and a rhombus?

   b. Determine the slope of each line segment in the quadrilateral. Describe the relationship between the slopes. Can you identify the figure? If so, identify the type of figure. If not, explain why not.

3. **Graph quadrilateral *ABCD* using points *A* (8, 8), *B* (3, −7), *C* (10, −6), and *D* (13, 3). Classify this quadrilateral as a trapezoid, a rhombus, a rectangle, a square, or none of these. Explain your reasoning.**

Which types of figures can you eliminate as you determine information about the figure?

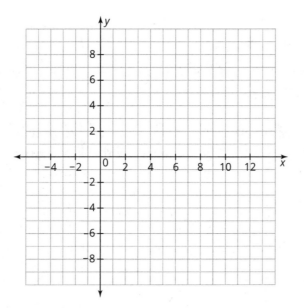

Classifying a Quadrilateral Formed by Midpoints

You have used the Distance Formula to determine the distance between two points. A **midpoint** is a point that is exactly halfway between two given points. To determine the coordinates of a midpoint, you can use the *Midpoint Formula*.

The **Midpoint Formula** states that if (x_1, y_1) and (x_2, y_2) are two points on the coordinate plane, then the midpoint of the line segment that joins these two points is $\left(\dfrac{x_1 + x_2}{2}, \dfrac{y_1 + y_2}{2}\right)$.

Use the Midpoint Formula to determine the midpoints of each side of the given figures.

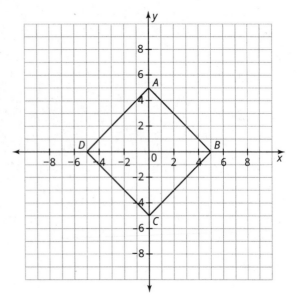

1. **Given square *ABCD*.**

   a. **Determine and label the midpoint of each side of the square.**

   b. **Determine the polygon formed by connecting the consecutive midpoints of each side of a square and justify your conclusion.**

   c. **If the same process was repeated one more time by connecting the consecutive midpoints of each side of the polygon determined in part (a), describe the polygon that would result.**

2. Sketch any rhombus that is not a square. Label the midpoint of each side of the rhombus.

a. Determine the polygon formed by connecting the consecutive midpoints of each side of a rhombus and justify your conclusion.

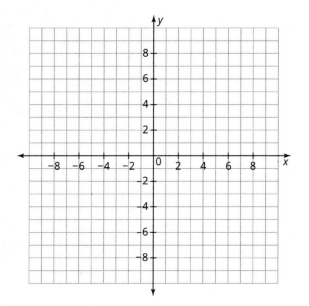

b. If the same process was repeated one more time by connecting the consecutive midpoints of each side of the polygon determined in part (a), describe the polygon that would result.

TALK the TALK

What's the Point?

Consider points A (2, 2), B (7, 8), and C (13, 8).

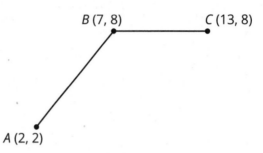

1. **Describe all possible locations for the coordinates of point D such that quadrilateral ABCD is a parallelogram.**

2. **Describe how point D can be located using a translation.**

Shape Cards

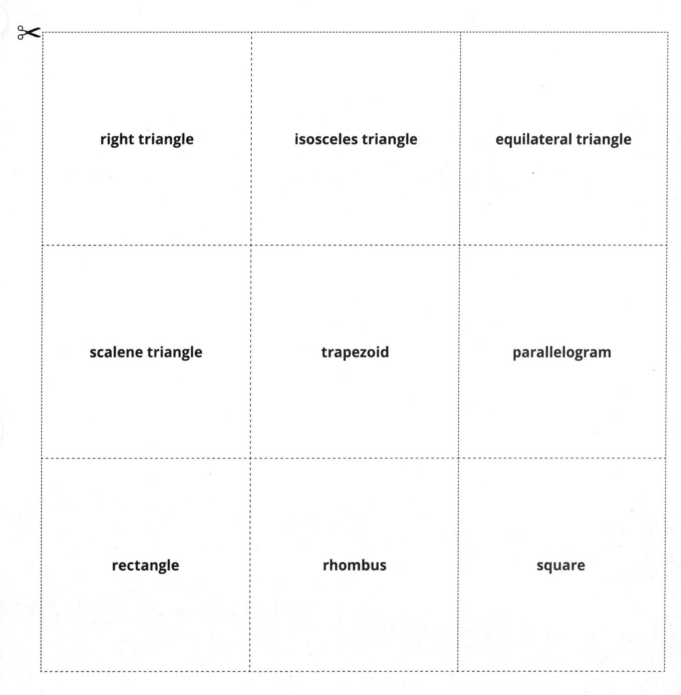

right triangle	isosceles triangle	equilateral triangle
scalene triangle	trapezoid	parallelogram
rectangle	rhombus	square

Assignment

Write

Describe how the Distance Formula and the slope formula can be used to classify triangles and quadrilaterals on the coordinate plane.

Remember

The Distance Formula states that if (x_1, y_1) and (x_2, y_2) are two points on the coordinate plane, then the distance d between the points is given by $d = \sqrt{(x_2 - x_1)^2 + (y_2 - y_1)^2}$.

Practice

1. The grid represents a map of Jose's neighborhood. It shows the locations of his house as well as the houses of four friends.

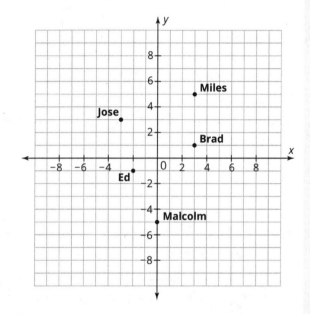

   a. Draw a triangle between the houses of Jose, Ed, and Brad. Determine whether this triangle is a scalene, isosceles, or equilateral triangle. Explain your reasoning.

   b. Determine whether the triangle is a right triangle. Explain your reasoning. If it is not a right triangle, determine whether it is acute or obtuse.

   c. Jose, Miles, and Brad are meeting for band rehearsal. Miles claims that the distance from Jose's house to his house is the same as the distance from Jose's house to Brad's house. Is his claim correct? Explain your answer. What kind of triangle is formed if you connect their houses?

   d. A new boy, James, moved into the neighborhood at the location $(-3, -5)$. Plot and label James's house on the grid. Then, determine whether the triangle formed by connecting his house, Jose's house, and Malcolm's house is a right triangle.

2. Susan is an interior floor designer. When designing a new floor, she uses a coordinate grid to represent the room. The client wants a rectangular tile insert to be placed in the floor of the room. The coordinates for 3 of the corners of the insert are $A(-7, -4)$, $B(1, 6)$, and $C(6, 2)$.

   a. Plot and label the points on a coordinate plane, then determine the coordinates of the fourth point of the rectangular tile insert. Plot this as point D and connect the points to form the rectangle.

   b. To prove the figure you drew is a rectangle, verify that the length of opposite sides are equal.

3. A client of Susan's has asked her to create a new wood floor for his living room. The design will be created by laying wood strips in different directions, as shown on the coordinate grid. Determine whether Quadrilateral *ABCD* can best be described as a trapezoid, a rhombus, a rectangle, or a square. Explain your reasoning.

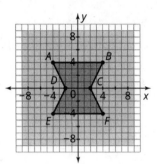

Stretch

The lines that connect points *A*, *B*, and *C* in a coordinate plane form a right triangle. Point *A* is located at $(-2, 5)$. Point *B* is located 6 units down from point *A* and to the left of point *A*. Point *C* is located 4 units to the right of point *A* and down from point *A*. The angle at point *B* is a right angle. The slope of the line between point *B* and point *C* is $-\frac{1}{3}$. The distance between point *A* and point *B* is $\sqrt{40}$. Determine the coordinates of point *B* and point *C*.

Review

1. The Build-A-Dream construction company has plans for two models of the homes they build, Model A and Model B. The Model A home requires 18 single windows and 3 double windows. The Model B home requires 20 single windows and 5 double windows. A total of 1,800 single windows and 375 double windows have been ordered for the developments.

   a. Write and solve a system of equations to represent this situation. Define your variables.

   b. Interpret the solution of the linear system in terms of the problem situation.

2. A company produces two types of TV stands. Type I has 6 drawers. It requires 3 single drawer pulls and 3 double drawer pulls. The company needs 75 hours of labor to produce the Type I TV stand. Type II has 3 drawers. It requires 6 single drawer pulls. The company needs 50 hours of labor to produce the Type II TV stand. The company only has 600 labor hours available each week, and a total of 60 single drawer pulls available in a week. For each Type I stand produced and sold, the company makes $200 in profit. For each Type II stand produced and sold, the company makes $150 in profit.

   a. Identify the constraints as a system of linear inequalities. Let *x* represent the number of 6 drawer TV stands produced and let *y* represent the number of 3 drawer TV stands produced.

   b. Graph the solution set for the system of linear inequalities. Label all points of the intersection of the boundary lines.

   c. Write an equation in standard form for the profit, *P*, that the company can make.

   d. How many of each type of stand should the company make if they want to maximize their profit? What is the maximum profit?

3. Each function is a transformation of the linear basic function $f(x) = x$. Graph each transformation.

   a. $g(x) = \frac{1}{3}x - 2$ b. $h(x) = -2x + 1$

Know It Inside Out

Area and Perimeter of Triangles and Rectangles on the Coordinate Plane

Warm Up

Determine the distance between each set of points. Round your answer to the nearest tenth, if necessary.

1. $(2, -3)$ and $(-4, 1)$

2. $(-4.75, -8.5)$ and $(3.25, 5.5)$

3. $\left(\frac{5}{4}, \frac{9}{4}\right)$ and $(0, 10)$

Learning Goals

- Determine the perimeter and area of rectangles on the coordinate plane.
- Determine the perimeter and area of triangles on the coordinate plane.
- Use transformations to discover efficient strategies to determine the perimeter and area of rectangles and triangles.

You have used the Distance Formula and the slope formula to classify geometric figures on the coordinate plane. How can you use these same formulas to determine the perimeter and area of rectangles and triangles on the coordinate plane?

It's Child's Play

A city uses a coordinate grid to map out the locations of two play areas at the park that need to be covered with a rubber surface to prevent injuries. Rectangle *JKLM* represents an area under a swing set and △*NOP* represents an area under a play structure. Each square on the coordinate grid represents one square foot.

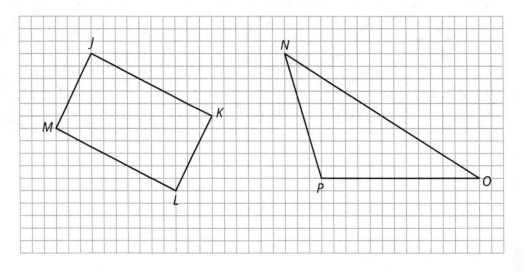

1. **Describe a way you can use the grid to determine the area of rectangle *JKLM* and △*NOP*.**

Remember:

The altitude, or height, of a triangle is the perpendicular distance from a vertex to the line containing the opposite side, represented by a line segment.

© Carnegie Learning, Inc.

Perimeter and Area of Figures on the Coordinate Plane

Previously, you classified geometric figures on the coordinate plane by examining the lengths and relationships of their sides. Now, you will determine the perimeter and the area of geometric figures.

1. **Consider rectangle *ABCD*.**

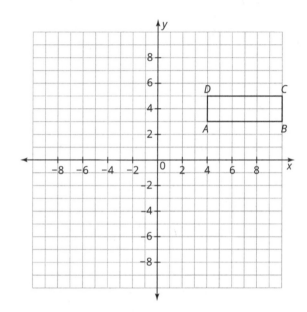

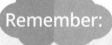

Remember:

The perimeter of a geometric figure is calculated by adding the side lengths.

Remember:

The formula for area of a rectangle is $A = bh$, where *A* represents the area, *b* represents the base, and *h* represents the height.

   a. **Determine the perimeter of rectangle *ABCD*.**

   b. **Determine the area of rectangle *ABCD*.**

2. **Horace says that he determined the area of rectangle *ABCD* by determining the product *CD*(*CB*). Bernice says that Horace is incorrect because he needs to use the base of the rectangle and that the base is $\overline{AB}$, not $\overline{CD}$. Horace responded by saying that $\overline{CD}$ is one of the bases. Who's correct? Explain your reasoning.**

When a rectangle is graphed along gridlines, you can determine the perimeter and area by simply counting units or square units on the coordinate plane.

Analyze rectangle *RSTU* on the coordinate plane shown.

Think about:

Notice the intervals along the axes.

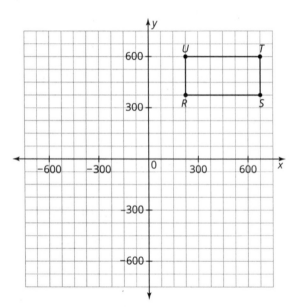

3. **Calculate the perimeter and area of rectangle *RSTU*.**

4. **How would doubling the height of the rectangle affect the area?**

5. **How would doubling the length of the base of the rectangle affect the area?**

When the sides of a rectangle do not lie on the gridlines of the coordinate plane, you can use the Distance Formula to determine the lengths of the sides.

6. Consider quadrilateral *LMNO*.

   a. Determine the perimeter and area of quadrilateral *LMNO*. Round your answer to the nearest hundredth, if necessary.

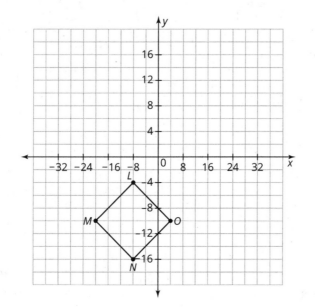

Think
about:

Is the quadrilateral a square, a rectangle, or a rhombus?

   b. Double the side lengths of quadrilateral *LMNO*. How does this affect the area? What are the new coordinates?

7. Consider △*DEF* with vertices *D* (−9, −4), *E* (−9, −14), and *F* (−2, −14).

a. Determine the perimeter and area of △*DEF*. Round your answer to the nearest hundredth, if necessary.

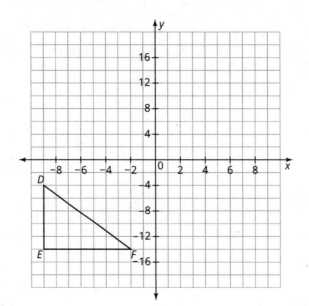

b. Double the height. What are the coordinates of the new triangle? How did this affect the area?

c. Double the length of the base. What are the coordinates of the new triangle? How did this affect the area?

d. Double the length of both the base and the height. How does this affect the area?

Consider △ABC with vertices A (−7.5, 2), B (−5.5, 13), and C (2.5, 2).

8. Determine the perimeter of △ABC. Round your answer to the nearest hundredth, if necessary.

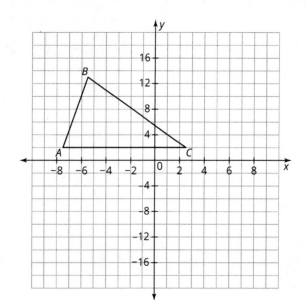

9. Determine the area of △ABC.

   a. What information is needed about △ABC to determine its area?

   b. Arlo says that $\overline{AB}$ can be used as the height. Trisha disagrees and says that $\overline{BC}$ can be used as the height. Randy disagrees with both of them and says that none of the line segments currently on the triangle can be used as the height. Who is correct? Explain your reasoning.

   c. Draw and label $\overline{BD}$ to represent the height of △ABC. Then, determine the height of △ABC.

   d. Determine the area of △ABC.

Shantelle claimed she used another strategy to determine the perimeter and area of rectangle *RSTU* from the previous activity. She explained the strategy she used.

> **Shantelle**
>
> If I translate rectangle *RSTU* to have at least one point of image *R'S'T'U'* on the origin, it is easier to calculate the perimeter and area of rectangle *RSTU* because one of the points will have coordinates (0, 0).

1. **How do you know a translation of rectangle *RSTU* will have the same area and perimeter as the pre-image *RSTU*? Explain your reasoning.**

2. **Explain why Shantelle's rationale is correct.**

As you learned previously, translations are rigid motions that preserve size and shape. The pre-image and the image are congruent because in a translation, all vertices are rigidly moved from one location to another location.

So, you know that the lengths of the sides of rectangle *RSTU* will be preserved if the rectangle is translated. That means that the perimeter of the rectangle is preserved when translated.

3. **Once again, consider rectangle *RSTU*.**

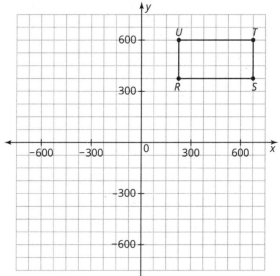

a. **Translate the rectangle so that point *R* is located at the origin. Then, list the coordinates of rectangle *R'S'T'U'*.**

b. **Determine the perimeter and area of *R'S'T'U'*. What do you notice?**

4. Mr. Young gives his class $\triangle DEF$ and asks them to determine the area and perimeter.

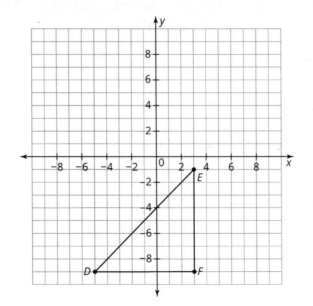

Four of his students decide to first transform the figure and then determine the perimeter and area. Their transformations are shown.

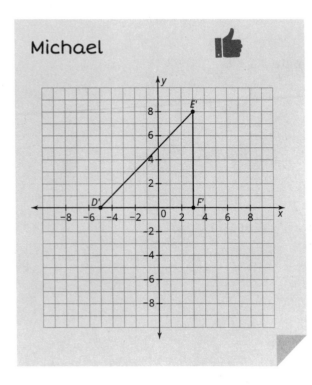

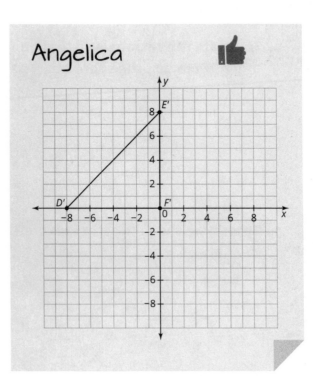

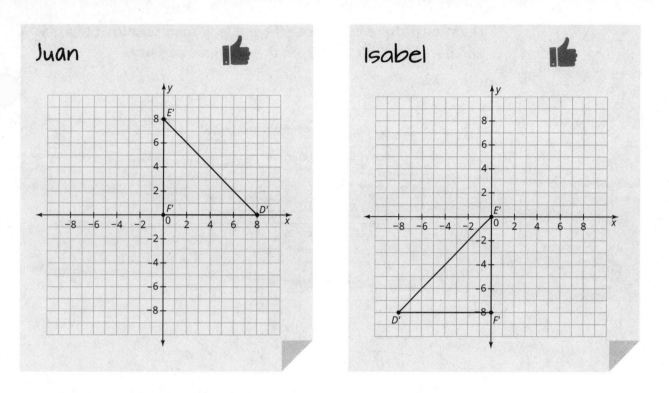

a. Describe the transformation(s) each student made to △DEF.

b. Whose method do you think is most efficient? Explain your reasoning.

c. What do you know about the perimeter and area of all the triangles? Explain your reasoning.

d. Calculate the perimeter and area of △DEF.

5. Let's see if there is a more efficient way to determine the area and perimeter of △*ABC* from the previous activity.

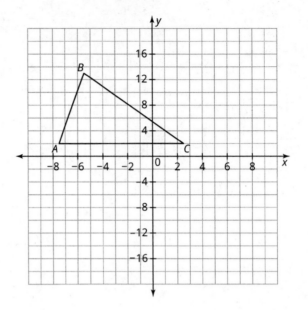

a. Transform △*ABC* on the coordinate plane. Label the image *A'B'C'*. Describe the transformation(s) completed and explain your reasoning.

b. Determine the perimeter and area of △*A'B'C'*. Round your answer to the nearest hundredth, if necessary.

c. Compare these calculations to your previous calculations. How did the translation change your calculations?

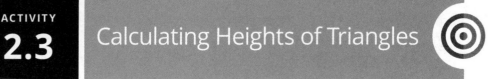
Consider $\triangle XYZ$ with vertices X (2, 5), Y (10, 9), and Z (6, 1).

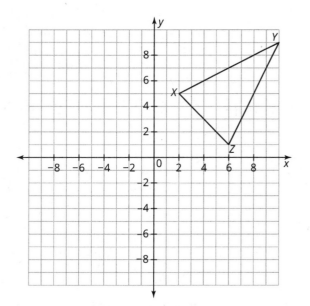

1. **Determine the perimeter of $\triangle XYZ$. Round your answer to the nearest hundredth, if necessary.**

2. **To determine the area, you will need to determine the height. How will determining the height of this triangle be different from determining the height of the triangles in previous activities?**

Let's use $\overline{XY}$ as the base of $\triangle XYZ$. You can draw $\overline{ZW}$ to represent the height. Remember that the height is perpendicular to the base. To determine the length of the height, you need to locate point W, which is located at the intersection of $\overline{XY}$ and $\overline{ZW}$.

Remember:

The slopes of perpendicular lines are opposite reciprocals.

Worked Example

Calculate the slope of the base, $\overline{XY}$.
$$m = \frac{y_2 - y_1}{x_2 - x_1} = \frac{9 - 5}{10 - 2} = \frac{4}{8} = \frac{1}{2}$$

Determine the slope of the height, $\overline{ZW}$.
$$m = -2$$

You can write equations for $\overleftrightarrow{XY}$ and $\overleftrightarrow{ZW}$ and solve the system to determine where the two lines intersect.

Determine the equations of the lines containing the base and the height.

	Base $\overleftrightarrow{XY}$	Height $\overleftrightarrow{ZW}$
	$X\,(2, 5),\ m = \frac{1}{2}$	$Z\,(6, 1),\ m = -2$
	$y - y_1 = m(x - x_1)$	$y - y_1 = m(x - x_1)$
	$y - 5 = \frac{1}{2}(x - 2)$	$y - 1 = -2(x - 6)$
	$y = \frac{1}{2}x + 4$	$y = -2x + 13$

Solve the system of equations to determine the coordinates of the point of intersection.

$$\frac{1}{2}x + 4 = -2x + 13 \qquad\qquad y = -2x + 13$$
$$\frac{5}{2}x = 9 \qquad\qquad\qquad\qquad y = -2\left(\frac{18}{5}\right) + 13$$
$$x = \frac{18}{5} \qquad\qquad\qquad\qquad\quad y = \frac{29}{5}$$

3. **Identify the coordinates of the point of intersection. Plot this point on the coordinate plane and label it point W. Draw $\overline{ZW}$ to represent the height.**

4. **Determine the area of $\triangle XYZ$.**

   a. **Determine the height of the triangle.**

   b. **Determine the area of the triangle.**

© Carnegie Learning, Inc.

M2-280 • TOPIC 4: Shapes on a Coordinate Plane

You know that any side of a triangle can be thought of as the base of the triangle.

5. **Predict whether using a different side as the base will result in a different area of the triangle. Explain your reasoning.**

Let's consider your prediction.

6. **Triangle *XYZ* is graphed on the coordinate plane. This time consider side $\overline{XZ}$ as the base.**

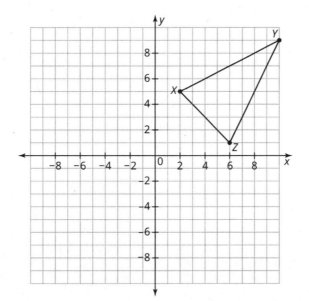

a. **Let point *V* represent the intersection point of the height, $\overline{YV}$, and the base. Determine the coordinates of point *V*.**

b. Determine the height of △*XYZ*.

c. Determine the area of △*XYZ*.

7. Triangle *XYZ* is graphed on the coordinate plane. Determine the area of △*XYZ* using side $\overline{YZ}$ as the base.

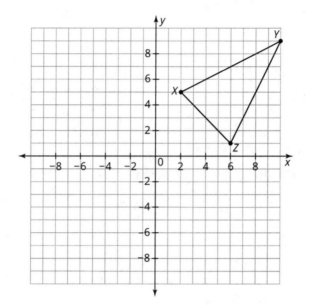

8. Compare the three areas you determined for △*XYZ*.
   Was your prediction in Question 5 correct?

TALK the TALK

Three's Company

Kaycee wants to paint an enlarged version of her company's triangular logo on the wall of the reception room for clients to see when they first walk into the building. To get the proportions correct, she constructs a removable coordinate grid on the wall using tape and sets the intervals of each axis 1 foot apart. Kaycee marks the vertices of the logo at A (0, 6), R (4, 2), and T (8, 4) and connects the points with straight lines.

1. **A four-ounce bottle of the paint Kaycee wants to use costs $12 and covers 8 square feet. She plans to use 3 coats of paint on the logo to really make the color stand out. Determine how much Kaycee will spend on paint. Explain your reasoning.**

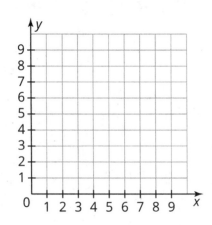

Assignment

Write

Describe how the Distance Formula and the slope formula can be used to find the height of a triangle on the coordinate plane.

Remember

Rigid transformations can make calculating the perimeter and area of figures on the coordinate plane more efficient.

Any side of a triangle can be considered its base, and the height of the triangle is the perpendicular distance from the base to the opposite vertex.

Practice

1. Franco translates rectangle *JKLM* so that it has one vertex on the origin. The result is rectangle *J'K'L'M'*. He claims that he doesn't even have to use the Distance Formula to calculate the perimeter and area of this translated rectangle.

   a. Is Franco correct? Why or why not?

   b. Maeko claims that you don't have to use the Distance Formula or translate the rectangle in order to calculate the perimeter and area of the original rectangle. Is she correct? Why or why not?

   c. Give an example of a case in which translating a rectangle to the origin would be extremely helpful in simplifying the calculations for determining the perimeter and area of the rectangle.

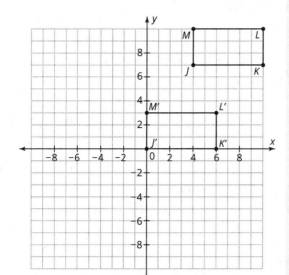

2. Olivia translates rectangle *WXYZ* vertically up 1 unit and horizontally to the right 4 units to produce the image *W'X'Y'Z'*. Thom translates the rectangle vertically up 6 units and horizontally to the right 5 units to produce the image *W"X"Y"Z"*.

   a. Would you prefer to use Olivia's translation or Thom's translation to determine the perimeter and area of the rectangle? Explain your reasoning.

   b. Calculate the perimeter and area of the rectangle. Show your work.

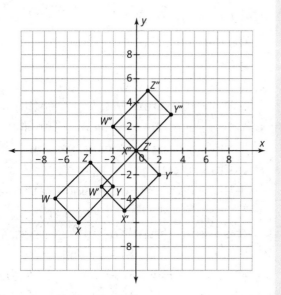

3. Cisco claims that $\overline{GH}$ is the height of $\triangle EFG$, and Beth claims that $\overline{GJ}$ is the height of $\triangle EFG$.

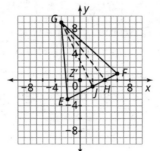

   a. Who is correct? Justify your response.

   b. Calculate the area of $\triangle EFG$. Show your work.

Stretch

1. A few years ago, Leon planted a small triangular garden in his backyard. Recently he has been thinking that the garden is too small. He now wants to double the area of the garden. His original garden is shown on the coordinate plane. Each unit represents one square foot.

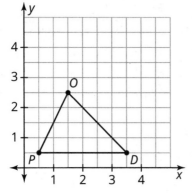

   a. Describe two ways Leon could double the area of his garden.

   b. Because of the location of Leon's neighbors, he cannot extend the garden any further horizontally. Use this information to manipulate $\triangle POD$ representing Leon's garden to double the area. Label the vertices of $\triangle PO'D$.

   c. Determine the area of the original garden and the new garden to verify that the area has doubled.

Review

1. The members of a youth football program are required to sell tickets to chicken dinners for the program's fundraiser. They can sell adult tickets for $10 and child tickets for $5. Each athlete must bring in at least $350 from the ticket sales.

   a. Write an expression to represent the total amount of money an athlete makes from ticket sales. Let x represent the number of adult tickets sold and let y represent the number of child tickets sold.

   b. Write an inequality in two variables to represent the amount an athlete must make.

   c. Graph the inequality from part (b).

   d. Use the graph to determine whether an athlete will bring in at least $350 if they sell 10 adult tickets and 30 child tickets. Explain your reasoning.

2. The quadrilateral $ABCD$ has the vertices A $(-5, 4)$, B $(0, 6)$, C $(1, 3)$, and D $(-4, 1)$. Determine whether it can be classified as a parallelogram. Justify your reasoning.

3. Triangle DEF has the vertices D $(-2, 3)$, E $(2, -1)$, and F $(-5, -4)$. Determine whether it is scalene, isosceles, or equilateral. Explain your reasoning.

4. Solve for b in the equation $\frac{a - b}{12} = 11 - 6a$.

In All Shapes and Sizes

Area and Perimeter of Polygons on the Coordinate Plane

3

Warm Up

Determine the perimeter and area of each figure with the given coordinates. Round your answer to the nearest hundredth, if necessary.

1.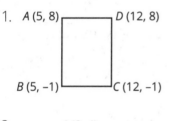
A (5, 8)   D (12, 8)

B (5, –1)   C (12, –1)

2.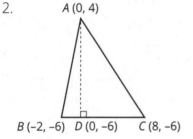
A (0, 4)

B (–2, –6) D (0, –6)   C (8, –6)

Learning Goals

- Determine the perimeter and area of parallelograms on a coordinate plane.
- Determine the perimeter and area of trapezoids and hexagons on a coordinate plane.
- Determine the perimeter and the area of composite figures on a coordinate plane.

Key Term

- composite figure

You have determined the perimeter and area of rectangles and triangles on the coordinate plane. How can you use these shapes to determine the areas of other polygons on the coordinate plane?

Tour de France

Luca is planning a biking trip around France. The polygon drawn on the map represents Luca's approximate route.

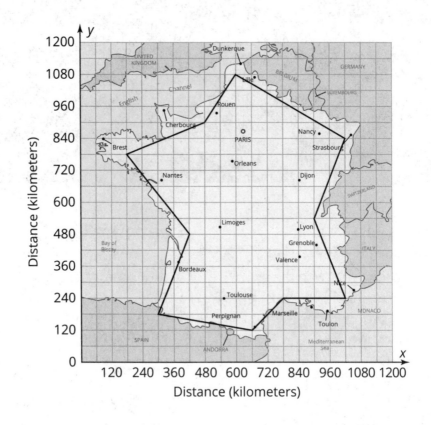

1. **Estimate the total length of Luca's route to the nearest kilometer.**

A pattern for a quilt patch is drawn on a coordinate plane where each interval represents one inch. Parallelogram *ABCD* represents the patch.

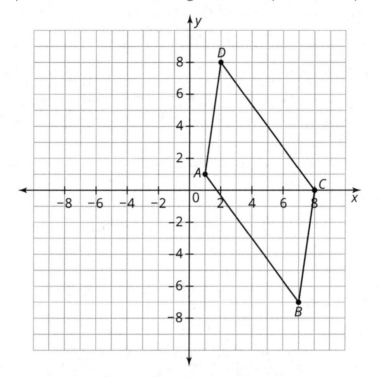

1. **Bryce is in charge of buying the ribbon that will be sewn around the outside of each patch. How many inches of ribbon are needed for each patch?**

The method you use to determine the perimeter of a rectangle or triangle can be used with any polygon. You can use the Distance Formula to calculate the distance between any set of vertices and then add the lengths of all the sides.

You can determine the area of a *composite figure* by dividing the figure into a combination of rectangles and triangles. A **composite figure** is a figure that is formed by combining different shapes.

Carter has an irregular backyard because it backs onto the foothill of a mountain and is very rocky. The composite figure graphed on the coordinate plane represents the useable area of Carter's backyard that is flat. Each interval of the coordinate plane represents two yards.

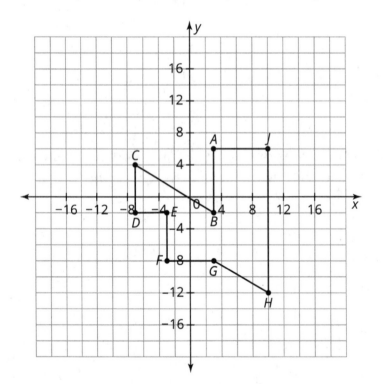

1. Carter will install fencing all around the flat area of his backyard. Determine the amount of fencing he needs to the nearest whole yard.

2. Carter wants to lay grass sod in the flat area of his backyard. Determine the total area of sod he needs.

3. Compare the method you used to determine the area of sod Carter needs to your classmates' methods. If you had a different way of dividing up the composite figure, did your answers differ? Explain why or why not.

4. The fencing costs $5.45 per foot and the sod costs $0.62 per square foot. In order to have room for error, Carter plans to buy an extra 10% of both materials. How much will it cost Carter to purchase these materials?

Aida's bedroom is on the top floor of her house. In her room, the roof slants downward, creating two congruent trapezoid-shaped walls. One of the walls in her room is represented on the coordinate plane by quadrilateral *ABCD*. Each interval on the coordinate plane represents one foot.

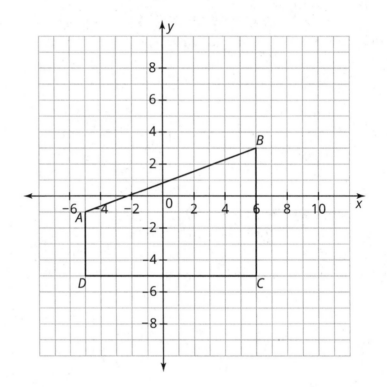

Aida and Marco are going to paint the two walls and want to place a strip of painter's tape along each edge of the walls so the paint does not touch any other wall, the ceiling, or the floor.

1. **What is the length of painter's tape to the nearest whole foot that Aida and Marco need to be able to cover the edges of both walls?**

Ask

yourself:

How can you use a transformation of trapezoid *ABCD* on the coordinate plane as part of your strategy?

2. Marco says he can draw a diagonal to divide trapezoid *ABCD* into a right and an isosceles triangle to determine the area of the trapezoid. Aida says she can draw a horizontal line segment to divide trapezoid *ABCD* into a rectangle and a right triangle to determine the area of the trapezoid. Who's correct? Explain your reasoning.

3. One gallon of paint covers approximately 400 square feet. Aida estimates she has about one fourth of a gallon of paint remaining of the color she wants to use. Does she have enough paint for both walls? Explain your reasoning.

Perimeter and Area of a Hexagon

Emma and Kevin are designing a gazebo for the local park. The polygon shown on the coordinate plane represents the base of the gazebo. Each interval on the coordinate plane represents two feet.

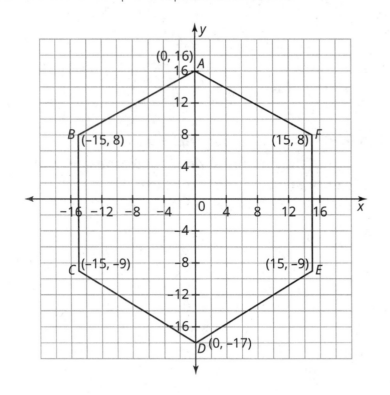

1. **The base of the gazebo needs to be built with lengths of lumber around the outside to support the floorboards. What is the length of lumber needed for the outside of the base?**

2. **How many square feet of floorboards are needed for the base of the gazebo? Describe how you determined your answer and show your work.**

Area Under a Curve

The graph shows the constant speed of a car on the highway over the course of 2.5 hours.

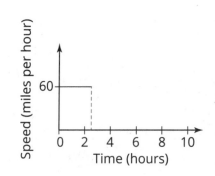

1. **Describe how you could calculate the distance the car traveled in 2.5 hours using what you know about area.**

2. **How far did the car travel in 2.5 hours?**

The graph you used is called a velocity-time graph. In a velocity-time graph, the area under the line or curve gives the distance.

The graph shown describes the speed and the time of a passenger jet's ascent.

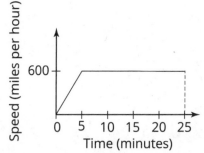

3. **How can you use the graph to determine the distance the jet has traveled in 25 minutes?**

4. Determine the distance the jet has traveled:

   a. in 25 minutes.

   b. in the first 5 minutes.

5. Consider the ascent of a passenger jet.

   a. Draw a velocity-time graph to model the ascent of a
      passenger jet using the information given.
      • The jet took 7 minutes to reach a top speed of
        600 miles per hour.
      • The jet continued to travel at a constant speed of
        600 miles per hour.
      • The jet left the airport 4 hours ago.

   b. How many miles has the jet traveled?

TALK the TALK

Vive les Maths!

Eva is using a map to estimate the area of France. She thinks the country looks like a hexagon and draws the polygon shown to approximate its shape.

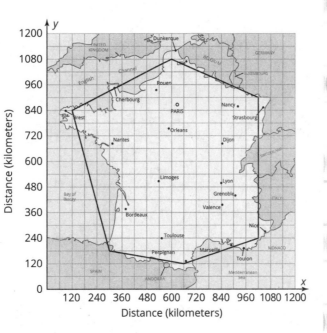

1. Determine which statements are true. Justify your answers.
   - The coastline of France is greater than 5000 km.

   - The coastline of France is less than 5000 km.

   - The coastline of France is approximately 5000 km.

   - The area of France is greater than 1,000,000 sq km.

   - The area of France is less than 1,000,000 sq km.

   - The area of France is approximately 1,000,000 sq km.

2. If the population of France is approximately 104 people per square kilometer, how many people live in the country of France?

Write

Describe how you can determine the area of a composite figure.

Remember

The perimeter of any polygon on the coordinate plane can be determined by using the Distance Formula and adding the lengths of the sides.

Practice

1. Trapezoid *QRST* is given.
   a. Determine the perimeter of trapezoid *QRST*. Show your work. Round your answer to the nearest hundredth, if necessary.
   b. Determine the area of trapezoid *QRST*. Show your work and explain how you determined your answer.

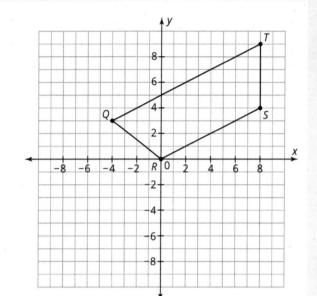

2. Composite figure *ABCDEFG* is given.
   a. Determine the perimeter of figure *ABCDEFG*.
   b. Determine the area of figure *ABCDEFG*.

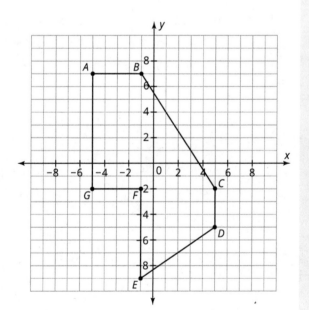

Stretch

Parallelograms *JKLM* and *JKPR* are given. Without calculating each area, determine whether or not the area of parallelogram *JKPR* is twice that of the area of parallelogram *JKLM*. Explain how you determined your answer.

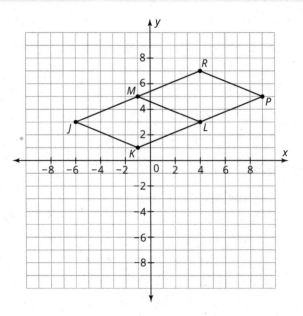

Review

1. Lucia and Danna both recently purchased fitness watches. The watches count the number of steps they walk in a day. At lunchtime, Lucia has 5445 steps and Danna has 4995 steps. Lucia averages 800 steps per hour and Danna averages 900 steps per hour.

   a. Write and solve a system of linear equations that represent the total number of steps each person takes after lunch.

   b. Interpret the meaning of the solution in terms of the problem situation.

2. Triangle *PQR* is given. Determine the area of △*PQR* using $\overline{QR}$ as the base. Show your work.

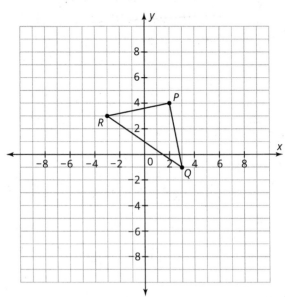

3. Calculate the average rate of change of the function $f(x) = 2x - 2$ from $x_1 = 5$ to $x_2 = 11$.

Shapes on a Coordinate Plane Summary

KEY TERMS

- Distance Formula
- midpoint
- Midpoint Formula
- composite figure

LESSON 1

The Shape of Things

You can use the Pythagorean Theorem to calculate the distance between two points on the coordinate plane. This method can be written as the **Distance Formula**. The Distance Formula states that if (x_1, y_1) and (x_2, y_2) are two points on the coordinate plane, then the distance d between (x_1, y_1) and (x_2, y_2) is given by $d = \sqrt{(x_2 - x_1)^2 + (y_2 - y_1)^2}$.

Note that absolute value symbols are used because length is always positive.

You can apply the Distance Formula to determine the lengths of the sides of polygons on the coordinate plane.

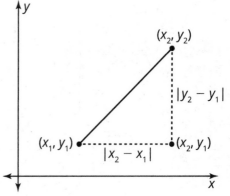

For example, classify △ABC as scalene, isosceles, or equilateral by determining AC, CB, and AB.

Since points A and B have the same x-value, determine the length of AB by determining the absolute value of the difference in the y-values.

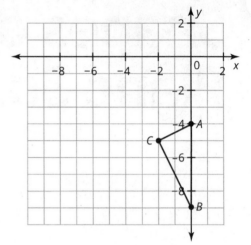

$AB = |-4 - (-9)|$
$AB = 5$

Then, use the Distance Formula to determine AC and CB.

$d = \sqrt{(2)^2 + (1)^2}$ $d = \sqrt{(4)^2 + (2)^2}$
$d = \sqrt{5}$ $d = \sqrt{20}$
$AC \approx 2.24$ $CB \approx 4.47$

Since all sides of the triangle are different lengths, the triangle is scalene.

The slopes of adjacent sides of a polygon can also be used to determine if the sides form a right angle since the slopes of perpendicular lines are negative reciprocals of each other. For example, in △ABC, $\overline{AC}$ has a slope of $\frac{1}{2}$ and $\overline{BC}$ has a slope of −2. Since $\frac{1}{2}$ and −2 are negative reciprocals, the line segments form a right angle and △ABC can be classified as a right scalene triangle.

Given three points of a quadrilateral, the fourth point can be determined using the Distance Formula and the characteristics of the specific quadrilateral.

For example, given points A, B, and C, point D can be placed at (5, 3) to create a square or at (3, −2) to create a trapezoid.

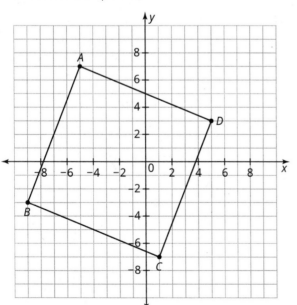

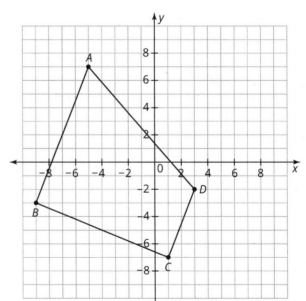

The Distance Formula can be used to determine the perimeter and area of rectangles and triangles on the coordinate plane. The perimeter of a geometric figure is calculated by adding the side lengths. The formula for the area of a rectangle is $A = bh$, where A represents area, b represents the base, and h represents height.

Consider rectangle $ABCD$ on the coordinate plane.

$P = 2 + 6 + 2 + 6$
$\quad = 16$

The perimeter is 16 units.

$A = 6 \times 2$
$\quad = 12$

The area is 12 square units.

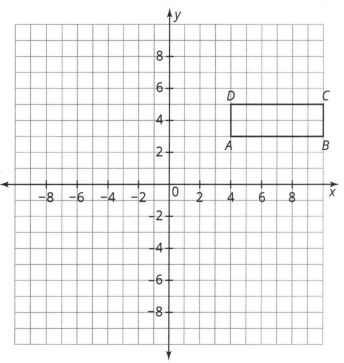

Next, consider $\triangle ABC$ with vertices $A\,(-7.5, 2)$, $B\,(-5.5, 13)$, and $C\,(2.5, 2)$.

You can use the Distance Formula to determine the lengths of the sides, and then determine the sum of the lengths of the sides to calculate the perimeter of the triangle.

$AB = \sqrt{2^2 + 11^2} \approx 11.18$

$BC = \sqrt{8^2 + 11^2} \approx 13.6$

$AC = |-7.5 - 2.5| = 10$

$P \approx 11.18 + 13.6 + 10 \approx 34.78$

The formula for the area of a triangle is $A = \frac{1}{2}bh$, where A represents area, b represents the base, and h represents height. To determine the area of the triangle, first determine the height of the triangle. The altitude, or height, of a triangle is the perpendicular distance from a vertex to the line containing the opposite side, represented by a line segment.

For example, again consider $\triangle ABC$ with vertices $A\,(-7.5, 2)$, $B\,(-5.5, 13)$, and $C\,(2.5, 2)$. The height of the triangle can be created using a line segment from vertex B to base $\overline{AC}$.

The height is $13 - 2 = 11$ units.

The length of the base, $\overline{AC}$, is $|-7.5 - 2.5|$ $= 10$ units.

$A = \frac{1}{2}(11 \times 10) = 55$

The area of the triangle is 55 square units.

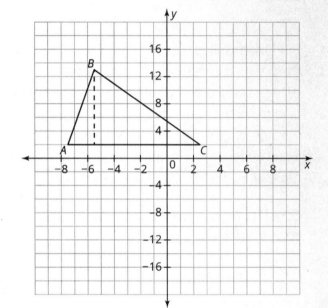

You can translate shapes on the coordinate plane to make the process of determining the perimeter and area more efficient. Translations are rigid motions that preserve the size and shape of a figure. The pre-image and the image are congruent because in a translation, all vertices must be rigidly moved from one location to another location.

The image of $\triangle ABC$, $\triangle A'B'C'$, has the same area and perimeter as the pre-image.

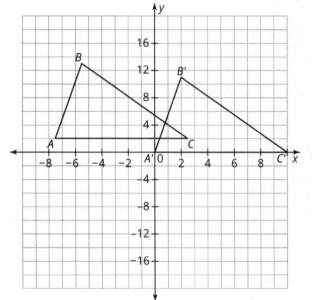

When the base of a triangle is not horizontal, the points that can be used to create a height perpendicular to the base must be identified.

For example, consider $\triangle XYZ$ with vertices X (2, 5), Y (10, 9), and Z (6, 1).

Using $\overline{XY}$ as the base of $\triangle XYZ$, you can draw $\overline{ZW}$ to represent the height, such that $\overline{ZW}$ is perpendicular to $\overline{XY}$.

First, calculate the slope of the base.

$$m = \frac{y_2 - y_1}{x_2 - x_1} = \frac{9 - 5}{10 - 2} = \frac{4}{8}$$

$$m = \frac{1}{2}$$

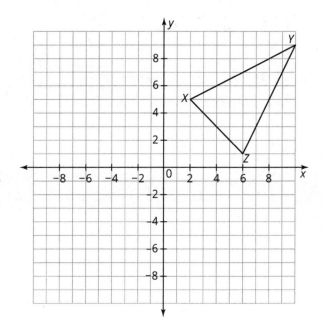

Determine the slope of the height, using the fact that the slopes of perpendicular lines are negative reciprocals.

$$m = -2$$

Write equations for lines XY and ZW and solve the system to determine where the two lines intersect.

Determine the equation of the base and the equation of the height.	Height ZW	Base XY
	Z (6, 1), $m = -2$	X (2, 5), $m = \frac{1}{2}$
	$(y - y_1) = m\,(x - x_1)$	$(y - y_1) = m\,(x - x_1)$
	$(y - 1) = -2(x - 6)$	$(y - 5) = \frac{1}{2}(x - 2)$
	$y = -2x + 13$	$y = \frac{1}{2}x + 4$

Solve the system of equations to determine the coordinates of the point of intersection.	$-2x + 13 = \frac{1}{2}x + 4$	$y = -2x + 13$
	$9 = \frac{5}{2}x$	$y = -2\left(\frac{18}{5}\right) + 13$
	$x = \frac{18}{5}$	$y = \frac{29}{5}$

The location of point W is at $\left(\frac{18}{5}, -\frac{29}{5}\right)$. This can be used to determine the height, ZW.

The method you use to determine the perimeter of a rectangle or triangle can be used with any polygon. You can use the Distance Formula to calculate the distance between any set of vertices and then add the lengths of all the sides.

You can determine the area of a **composite figure** by dividing the figure into a combination of rectangles and triangles. A composite figure is a figure that is formed by combining different shapes.

For example, suppose Aida has a bedroom that is on the top floor of her house. The roof slants downward, creating two congruent trapezoid shaped walls. One of the walls in her room is represented on the coordinate plane by quadrilateral *ABCD*. Each interval on the coordinate plane represents one foot.

You can determine the area of quadrilateral *ABCD* by breaking it into a triangle and a rectangle and determining the area of each.

The area of the triangle with vertices at (−5, −1), (6, 3), and (6, −1), is 22 square feet.

The area of the rectangle with vertices at (−5, −1), (6, −1), (6, −5), and (−5, −5) is 44 square feet.

The area of the wall is 22 square feet + 44 square feet = 66 square feet.

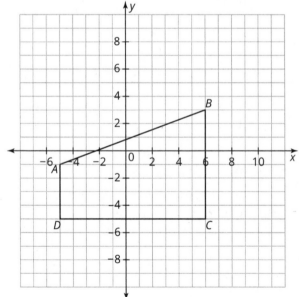

A
---

absolute maximum

A function has an absolute maximum if there is a point that has a y-coordinate that is greater than the y-coordinates of every other point on the graph.

Example

The ordered pair (4, 2) is the absolute maximum of the graph of the function $f(x) = -\frac{1}{2}x^2 + 4x - 6$.

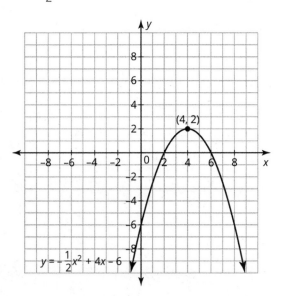

absolute minimum

A function has an absolute minimum if there is a point that has a y-coordinate that is less than the y-coordinates of every other point on the graph.

Example

The ordered pair (1, −4) is the absolute minimum of the graph of the function $y = \frac{2}{3}x^2 - \frac{4}{3}x - \frac{10}{3}$.

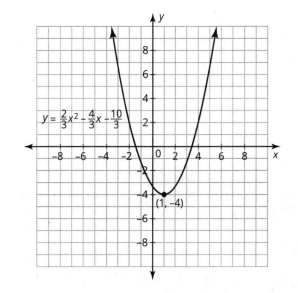

---

angle

An angle is formed by two rays that share a common endpoint.

Angle Addition Postulate

The Angle Addition Postulate states: "If point D lies in the interior of $\angle ABC$, then $m\angle ABD + m\angle DBC = m\angle ABC$."

angle bisector

An angle bisector is a ray drawn through the vertex of an angle that divides the angle into two angles of equal measure, or two congruent angles.

Example

Ray *BY* is an angle bisector.

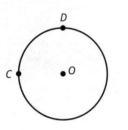

Angle-Side-Angle Congruence Theorem (ASA)

The Angle-Side-Angle Congruence Theorem (ASA) states that if two angles and the included side of one triangle are congruent to the corresponding two angles and the included side of another triangle, then the triangles are congruent.

arc

An arc is a part of a circle that is the curve between two points on the circle. An arc is named using its two endpoints.

Example

Arc *CD* is an arc of circle *O*. The symbol used to describe arc *CD* is $\overset{\frown}{CD}$.

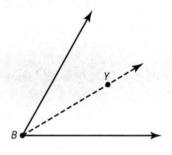

arithmetic sequence

An arithmetic sequence is a sequence of numbers in which the difference between any two consecutive terms is a constant.

Example

The sequence 1, 3, 5, 7 is an arithmetic sequence with a common difference of 2.

average rate of change

Another name for the slope of a linear function is average rate of change. The formula for the average rate of change is $\frac{f(t) - f(s)}{t - s}$.

Example

The average rate of change of the function shown is 3.

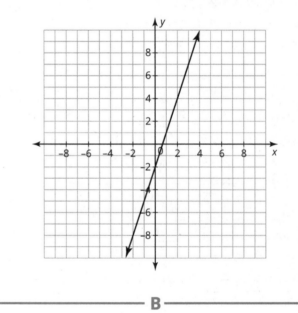

--------- B ---------

basic function

A basic function is the simplest function of its type.

Example

The basic linear function is $f(x) = x$.
The basic exponential function is $g(x) = 2^x$.
The basic quadratic function is $h(x) = x^2$.

bin

The width of a bar in a histogram represents an interval of data and is often referred to as a bin.

boundary line

A boundary line, determined by the inequality in a linear inequality, divides the plane into two half-planes and the inequality symbol indicates which half-plane contains all the solutions.

Example

For the linear inequality $y > -x + 8$, the boundary line is a dashed line because no point on that line is a solution.

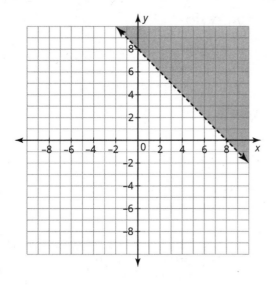

box-and-whisker plot

A box-and-whisker plot displays a data distribution based on a five-number summary.

Example

The box-and-whisker plots compare the test scores from two algebra classes.

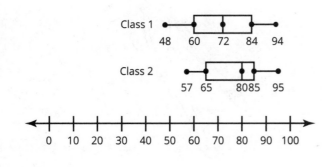

── C ──

categorical data

Data that can be grouped into categories are called categorical data.

causation

Causation is when one event causes a second event.

center

The center of a circle is a fixed point in the plane that is at an equal distance from every point on the circle.

Example

Point H is the center of the circle.

central angle

A central angle of a circle is an angle whose sides are radii. The measure of a central angle is equal to the measure of its intercepted arc.

Example

In circle O, $\angle AOC$ is a central angle and $\overset{\frown}{AC}$ is its intercepted arc. If $m\angle AOC = 45°$, then $m\overset{\frown}{AC} = 45°$.

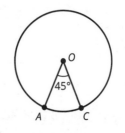

centroid

The centroid is a point whose x-value is the mean of all the x-values of the points on the scatter plot and its y-value is the mean of all the y-values of the points on the scatter plot.

Example

For the data points (1, 3), (1, 7), (2, 6), (3, 5), and (3, 4), the centroid is (2, 5).

chord

A chord is a line segment whose endpoints are points on a circle. A chord is formed by the intersection of the circle and a secant line.

Example

Segment *CD* is a chord of circle *O*.

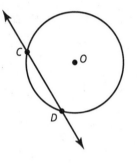

coefficient of determination

The coefficient of determination measures how well the graph of a regression fits the data. It is calculated by squaring the correlation coefficient and represents the percentage of variation of the observed values of the data points from their predicted values.

Example

The correlation coefficient for a data set is −0.9935. The coefficient of determination for the same data set is approximately 0.987, which means 98.7% of the data values should fall on the graph.

collinear points

Collinear points are points that are located on the same line.

Example

Points *A*, *B*, and *C* are collinear.

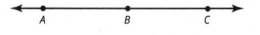

common difference

The difference between any two consecutive terms in an arithmetic sequence is called the common difference. It is typically represented by the variable *d*.

Example

The sequence 1, 3, 5, 7 is an arithmetic sequence with a common difference of 2.

common ratio

The ratio between any two consecutive terms in a geometric sequence is called the common ratio. It is typically represented by the variable *r*.

Example

The sequence 2, 4, 8, 16 is a geometric sequence with a common ratio of 2.

common response

A common response is when a variable other than the ones measured cause the same result as the one observed in the experiment.

compass

A compass is a tool used to create arcs and circles.

Example

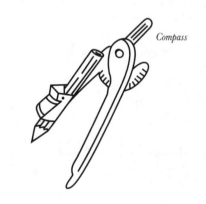

Compass

composite figure

A composite figure is a figure that is formed by combining different shapes.

compound inequality

A compound inequality is an inequality that is formed by the union, "or," or the intersection, "and," of two simple inequalities.

Example

The statement $x > 5$ or $x < -5$ is a compound inequality.

compound interest

In a compound interest account, the balance is multiplied by the same amount at each interval.

Example

Sonya opens a savings account with $100. She earns $4 in compound interest the first year. The compound interest y is found by using the equation $y = 100(1 + 0.04)^t$, where t is the time in years.

concentric circles

Concentric circles are circles in the same plane that have a common center.

Example

The circles shown are concentric because they are in the same plane and have a common center H.

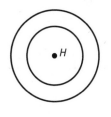

conclusion

The conclusion is the "then" part of an "if-then" or conditional statement.

conditional relative distribution

A conditional relative frequency distribution is the percent or proportion of occurrences of a category given the specific value of another category.

Example

Grades of Mr. Lewis's Science Students

Science Classes		A	B	C	D	F	Total
	Biology	$\frac{6}{20} = 30\%$	$\frac{6}{20} = 30\%$	$\frac{5}{20} = 25\%$	$\frac{1}{20} = 5\%$	$\frac{2}{20} = 10\%$	$\frac{20}{20} = 100\%$
	Chemistry	$\frac{4}{30} \approx 13.3\%$	$\frac{8}{30} \approx 26.7\%$	$\frac{12}{30} = 40\%$	$\frac{4}{30} \approx 13.3\%$	$\frac{2}{30} \approx 6.7\%$	$\frac{30}{30} = 100\%$
	Physics	$\frac{2}{15} \approx 13.3\%$	$\frac{5}{15} \approx 33.3\%$	$\frac{6}{15} = 40\%$	$\frac{1}{15} \approx 6.7\%$	$\frac{1}{15} \approx 6.7\%$	$\frac{15}{15} = 100\%$

conditional statement

A conditional statement is a statement that can be written in the form "If p, then q."

confounding variable

A confounding variable is when there are other variables in an experiment that are unknown or unobserved.

conjecture

A conjecture is a mathematical statement that appears to be true, but has not been formally proved.

conjunction

A compound inequality in the form $a < x < b$, where a and b are any real numbers, is a conjunction.

Example

The compound inequality $x \leq 1$ and $x > -3$ is a conjunction.

consistent systems

Systems that have one or many solutions are called consistent systems.

constant function

If the dependent variable of a function does not change or remains constant over the entire domain, then the function is called a constant function.

Example

The function shown is a constant function.

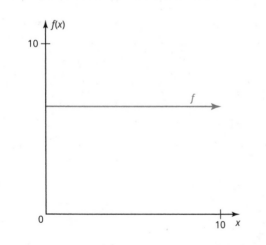

constraints

In a system of linear inequalities, the inequalities are known as constraints because the values of the expressions are "constrained" to lie within a certain region on the graph.

construct

When you construct geometric figures, you create exact figures without measurements, using paper folding or a compass and a straightedge—and geometric reasoning.

continuous graph

A continuous graph is a graph of points that are connected by a line or smooth curve on the graph. Continuous graphs have no breaks.

Example

The graph shown is a continuous graph.

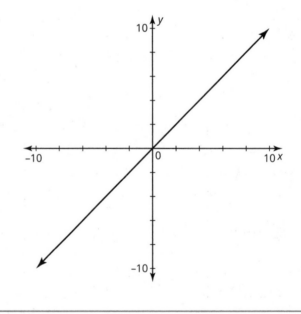

correlation

A measure of how well a regression fits a set of data is called a correlation.

correlation coefficient

The correlation coefficient is a value between −1 and 1, which indicates how close the data are to the graph of the regression equation. The closer the correlation coefficient is to −1 or 1, the stronger the relationship is between the two variables. The variable r is used to represent the correlation coefficient.

Example

The correlation coefficient for these data is −0.9935. The value is negative because the equation has a negative slope. The value is close to −1 because the data are very close to the graph of the equation of the line.

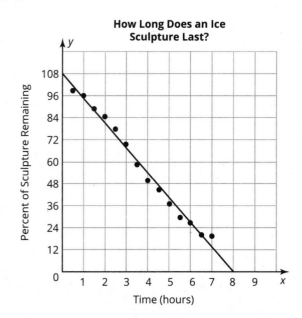

corresponding parts of congruent triangles are congruent (CPCTC)

CPCTC states that if two triangles are congruent, then each part of one triangle is congruent to the corresponding part of the other triangle.

Example

In the triangles shown, $\triangle XYZ \cong \triangle LMN$. Because corresponding parts of congruent triangles are congruent (CPCTC), the following corresponding parts are congruent.

- $\angle X \cong \angle L$
- $\angle Y \cong \angle M$
- $\angle Z \cong \angle N$
- $\overline{XY} \cong \overline{LM}$
- $\overline{YZ} \cong \overline{MN}$
- $\overline{XZ} \cong \overline{LN}$

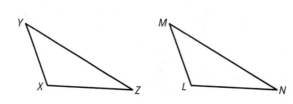

counterexample

A counterexample is a single example that shows that a statement is not true.

Example

Your friend claims that you add fractions by adding the numerators and then adding the denominators. A counterexample is $\frac{1}{2} + \frac{1}{2}$. The sum of these two fractions is 1. Your friend's method results in $\frac{1 + 1}{2 + 2}$, or $\frac{1}{2}$. Your friend's method is incorrect.

— D —

decreasing function

If a function decreases across the entire domain, then the function is called a decreasing function.

Example

The function shown is a decreasing function.

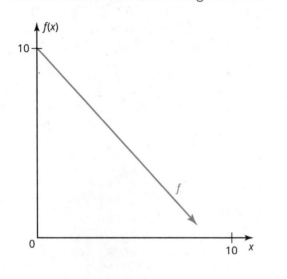

degree of a polynomial

The greatest exponent for any variable term in a polynomial determines the degree of the polynomial.

Example

The polynomial $2x^3 + 5x^2 - 6x + 1$ has a degree of 3.

dependent quantity

When one quantity depends on another in a problem situation, it is said to be the dependent quantity.

Example

In the relationship between driving time and distance traveled, distance is the dependent quantity, because distance depends on the driving time.

diagonal

A diagonal is a line segment joining two vertices of a polygon but is not a side of the polygon.

diameter

The diameter of a circle is a line segment with each endpoint on the circle that passes through the center of the circle.

Example

In circle O, $\overline{AB}$ is a diameter.

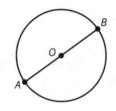

discrete graph

A discrete graph is a graph of isolated points.

Example

The graph shown is a discrete graph.

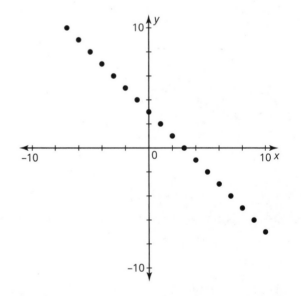

disjunction

A compound inequality in the form $x < a$ or $x > b$, where a and b are any real numbers, is a disjunction.

Example

The compound inequality $x < -2$ or $x > 1$ is a disjunction.

Distance Formula

The Distance Formula states that if (x_1, y_1) and (x_2, y_2) are two points on the coordinate plane, then the distance d between (x_1, y_1) and (x_2, y_2) is given by $d = \sqrt{(x_2 - x_1)^2 + (y_2 - y_1)^2}$.

Example

To find the distance between the points $(-1, 4)$ and $(2, -5)$, substitute the coordinates into the Distance Formula.

$$d = \sqrt{(x_2 - x_1)^2 + (y_2 - y_1)^2}$$
$$d = \sqrt{(2 + 1)^2 + (-5 - 4)^2}$$
$$d = \sqrt{3^2 + (-9)^2}$$
$$d = \sqrt{9 + 81}$$
$$d = \sqrt{90}$$
$$d \approx 9.49$$

So, the distance between the points $(-1, 4)$ and $(2, -5)$ is approximately 9.49 units.

domain

The domain is the set of input values in a relation.

Example

The domain of the function $y = 2x$ is the set of all real numbers.

dot plot

A dot plot is a graph that shows how discrete data are graphed using a number line.

Example

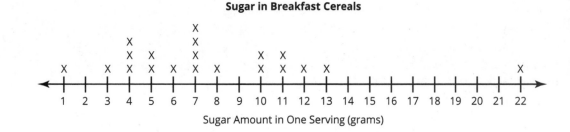

Sugar in Breakfast Cereals

Sugar Amount in One Serving (grams)

draw

To draw is to create a geometric figure using tools such as a ruler, straightedge, compass, or protractor. A drawing is more accurate than a sketch.

──────────── E ────────────

Euclidean geometry

Euclidean geometry is a geometry of straight lines and flat planes based on postulates developed by the ancient Greek mathematician Euclid. There are other types of geometry, such as spherical geometry and hyperbolic geometry, which are used to study curved space.

explicit formula

An explicit formula of a sequence is a formula for calculating the value of each term of a sequence using the term's position in the sequence. The explicit formula for an arithmetic sequence is $a_n = a_1 + d(n - 1)$. The explicit formula for a geometric sequence is $g_n = g_1 \cdot r^{n-1}$.

Example

The sequence 1, 3, 5, 7, 9, . . . can be described by the rule $a_n = 2n - 1$ where n is the position of the term. The fourth term of the sequence a_4 is $2(4) - 1$, or 7.

exponential decay function

An exponential decay function is an exponential function with a b-value greater than 0 and less than 1 and is of the form $y = a \cdot (1 - r)^x$, where r is the rate of decay.

Example

Greenville has a population of 7000. Its population is decreasing at a rate of 1.75%. The exponential decay function that models this situation is $f(x) = 7000 \cdot 0.9825^x$.

exponential functions

The family of exponential functions includes functions of the form $f(x) = a \cdot b^x$, where a and b are real numbers, and b is greater than 0 but is not equal to 1.

Example

The function $f(x) = 2^x$ is an exponential function.

exponential growth function

An exponential growth function is an exponential function with a b-value greater than 1 and is of the form $y = a \cdot (1 + r)^x$, where r is the rate of growth.

Example

Blueville has a population of 7000. Its population is increasing at a rate of 1.4%. The exponential growth function that models this situation is $f(x) = 7000 \cdot 1.014^x$.

extrapolation

To make predictions for values of x that are outside of the data set is called extrapolation.

──────────── F ────────────

finite sequence

If a sequence terminates, it is called a finite sequence.

Example

The sequence 22, 26, 30 is a finite sequence.

first differences

First differences are the values determined by subtracting consecutive output values in a table when the input values have an interval of 1.

Example

Time (minutes)	Height (feet)	First Differences
0	0	
1	1800	1800 − 0 = 1800
2	3600	3600 − 1800 = 1800
3	5400	5400 − 3600 = 1800

1 − 0 = 1
2 − 1 = 1
3 − 2 = 1

---

five-number summary

The five-number summary consists of the minimum value, the first quartile (Q1), the median, the third quartile (Q3), and the maximum value of a data set.

Example

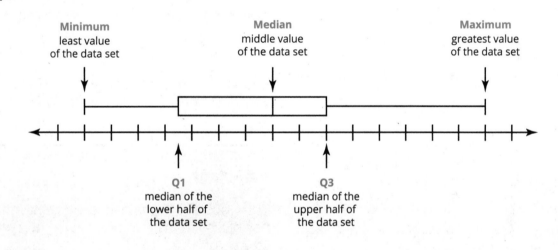

Minimum
least value
of the data set

Median
middle value
of the data set

Maximum
greatest value
of the data set

Q1
median of the
lower half of
the data set

Q3
median of the
upper half of
the data set

---

frequency

The height of each bar in a histogram indicates the frequency, which is the number of data values included in any given bin.

frequency distribution

A frequency distribution displays the frequencies for categorical data in a two-way table.

Example

Favorite Meals of Students

	Burgers	Chicken Nuggets	Pizza	Salad Bar
9th grade	4	1	3	5
10th grade	3	7	3	4

Grade Level

function

A function is a relation that assigns to each element of the domain exactly one element of the range.

Example

The equation $y = 2x$ is a function. Every value of x has exactly one corresponding y-value.

function family

A function family is a group of functions that share certain characteristics.

Example

Linear functions and exponential functions are examples of function families.

function notation

Function notation is a way of representing functions algebraically.

Example

In the function $f(x) = 0.75x$, f is the name of the function, x represents the domain, and $f(x)$ represents the range.

G

geometric sequence

A geometric sequence is a sequence of numbers in which the ratio between any two consecutive terms is a constant.

Example

The sequence 2, 4, 8, 16 is a geometric sequence with a common ratio of 2.

H

half-plane

The graph of a linear inequality is a half-plane, or half of a coordinate plane.

Example

The shaded portion of the graph is a half-plane.

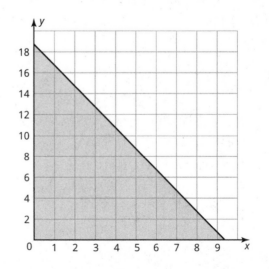

histogram

A histogram is a graphical way to display quantitative data using vertical bars.

Example

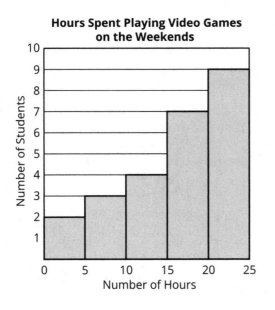

Hours Spent Playing Video Games on the Weekends

horizontal asymptote

A horizontal asymptote is a horizontal line that a function gets closer and closer to, but never intersects.

Example

The graph shows a horizontal asymptote at $y = -1$.

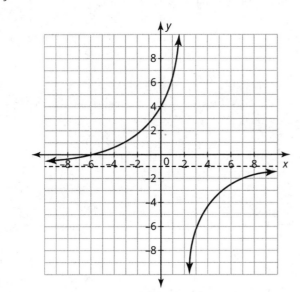

hypothesis

The hypothesis is the "if" part of an "if-then" or conditional statement.

— I —

included angle

An included angle is the angle formed by two sides of a triangle.

included side

An included side is the side between two angles of a triangle.

inconsistent systems

Systems with no solution are called inconsistent systems.

increasing function

If a function increases across the entire domain, then the function is called an increasing function.

Example

The function shown is an increasing function.

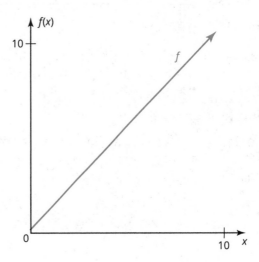

independent quantity

The quantity that the dependent quantity depends upon is called the independent quantity.

Example

In the relationship between driving time and distance traveled, driving time is the independent quantity, because it does not depend on any other quantity

infinite sequence

If a sequence continues on forever, it is called an infinite sequence.

Example

The sequence 22, 26, 30, 34 . . . is an infinite sequence.

infinite solutions

An equation with infinite solutions means that any value for the variable makes the equation true.

Example

The equation $2x + 1 = 2x + 1$ has infinite solutions.

inscribed angle

An inscribed angle is an angle whose vertex is on a circle and whose sides contain chords of the circle.

Example

Angle BAC is an inscribed angle. The vertex of $\angle BAC$ is on the circle and the sides of $\angle BAC$ contain the chords $\overline{AB}$ and $\overline{AC}$.

inscribed polygon

An inscribed polygon is a polygon drawn inside another polygon or circle in which all the vertices of the interior polygon lie on the outer figure.

Example

Quadrilateral $KLMN$ is inscribed in circle J.

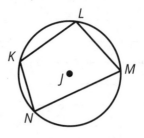

interpolation

Using a linear regression to make predictions within the data set is called interpolation.

interquartile range (IQR)

The interquartile range, IQR, measures how far the data are spread out from the median.

Example

In the data set 13, 17, 23, 24, 25, 29, 31, 45, 46, 53, 60, the median, 29, divides the data into two halves. The first quartile, 23, is the median of the lower half of the data. The third quartile, 46, is the median of the upper half of the data. The interquartile range is $46 - 23$, or 23.

isometry

An isometry is a rigid motion transformation that preserves size and shape.

— J —

joint frequency

Any frequency recorded within the body of a two-way frequency table is known as a joint frequency.

leading coefficient

The leading coefficient of a polynomial is the numeric coefficient of the term with the greatest power.

Example

In the polynomial $-7x^2 + x + 25$, the value -7 is the leading coefficient.

Least Squares Method

The Least Squares Method is a method that creates a regression line for a scatter plot that has two basic requirements: 1) the line must contain the centroid of the data set, and 2) the sum of the squares of the vertical distances from each given data point is at a minimum with the line.

Example

The regression line shown was created using the Least Squares Method.

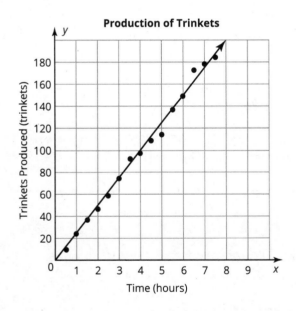

line

A line is made up of an infinite number of points that extend infinitely in two opposite directions. A line is straight and has only one dimension.

Example

The line below can be called line k or line AB.

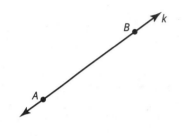

line segment

A line segment is a portion of a line that includes two points and all of the collinear points between the two points.

Example

The line segment shown is named $\overline{AB}$ or $\overline{BA}$.

linear absolute value functions

The family of linear absolute value functions includes functions of the form $f(x) = a|x + b| + c$, where a, b, and c are real numbers, and a is not equal to 0.

Example

The function $f(x) = |x - 3| - 2$ is a linear absolute value function.

linear combinations method

The linear combinations method is a process used to solve a system of equations by adding two equations together, resulting in an equation with one variable.

Example

Solve the following system of equations by using the linear combinations method:

$$\begin{cases} 6x - 5y = 3 \\ 2x + 2y = 12 \end{cases}$$

First, multiply the second equation by -3. Then, add the equations and solve for the remaining variable. Finally, substitute $y = 3$ into the first equation and solve for x. The solution of the system is $(3, 3)$.

linear functions

The family of linear functions includes functions of the form $f(x) = ax + b$, where a and b are real numbers.

Example

The function $f(x) = 3x + 2$ is a linear function.

Linear Pair Postulate

The Linear Pair Postulate states: "If two angles form a linear pair, then the angles are supplementary."

linear piecewise functions

Linear piecewise functions include linear functions that have equation changes for different parts, or pieces, of the domain.

Example

The function $f(x)$ is a linear piecewise function.

$$f(x) = \begin{cases} x + 5, & x \le -2 \\ -2x + 1, & -2 < x \le 2 \\ 2x - 9, & x > 2 \end{cases}$$

linear programming

Linear programming is a branch of mathematics that determines the maximum and minimum value of linear expressions on a region produced by a system of linear inequalities.

literal equation

Literal equations are equations in which the variables represent specific measures.

Example

The equations $I = Prt$ and $A = lw$ are literal equations.

lower fence

The value of $Q1 - (IQR \cdot 1.5)$ is known as the lower fence of a data set.

— M —

marginal frequency distribution

A marginal frequency distribution displays the total of the frequencies of the rows or columns of a frequency distribution.

Example

Favorite Meals of Students

	Burgers	Chicken Nuggets	Pizza	Salad Bar	Total
9th grade	4	1	3	5	13
10th grade	3	7	3	4	17
Total	7	8	6	9	30

Grade Level

marginal relative frequency distribution

Displaying the relative frequencies for the rows or columns in a two-way table is called a marginal relative frequency distribution. The marginal relative frequency distribution provides the ratio of total occurrences for each category to the total number of occurrences.

Example

Activities Preferred During Hot Weather

	Sports	Movies	Reading	Walking	Total
Students Age 18 Years Old and Under	$\frac{20}{280} \approx 7.1\%$	$\frac{30}{280} \approx 10.7\%$	$\frac{22}{280} \approx 7.9\%$	$\frac{8}{280} \approx 2.9\%$	$\frac{80}{280} \approx 28.6\%$
Adults Age 19 Thru 50 Years Old	$\frac{10}{280} \approx 3.6\%$	$\frac{32}{280} \approx 11.4\%$	$\frac{25}{280} \approx 8.9\%$	$\frac{43}{280} \approx 15.4\%$	$\frac{110}{280} \approx 39.3\%$
Adults Over 50 Years Old	$\frac{5}{280} \approx 1.8\%$	$\frac{20}{280} \approx 7.1\%$	$\frac{35}{280} \approx 12.5\%$	$\frac{30}{280} \approx 10.7\%$	$\frac{90}{280} \approx 32.1\%$
Total	$\frac{35}{280} \approx 12.5\%$	$\frac{82}{280} \approx 29.3\%$	$\frac{82}{280} \approx 29.3\%$	$\frac{81}{280} \approx 28.9\%$	$\frac{280}{280} \approx 100\%$

mathematical modeling

Mathematical modeling is explaining patterns in the real world based on mathematical ideas.

measure of central tendency

A measure of central tendency is a numeric value used to describe the overall clustering of data in a set.

Example

The mean, median, and mode are the most common measures of central tendency.

midpoint

A midpoint is a point that is exactly halfway between two given points.

Example

Because point B is the midpoint of segment AC, segment AB is congruent to segment BC.

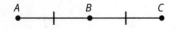

Midpoint Formula

The Midpoint Formula states that if (x_1, y_1) and (x_2, y_2) are two points on the coordinate plane, then the midpoint of the line segment that joins these two points is given by $\left(\frac{x_1 + x_2}{2}, \frac{y_1 + y_2}{2}\right)$.

Example

To find the midpoint between the points $(-1, 4)$ and $(2, -5)$, substitute the coordinates into the Midpoint Formula.

$$\left(\frac{x_1 + x_2}{2}, \frac{y_1 + y_2}{2}\right) = \left(\frac{-1 + 2}{2}, \frac{4 - 5}{2}\right)$$
$$= \left(\frac{1}{2}, \frac{-1}{2}\right)$$

So, the midpoint between the points $(-1, 4)$ and $(2, -5)$ is $\left(\frac{1}{2}, -\frac{1}{2}\right)$.

— N —

necessary condition

A correlation is a necessary condition for causation, meaning that for one variable to cause another, they must be correlated.

no solution

An equation with no solution means that there is no value for the variable that makes the equation true.

Example

The equation $2x + 1 = 2x + 3$ has no solution.

O

outlier

An outlier is a data value that is significantly greater or lesser than other data values in a data set.

Example

In the data set 1, 1, 3, 3, 4, 4, 5, 1000, the outlier is 1000.

P

perpendicular bisector

A perpendicular bisector is a line, line segment, or ray that intersects the midpoint of a line segment at a 90° angle.

Example

Line k is the perpendicular bisector of $\overline{AB}$. It is perpendicular to $\overline{AB}$, and intersects $\overline{AB}$ at midpoint M so that $AM = MB$.

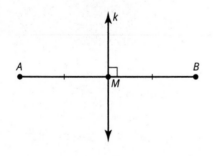

---

point

A point has no dimension, but can be visualized as a specific position in space, and is usually represented by a small dot.

Example

Point A is shown.

●A

---

polynomial

A polynomial is a mathematical expression involving the sum of powers in one or more variables multiplied by coefficients.

Example

The expression $3x^3 + 5x - 6x + 1$ is a polynomial.

---

postulate

A postulate is a mathematical statement that cannot be proved but is considered true.

---

proof

A proof is a series of statements and corresponding reasons forming a valid argument that starts with a hypothesis and arrives at a conclusion.

Q

quadratic functions

The family of quadratic functions includes functions of the form $f(x) = ax^2 + bx + c$, where a, b, and c are real numbers, and a is not equal to 0.

Examples

The equations $y = x^2 + 2x + 5$ and $y = -4x^2 - 7x + 1$ are quadratic functions.

R

radius

The radius of a circle is a line segment with one endpoint on the circle and one endpoint at the center.

Example

In circle O, $\overline{OA}$ is a radius.

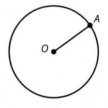

range

The range is the set of output values in a relation.

Example

The range of the function $y = x^2$ is the set of all numbers greater than or equal to zero.

ray

A ray is a portion of a line that begins with a single point and extends infinitely in one direction.

Example

The ray shown is ray AB.

recursive formula

A recursive formula expresses each new term of a sequence based on the preceding term in the sequence. The recursive formula for an arithmetic sequence is $a_n = a_{n-1} + d$. The recursive formula for a geometric sequence is $g_n = g_{n-1} \cdot r$.

Example

The formula $a_n = a_{n-1} + 2$ is a recursive formula. Each successive term is calculated by adding 2 to the previous term. If $a_1 = 1$, then $a_2 = 1 + 2 = 3$.

reflection

A reflection is a function, R_ℓ, which takes as its input, P, the location of a point with respect to some line of reflection ℓ and outputs $R_\ell (P)$, or the opposite of the location of P with respect to the line of reflection.

Example

$R_m (STUV) = S'T'U'V'$

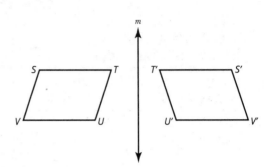

reflectional symmetry

A plane figure has reflectional symmetry if you can draw a line so that the figure to one side of the line is a reflection of the figure on the other side of the line.

Example

The figure shown has reflectional symmetry.

regression line

On a scatter plot, a regression line is a mathematical model that can be used to predict the values of a dependent variable based upon the values of an independent variable.

relation

A relation is the mapping between a set of input values called the domain and a set of output values called the range.

Example

The set of points {(0, 1), (1, 8), (2, 5), (3, 7)} is a relation.

relative frequency distribution

Representing the relative frequencies for joint data displayed in a two-way table is called a relative frequency distribution. The relative frequency distribution provides the ratio of occurrences in each category to the total number of occurrences.

Example

Activities Preferred During Hot Weather

	Sports	Movies	Reading	Walking
Students Age 18 Years Old and Under	$\frac{20}{280} \approx 7.1\%$	$\frac{30}{280} \approx 10.7\%$	$\frac{22}{280} \approx 7.9\%$	$\frac{8}{280} \approx 2.9\%$
Adults Age 19 Thru 50 Years Old	$\frac{10}{280} \approx 3.6\%$	$\frac{32}{280} \approx 11.4\%$	$\frac{25}{280} \approx 8.9\%$	$\frac{43}{280} \approx 15.4\%$
Adults Over 50 Years Old	$\frac{5}{280} \approx 1.8\%$	$\frac{20}{280} \approx 7.1\%$	$\frac{35}{280} \approx 12.5\%$	$\frac{30}{280} \approx 10.7\%$

residual

A residual is the distance between an observed data value and its predicted value using a regression equation.

residual plot

A residual plot is a scatter plot of the independent variable on the x-axis and the residuals on the y-axis.

Example

The graph on the right shows a residual plot of the braking distance data.

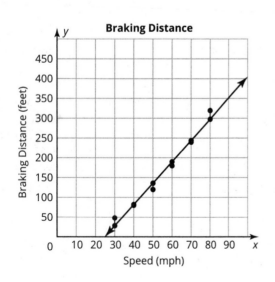

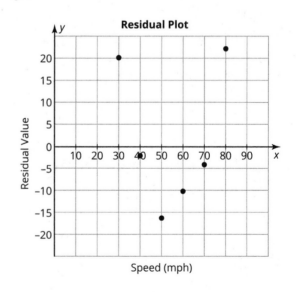

rotation

A rotation is a function that maps its input, a point P, to another location, $f(P)$. This movement to a new location is defined by a center of rotation, E, and a rotation angle, t. For this reason, a rotation function is written as $R_{E,t}(P)$

Example

$R_{A, 40}(\overline{JN}) = \overline{J'N'}$

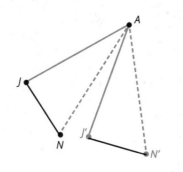

rotation angle

A rotation angle is a directed angle based on a circle. Positive rotation angles turn counterclockwise, and negative rotation angles turn clockwise.

Example

The rotation angle shown rotates point A 45° counterclockwise.

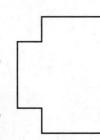
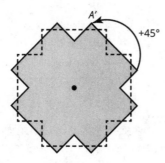

rotational symmetry

A plane figure can also have rotational symmetry if you can rotate the figure more than 0° but less than 360° and the resulting figure is the same as the original figure in the original position.

Example

The figure shown has rotational symmetry.

S

---

secant

A secant of a circle is a line that intersects the circle at two points.

Example

The line intersecting the circle through points A and B is a secant.

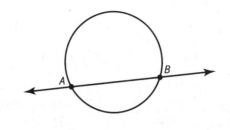

Segment Addition Postulate

The Segment Addition Postulate states: "If point B is on $\overline{AC}$ and between points A and C, then $AB + BC = AC$."

segment bisector

A segment bisector is a line, line segment, or ray that divides a line segment into two line segments of equal measure, or two congruent line segments.

Example

$\overline{AB}$ is a segment bisector of $\overline{CD}$.

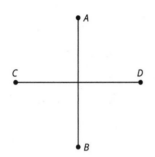

sequence

A sequence is a pattern involving an ordered arrangement of numbers, geometric figures, letters, or other objects.

Example

The numbers 1, 1, 2, 3, 5, 8, 13 form a sequence.

Side-Angle-Side Congruence Theorem (SAS)

The Side-Angle-Side Congruence Theorem (SAS) states that if two sides and the included angle of one triangle are congruent to the corresponding sides and the included angle of the second triangle, then the triangles are congruent.

Side-Side-Side Congruence Theorem (SSS)

The Side-Side-Side Congruence Theorem (SSS) states that if three sides of one triangle are congruent to the corresponding sides of another triangle, then the triangles are congruent.

simple interest

In a simple interest account, the interest earned at the end of each interval is a percent of the starting balance (also known as the original principal).

Example

Tonya deposits $200 in a 3-year certificate of deposit that earns 4% simple interest. The amount of interest that Tonya earns can be found using the simple interest formula.

$$I = (200)(0.04)(3)$$
$$I = 24$$

Tonya earns $24 in interest.

sketch

To sketch is to create a geometric figure without using tools such as a ruler, straightedge, compass, or protractor. A drawing is more accurate than a sketch.

solution

The solution to an equation is any value for the variable that makes the equation a true statement.

Example

The solution of the equation $3x + 4 = 25$ is 7 because 7 makes the equation true: $3(7) + 4 = 25$, or $25 = 25$.

solution of a compound inequality

The solution of a compound inequality is the part or parts of the solutions that satisfy both of the inequalities.

Example

The number line shows the solution of the compound inequality $x < -2$ or $x > 1$.

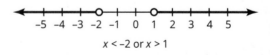

$x < -2$ or $x > 1$

solution of a system of linear inequalities

The solution of a system of linear inequalities is the intersection of the solutions to each inequality. Every point in the intersection region satisfies all inequalities in the system.

Example

The solution of this system of linear inequalities is shown by the shaded region, which represents the intersection of the solutions to each inequality.

$$\begin{cases} 200a + 100c \leq 800 \\ 75(a - 1) + 50c \geq 150 \end{cases}$$

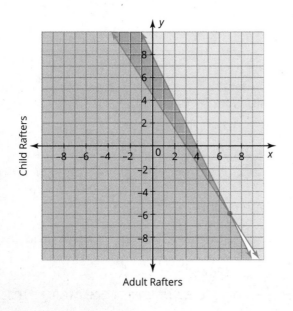

Adult Rafters

solve an inequality

To solve an inequality means to determine the values of the variable that make the inequality true.

Example

The inequality $x + 5 > 6$ can be solved by subtracting 5 from each side of the inequality. The solution is $x > 1$. Any number greater than 1 will make the inequality $x + 5 > 6$ true.

standard deviation

Standard deviation is a measure of how spread out the data are from the mean.

statistics

Statistics are numerical characteristics of data.

straightedge

A straightedge is a ruler with no numbers.

sufficient condition

A correlation is not a sufficient condition for causation, meaning that a correlation between two variables is not enough to establish that one variables causes another.

system of linear equations

When two or more equations define a relationship between quantities, they form a system of linear equations.

Example

The equations $y = 3x + 7$ and $y = -4x$ are a system of linear equations.

$$\begin{cases} y = 3x + 7 \\ y = -4x \end{cases}$$

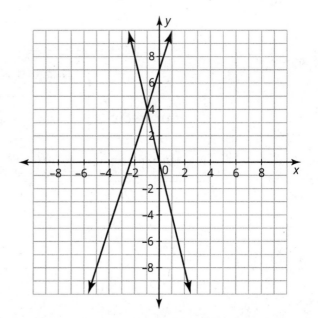

—————— T ——————

term of a sequence

A term of a sequence is an individual number, figure, or letter in the sequence.

Example

In the sequence 2, 4, 6, 8, 10, the first term is 2, the second term is 4, and the third term is 6.

theorem

A theorem is a statement that can be demonstrated to be true by accepted mathematical operations and arguments.

translation

A translation is a function, T, which takes as its input a set of pre-image points and outputs a set of image points. The pre-image points are translated a distance of AB in the direction AB.

Example

$T_{AB}(P) = P'$ and $T_{AC}(P) = P''$

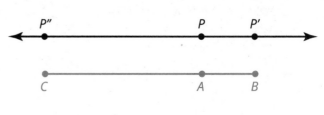

truth table

A truth table is a table that summarizes all possible truth values for a conditional statement $p \rightarrow q$.

truth value

The truth value of a conditional statement is whether the statement is true or false.

two-way frequency table

A two-way frequency table displays categorical data by representing the number of occurrences that fall into each group for two variables.

Example

Favorite Meals of Students

		Burgers	Chicken Nuggets	Pizza	Salad Bar
Grade Level	9th grade	////	/	///	////
	10th grade	///	//// //	///	////

—————— U ——————

upper fence

The value of Q3 + (IQR · 1.5) is known as the upper fence of a data set.

Vertical Line Test

The Vertical Line Test is a visual method used to determine whether a relation represented as a graph is a function.

Example

The equation $y = 3x^2$ is a function. The graph passes the Vertical Line Test because there are no vertical lines that can be drawn that would intersect the graph at more than one point.

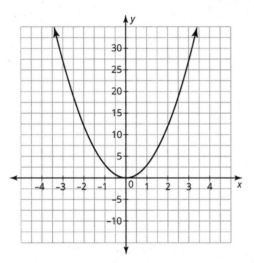

The equation $x^2 + y^2 = 9$ is not a function. The graph fails the Vertical Line Test because a vertical line can be drawn that intersects the graph at more than one point.

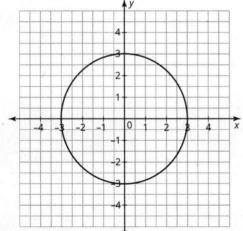

x-intercept

The point where a graph crosses the x-axis is the x-intercept.

y-intercept

The point where a graph crosses the y-axis is the y-intercept.

zero of a function

A zero of a function is a real number that makes the value of the function equal to zero, or $f(x) = 0$.

Example

The zero of the linear function $f(x) = 2(x - 4)$ is (4, 0).

© Carnegie Learning, Inc.

A

Absolute maximum of
function, M1-51–M1-53,
M1-77

Absolute minimum of
function, M1-51–M1-53,
M1-77

Absolute value functions,
linear, M1-53, M1-77

Adders, M3-24

Adding functions, M3-81–
M3-82

Additive inverses, M2-177
system of linear equations
and, M2-177–M2-179

Analytic geometry, M5-6

Angle
bisecting, M5-35–M5-36,
M5-48
defined, M5-60, M5-118
duplicating, M5-27–M5-28
included, M5-150, M5-174
inscribed, M5-9
rotation, M5-60, M5-118

Angle Addition Postulate,
M5-139, M5-173

Angle bisector
constructing, M5-6
defined, M5-5, M5-35,
M5-47

Angle-side-angle (ASA)
congruence theorem
on coordinate plane,
M5-164–M5-166
description of, M5-152
statement of, M5-152,
M5-175
using, M5-161–M5-163

Anscombe, Francis J.,
M1-208

Arc markers, M5-145,
M5-173

Arc of circle, M5-9, M5-41

Area
of composite figure,
M2-290–M2-291
under a curve, M2-295–
M2-296
formula for, M2-269
of geometric figures on
coordinate plane,
M2-269–M2-273
of hexagon, M2-294
of polygons on coordinate
plane, M2-287–M2-297
of trapezoid, M2-292–
M2-293
of triangle, M2-304

Argument of function, M3-40,
M3-62

Arithmetic sequences,
M1-117–M1-121
connecting constant
difference, slope, and
average rate of change,
M2-15–M2-16
connecting constant
difference and slope,
M2-12–M2-14
connecting forms,
M2-9–M2-11
constant sequences,
M2-18–M2-19
defined, M1-82, M1-101,
M1-156, M2-10
explicit formulas for,
M1-134–M1-135,
M1-157
formulas for, M1-133–
M1-135
linear functions and, M2-7–
M2-22
recursive formula for,
M1-133–M1-134,
M1-156

Asymptote, horizontal, M3-6,
M3-18–M3-19, M3-60

Average rate of change,
M2-6, M2-16, M2-86
constant difference and,
M2-15–M2-16
formula for, M2-86
slope and, M2-15–M2-16

B

Bar graph, M4-78, M4-106

Basic function, M2-44,
M2-88

Bici Bicycle Company,
M2-219

Bin, M4-9, M4-45

Bisecting angle, M5-35–
M5-36

Bisecting line segment,
M5-10

Blood Alcohol Content (BAC),
M3-110
data analysis, M3-100
defined, M3-98
level, M3-98–M3-99
result summarization,
M3-102

Boundary line, M2-156,
M2-192, M2-239

Box-and-whisker plot,
M4-11–M4-12, M4-46
outlier represented on,
M4-23

C

Categorical data, M4-54
defined, M4-56
in two variables, M4-57–
M4-58

Causation
vs. correlation, M1-184–
M1-187

© Carnegie Learning, Inc.

Inequality signs, M2-128–M2-129

Infinite sequence, M1-95, M1-155

Infinite solutions, M2-96

Inscribed angle, M5-9

Inscribed hexagon, constructing, M5-29

Inscribed polygon, defined, M5-6, M5-19, M5-44

Inscribed square, constructing, M5-19–M5-21

Inscribing equilateral triangle, M5-37

Interpolation
  defined, M1-162, M1-219
  from linear regression, M1-162, M1-171, M1-220

Interquartile range (IQR), M4-6
  defined, M4-22, M4-47
  for identifying outliers, M4-24
  outlier, M4-22–M4-23

Interval of data, M4-9, M4-45

Isometry
  defined, M5-52, M5-72, M5-118
  sequences of, M5-99
    using transactions and reflections, M5-87–M5-88

J

Joint frequency, M4-60

L

Leading coefficient of polynomial, M2-32, M2-87

Least Squares Method, M1-167, M1-219

Line(s)
  defined, M5-59, M5-118
  horizontal, M2-66–M2-67
  parallel, M2-47–M2-48
  perpendicular, M2-61–M2-72
  vertical, M2-66–M2-67

Linear combinations method, M2-155, M2-176, M2-180–M2-181, M2-238

Linear equation(s)
  creating, M2-98
  determining the solution to system of, M2-162–M2-163
  factored form, M2-111–M2-112, M2-150
  as function, M1-5
  general form, M2-111–M2-112, M2-150
  infinite solutions, M2-149
  with infinite solutions, M2-102
  with no solution, M2-102, M2-149
  solutions, M2-101–M2-102
  Tic-Tac-Bingo, M2-103
    using linear combinations to, M2-173–M2-186
    using properties to justify, M2-99–M2-100
  solving, M2-97–M2-105
  standard form, M2-111–M2-112, M2-150
  See also Systems of equations

Linear functions, M1-50, M1-56, M1-77
  arithmetic sequences and, M2-7–M2-22
    connecting constant difference, slope, and average rate of change, M2-15–M2-16
    connecting constant difference and slope, M2-12–M2-14
    connecting forms, M2-9–M2-11
    constant sequences, M2-18–M2-19
  average rate of change, M2-6
  comparing, M2-73–M2-79
    descriptions and graphs, M2-78
    equations and tables, M2-77
    slopes of linear relationships, M2-75
    tables and graphs, M2-76
  degree, M2-6

determining best model with, M1-210–M1-213

factored form of, M2-35, M2-87

first differences, M2-6

in general form, M2-11, M2-35

graph of
  interpreting, M2-27–M2-29
  interpreting changes to, M2-30–M2-33
  interpreting more changes to, M2-34–M2-35

interpreting, M2-25–M2-26, M2-27–M2-29

changes to graph of, M2-30–M2-33

graphs of, M2-27–M2-29

more changes to graph of, M2-34–M2-35

representations of, M2-23–M2-40

transforming, M2-41–M2-59
  applying, M2-54–M2-55
  slopes of parallel lines, M2-47–M2-48
  vertical dilations of functions, M2-49–M2-51, M2-52–M2-53
  vertical translations of functions, M2-44–M2-46, M2-52–M2-53

zero of a function, M2-6

See also Linear regression equations

Linear inequalities
  determining graphs of, M2-192–M2-196
  interpreting graph of, M2-197–M2-198
  modeling, M2-123–M2-125
  reversing inequality signs, M2-128–M2-129
  solving
    other, M2-130
    two-step, M2-126–M2-127
  two-step, M2-126–M2-127
  in two variables, M2-189–M2-191

Linear Pair Postulate,
    M5-137, M5-172
Linear piecewise functions,
    M1-53, M1-78
Linear programming,
    M2-227–M2-234
  defined, M2-229, M2-242
  introduction, M2-229–
    M2-231
  profit maximization,
    M2-232–M2-33
Linear regression
  extrapolation from,
    M1-162, M1-172,
    M1-220
  graph of, M1-167
    graphing calculator, use
      of, M1-167
  interpolation from, M1-162,
    M1-171, M1-220
  making predictions,
    M1-169–M1-172
  to model data, M1-171–
    M1-172
Linear regression equations,
    M1-170, M1-224
  graphing calculator to
    determine, M1-171,
    M1-224
Line of reflection, M3-44,
    M3-62
Line segment
  bisecting, M5-10
  defined, M5-59, M5-118
  diagonal in, M5-18, M5-45
  duplicating, M5-16–M5-18,
    M5-26–M5-27
Lines of best fit
  correlation coefficient and,
    M1-183
  linear regression and,
    M1-165–M1-166
  residual plot and, M1-210–
    M1-213
Literal equations, M2-96,
    M2-109–M2-120
  defined, M2-113, M2-150
  in different forms, M2-111–
    M2-112
  rewriting, M2-113–M2-115
  solving for specific variables,
    M2-116–M2-117
Lower fence, M4-22, M4-48

M
Marginal frequency
    distribution, M4-54,
    M4-61–M4-62
Mathematical modeling,
    M1-149
  defined, M1-82, M1-144,
    M1-157
  information gathering,
    M1-144, M1-157
  interpreting and testing
    predictions, M1-147,
    M1-158
  organizing information,
    M1-145, M1-157
  predicting and analyzing
    results, M1-146,
    M1-157
  using mathematical
    notation, M1-145,
    M1-157
  See also Modeling
Matthew effect, M3-6
Measures of central
    tendency, M4-19–
    M4-23
  defined, M4-19, M4-46
  mean, M4-19–M4-20,
    M4-25, M4-47
  median, M4-19–M4-20,
    M4-47
Midpoint
  classifying a quadrilateral
    formed by, M2-260–
    M2-261
  defined, M2-260
Midpoint Formula, M2-260–
    M2-261
Midpoint of segment, M5-10,
    M5-41
Modeling
  exponential functions,
    M3-87–M3-93
    best fit model, M3-91–
      M3-93
    decreasing, M3-89–
      M3-90
  See also Mathematical
    modeling
Multiplicative inverses,
    M2-63. *See also*
    Reciprocal numbers
Multipliers, M3-24

N
Necessary condition for
    causation, M1-185,
    M1-221
Negative common difference,
    M1-101
Negative exponents, M3-18–
    M3-19
Non-linear regression, and
    residual plot, M1-214–
    M1-215
Numbers, reciprocal, M2-63

O
One-variable statistics
  box-and-whisker plot,
    M4-11–M4-12, M4-46
  dot plot, M4-8, M4-45
  five-number summary,
    M4-11, M4-46
  histograms, M4-9–M4-10,
    M4-45–M4-46
  interquartile range (IQR),
    M4-6, M4-22, M4-24,
    M4-47
  measures of central
    tendency, M4-19–
    M4-23
  outlier(s), M4-6, M4-22–
    M4-24, M4-48
  standard deviation, M4-6,
    M4-25–M4-30, M4-49
  See also Data sets for one
    variable; Statistics
Outlier(s), M4-6, M4-22,
    M4-48
  interquartile range for
    identifying, M4-24
  lower fence, M4-22, M4-48
  represented on box-and-
    whisker plot, M4-23
  upper fence, M4-22, M4-48

P
Parallel lines
  constructing, M5-56–
    M5-58
  slopes of, M2-47–M2-48
Parallelogram, perimeter of,
    M2-289
Parallel postulate, M5-136
Pascal, Blaise, M1-88
Pascal's Triangle, M1-84

© Carnegie Learning, Inc.

© Carnegie Learning, Inc.